Computer Item Generator

with

Standardized Test Practice

Course 1

Prentice Hall
Needham, Massachusetts
Upper Saddle River, New Jersey

Your *Computer Item Generator with Standardized Test Practice* software is on the CD-ROM at the back of this book!

If you prefer diskettes,
call 1-800-468-8378,
and you will receive them at no charge.

PRENTICE HALL
Simon and Schuster Education Group

Printed in the United States of America.

ISBN 0-13-435403-6

1 2 3 4 5 6 7 8 9   03 02 01 00 99 98

Table of Contents

About Prentice Hall's Computer Item Generator with Standardized Test Practice .... *iv*

About the Dial-A-Test® Service .... *vii*

Dial-A-Test® Order Form .... *viii*

Middle Grades Math Course 1 Exercises on the Software

Chapter 1 Using Statistics to Analyze Data *1*

Chapter 2 Patterns and Algebraic Thinking *33*

Chapter 3 Adding and Subtracting Decimals *47*

Chapter 4 Multiplying and Dividing Whole Numbers and Decimals *69*

Chapter 5 Investigating Fractions *89*

Chapter 6 Using Fractions *113*

Chapter 7 Ratios, Proportions, and Percents *135*

Chapter 8 Tools of Geometry *159*

Chapter 9 Geometry and Measurement *195*

Chapter 10 Algebra: Integers and Graphing *221*

Chapter 11 Exploring Probability *245*

Answers to Exercises *267*

Standardized Test Practice Exercises on the Software

About Standardized Test Practice *292*

CAT5 Level 16 Exercises *293*

CTBS Terra Nova Level 16 Exercises *295*

ITBS Form M Level 12 Exercises *297*

MAT7 Intermediate 1 Exercises *299*

SAT9 Intermediate 2 Exercises *301*

TAAS Grade 6 Exercises *304*

NC End-of-Grade 6 Exercises *307*

System Requirements and Software Installation Instructions *312*

Software on CD-ROM .... *Affixed to back cover*

About Prentice Hall's Computer Item Generator with Standardized Test Practice

Contents of the Software

Items Corresponding to *Middle Grades Math* Student Editions

- Contains 10–15 items for *every* lesson in the Student Editions of Courses 1, 2, and 3
- Items arranged by chapter, lesson, and objective
- Items in Free-Response and Multiple-Choice formats

Items Corresponding to Standardized Test Objectives

- Contains 150–225 items for each of three levels of seven different standardized tests
- Items arranged according to test objectives
- Items in Multiple-Choice format

Standardized Test Practice

A Prentice Hall Exclusive!

Do your students need preparation for standardized tests? Prentice Hall's unique Computer Item Generator with Standardized Test Practice provides you with practice exercises that have been correlated to the mathematics objectives of the following standardized tests:

	Level of Prentice Hall *Middle Grades Math*		
	Course 1	**Course 2**	**Course 3**
California Achievement Tests, 5th Ed. (CAT5)	Level 16	Level 17	Level 18
Comprehensive Tests of Basic Skills (CTBS), Terra Nova	Level 16	Level 17	Level 18
Iowa Tests of Basic Skills, Form M (ITBS)	Level 12	Level 13	Level 14
Metropolitan Achievement Tests, 7th Ed. (MAT7)	Intermediate 1	Intermediate 2	Intermediate 3
Stanford Achievement Tests, 9th Ed. (SAT9)	Intermediate 2	Intermediate 3	Advanced 1
NC End-of-Grade	Grade 6	Grade 7	Grade 8
TAAS	Grade 6	Grade 7	Grade 8

To create worksheets for Standardized Test practice, simply select the test of your choice from the menu. Upon doing so, you'll find multiple-choice exercises, arranged according to the objectives of the test you've chosen. You can use all the regular Computer Item Generator features as you select individual exercises, groups of exercises, or randomly chosen exercises to make worksheets that will give your students practice in the skills they need to perform well on specific standardized tests.

No Computer? Use Dial-a-Test®

A Prentice Hall Exclusive!

If you don't have access to a computer, one way to create worksheets or tests is to photocopy and paste exercises from this print version of the Computer Item Generator. A far less tedious way to is to use Prentice Hall's **free** Dial-a-Test® service. With Dial-a-Test®, you tell Prentice Hall which items you want on a test and let us create the test for you. For details, see page vii.

Create Tests and Worksheets Easily

Item Selection Options

- Select single items from any combination of textbook chapters or standardized tests.
- Select a range of exercises within one chapter or standardized test.
- Direct the software to randomly select exercises according to criteria you have chosen.

Output Options

- The Print Preview feature allows you to view and adjust pages before printing.
- Tests can be printed in one-column or two-column format.
- The software provides a customized answer key and a matching student answer sheet for each test or worksheet.

Dynamic Items—A Powerful Tool

Some of the items in the Computer Item Generator are dynamic. Dynamic items are very powerful and useful, because one item can be used to generate a practically unlimited number of different items. Here's how dynamic items work:

- Select any dynamic item and add it *several times* to the test file that you are working on.

  1. [TAAS 6,7,8+ 1.3.1.49] Estimate with whole numbers and decimals.
  2. [TAAS 6,7,8+ 1.3.1.49] Estimate with whole numbers and decimals.
  3. [TAAS 6,7,8+ 1.3.1.49] Estimate with whole numbers and decimals.

- Print the test or choose Print Preview. You will see that the program automatically adjusts the item to appear differently each time.

  1. When all 5 runways are open, a large airport can handle 48 airplanes landing per hour. What is a good estimate for the number of planes that can land in a 6-hour period?

     [A] 350 [B] 50 [C] 200 [D] 300

  2. When all 5 runways are open, a large airport can handle 99 airplanes landing per hour. What is a good estimate for the number of planes that can land in an 8-hour period?

     [A] 700 [B] 800 [C] 1000 [D] 100

  3. When all 5 runways are open, a large airport can handle 97 airplanes landing per hour. What is a good estimate for the number of planes that can land in a 5-hour period?

     [A] 300 [B] 600 [C] 100 [D] 500

One dynamic item, therefore, represents a lot of opportunities for practice and assessment. In addition, if you use dynamic items to create an assessment, each time you print the assessment, you get a **different, yet equivalent form**, each with its own answer key.

Other Types of Items

Items that are not dynamic are called static items. The Computer Item Generator allows you to add your own exercises and to modify the exercises in the existing item bank. (All user-created items are static.) This functionality allows you to create tests and worksheets uniquely customized to your needs and preferences. On the software, item types and formats are indicated by these icons:

= dynamic item	**= static item**
= multiple-choice item	**= free response item**
= item included with software	**= item customized by user**

User's Guide and On-Screen Help

The User's Guide for the Computer Item Generator with Standardized Test Practice describes the complete functionality of the software. The User's Guide appears in PDF format on the CD-ROM that contains the software. You will need to use Acrobat Reader™ to open and print the User's Guide. If you don't already have Acrobat Reader™ installed on your computer, you can install it from the CD-ROM.

The Computer Item Generator has an on-screen Help feature with easy-to-follow directions so that even novices can use the software immediately.

Another Middle Grades Math Resource to Help Prepare Students for Standardized Tests

You will also find the *Computer Item Generator with Standardized Test Practice* CD-ROM in the Middle Grades Math Assessment Success Kits for Courses 1, 2, and 3. Assessment Success Kits contain the Computer Item Generator CD-ROM plus pages of materials that give teachers everything they need to ready students for local, state, and national tests.

About the Dial-A-Test® Service

If you do not have access to a computer or would like the convenience of designing your own tests without typing a word, you may want to take advantage of our free Dial-A-Test® Service. Available to all users of *Prentice Hall Math*, Dial-A-Test® is simple to use. At the right is an example of a filled-out form.

-ORDER FORM- CTS

DIAL-A-TEST®
PRENTICE HALL SCHOOL DIVISION
CUSTOMIZED TESTING SERVICE
TOLL-FREE NUMBER 800-468-8378 (H O-T-T-E-S-T)

-ORDER FORM- CTS

You may **call** the Dial-A-Test® toll-free number during our business hours (9:00 A.M.-4:30 P.M. EST).
Now you may also FAX your order to 1-614-771-7365 any time.

DIAL-A-TEST®
PRENTICE HALL SCHOOL DIVISION
4350 EQUITY DRIVE
COLUMBUS, OH 43228

FOR PH USE DATE REC. DATE SENT
_ PHONE _ MAIL _ FAX

EXACT TEXT TITLE/VOL. Middle Grades Math, Course1 **© DATE** 1999
CODE 134354036

CUSTOMER INFORMATION
NAME Ellen Mack
SCHOOL Riverside High School
ADDRESS 700 River Road
CITY Wells River STATE TN ZIP 38578
PHONE 208-555-2717 EXT. 34

OBJECTIVES TO USE (CHECK ONE)
X LESSON OBJECTIVES
_ STANDARDIZED TEST PRACTICE OBJECTIVES

VERSIONS (SEE REVERSE–INSTRUCTION #4) (CHECK ONE)
_ 1. ORIGINAL X 2. SCRAMBLE QUESTIONS

DATE BY WHICH TEST IS NEEDED 11/30/98

TEST IDENTIFICATION (This information will appear at the top of your test.)
Ellen Mack
Math Period 2
Chapter 1 Test

EXAMPLE: Mr. Holtzman
Math, Period 5
Chapter Test

1 1.3	26 1.74	51	76	101	126	151	176
2 1.5	27 1.80	52	77	102	127	152	177
3 1.6	28 1.81	53	78	103	128	153	178
4 1.7	29 1.82	54	79	104	129	154	179
5 1.11	30 1.83	55	80	105	130	155	180
6 1.12	31	56	81	106	131	156	181
7 1.14	32	57	82	107	132	157	182
8 1.17	33	58	83	108	133	158	183
9 1.18	34	59	84	109	134	159	184
10 1.21	35	60	85	110	135	160	185
11 1.32	36	61	86	111	136	161	186
12 1.34	37	62	87	112	137	162	187
13 1.35	38	63	88	113	138	163	188
14 1.38	39	64	89	114	139	164	189
15 1.40	40	65	90	115	140	165	190
16 1.41	41	66	91	116	141	166	191
17 1.45	42	67	92	117	142	167	192
18 1.47	43	68	93	118	143	168	193
19 1.55	44	69	94	119	144	169	194
20 1.57	45	70	95	120	145	170	195
21 1.66	46	71	96	121	146	171	196
22 1.67	47	72	97	122	147	172	197
23 1.69	48	73	98	123	148	173	198
24 1.70	49	74	99	124	149	174	199
25 1.71	50	75	100	125	150	175	200

HERE'S HOW IT WORKS

1. **Choose the questions you want** from those listed in this book.
2. **Enter the numbers of the questions** in the order you want on a Dial-A-Test® Order Form (see page viii for a master that you may photocopy). Be sure to include the chapter number or the standardized test number on the form. For example, in the case of test question 17, taken from Chapter 1, mark the order form with the designation 1.17. Also be sure to check the box telling which objectives to use.
3. **Use a separate Dial-A-Test® order form** for each original test you request. You may use one form, however, to order multiple versions of the same original test.
4. **If you would like another version** of your original test with the questions scrambled, or put in another sequence, simply check the box labeled *Scramble Questions* on the order form. If you would like more than one scrambled version of your original test, note this on your order form or inform the Dial-A-Test® operator. Please note that Prentice Hall reserves the right to limit the number of tests and versions you can request at any one time, especially during the busier times of the year when midterms and finals are given.
5. **Choose the method** by which you would like to order your original test and/or multiple versions of your original test. To order by telephone, call toll free 1-800-468-8378 between 9:00 A.M. and 4:30 P.M. Eastern Standard Time and read the test question numbers to our Dial-A-Test® operator. To order by mail, send your completed Dial-A-Test® order form to the address listed below. Now you may also FAX your order to 1-614-771-7365.
6. **You may order** up to 100 questions per test by telephone on our toll-free 800 number or up to 200 questions per test by fax or by mail.
7. **Please allow a minimum of two weeks** for shipping, especially if you are ordering by mail. Although we process your order within 48 hours of your call or the receipt of your form by mail, mailing may take up to two weeks. Thus we ask you to plan accordingly and expect to receive your original test, any alternate test versions that you requested, and complete answer keys within a reasonable amount of time.
8. **Tests are available all year.** You can order tests before the school year begins, during vacation, or as you need them.
9. **For additional order forms** or to ask questions regarding this service, please write to the following address:

Dial-A-Test®, Prentice Hall School Division
4350 Equity Drive, Columbus, OH 43228

-ORDER FORM-
CTS

DIAL-A-TEST®
PRENTICE HALL SCHOOL DIVISION
CUSTOMIZED TESTING SERVICE
TOLL-FREE NUMBER 800-468-8378 (H O-T-T-E-S-T)

-ORDER FORM-
CTS

You may **call** the Dial-A-Test® toll-free number during our business hours (9:00 A.M.-4:30 P.M. EST). Now you may also FAX your order to 1-614-771-7365 any time.

DIAL-A-TEST®
PRENTICE HALL SCHOOL DIVISION
4350 EQUITY DRIVE
COLUMBUS, OH 43228

FOR PH USE DATE REC. DATE SENT
__ PHONE __ MAIL __ FAX ________ ________

EXACT TEXT TITLE/VOL. Middle Grades Math, Course1 **© DATE** 1999
CODE 134354036

CUSTOMER INFORMATION
NAME ____________
SCHOOL ____________
ADDRESS ____________
CITY ____________ STATE ____ ZIP ____
PHONE ____________ EXT. ____

OBJECTIVES TO USE (CHECK ONE)
__ LESSON OBJECTIVES
__ STANDARDIZED TEST PRACTICE OBJECTIVES

DATE BY WHICH TEST IS NEEDED ________

VERSIONS (SEE REVERSE–INSTRUCTION #4) (CHECK ONE)
__ 1. ORIGINAL __ 2. SCRAMBLE QUESTIONS

TEST IDENTIFICATION (This information will appear at the top of your test.)
____
____
____
____

EXAMPLE: Mr. Holtzman
Math, Period 5
Chapter Test

1 ___	26 ___	51 ___	76 ___	101 ___	126 ___	151 ___	176 ___
2 ___	27 ___	52 ___	77 ___	102 ___	127 ___	152 ___	177 ___
3 ___	28 ___	53 ___	78 ___	103 ___	128 ___	153 ___	178 ___
4 ___	29 ___	54 ___	79 ___	104 ___	129 ___	154 ___	179 ___
5 ___	30 ___	55 ___	80 ___	105 ___	130 ___	155 ___	180 ___
6 ___	31 ___	56 ___	81 ___	106 ___	131 ___	156 ___	181 ___
7 ___	32 ___	57 ___	82 ___	107 ___	132 ___	157 ___	182 ___
8 ___	33 ___	58 ___	83 ___	108 ___	133 ___	158 ___	183 ___
9 ___	34 ___	59 ___	84 ___	109 ___	134 ___	159 ___	184 ___
10 ___	35 ___	60 ___	85 ___	110 ___	135 ___	160 ___	185 ___
11 ___	36 ___	61 ___	86 ___	111 ___	136 ___	161 ___	186 ___
12 ___	37 ___	62 ___	87 ___	112 ___	137 ___	162 ___	187 ___
13 ___	38 ___	63 ___	88 ___	113 ___	138 ___	163 ___	188 ___
14 ___	39 ___	64 ___	89 ___	114 ___	139 ___	164 ___	189 ___
15 ___	40 ___	65 ___	90 ___	115 ___	140 ___	165 ___	190 ___
16 ___	41 ___	66 ___	91 ___	116 ___	141 ___	166 ___	191 ___
17 ___	42 ___	67 ___	92 ___	117 ___	142 ___	167 ___	192 ___
18 ___	43 ___	68 ___	93 ___	118 ___	143 ___	168 ___	193 ___
19 ___	44 ___	69 ___	94 ___	119 ___	144 ___	169 ___	194 ___
20 ___	45 ___	70 ___	95 ___	120 ___	145 ___	170 ___	195 ___
21 ___	46 ___	71 ___	96 ___	121 ___	146 ___	171 ___	196 ___
22 ___	47 ___	72 ___	97 ___	122 ___	147 ___	172 ___	197 ___
23 ___	48 ___	73 ___	98 ___	123 ___	148 ___	173 ___	198 ___
24 ___	49 ___	74 ___	99 ___	124 ___	149 ___	174 ___	199 ___
25 ___	50 ___	75 ___	100 ___	125 ___	150 ___	175 ___	200 ___

Chapter 1: Using Statistics to Analyze Data

Lesson 1-1 Objective 1: Organize data into frequency tables.

Dynamic Item

1. A computer is used to generate the following random set of square numbers.
   16 1 729 36 1681 64,516 576 49,284 2025 1849 49 289 894,916
   Make a frequency table of numbers with same digit length from this set of data.

Dynamic Item

2. The students' scores on a math test are shown on the following frequency table:

Score	16	17	18	19	20	21	22	23	24	25
Number of Students	3	3	2	1	4	2	0	3	1	4

   How many students scored above 22?

   [A] 0 [B] 9 [C] 12 [D] 8

3. In your own words describe a frequency table and a line plot.

4. If oranges were not included in the data below, would the range be different? Explain.

			x
	x		x
x	x		x
x	x		x
x	x		x
x	x		x
x	x	x	x
x	x	x	x
x	x	x	x
x	x	x	x
x	x	x	x
x	x	x	x
Apples	Oranges	Pears	Bananas

5. How many tickets were sold on Friday, if the total sales for the five days is $234 and each ticket costs $4.50?

Day	Frequency
Monday	𝍸 |
Tuesday	𝍸 𝍸
Wednesday	𝍸 𝍸 ||
Thursday	𝍸 ||||
Friday	?

[A] 52 [B] 37 [C] 67 [D] 15

6. The frequency table below shows the number of books sold during one week at the local bookstore. How can the information in the frequency table be used by the bookstore?

Type of Book	Frequency
Fiction	235
Nonfiction	185
Adventure	79
Science Fiction	210
Mystery	150

7. An old Greek word for meat stew is the longest word in the world. The word translated in English is: Lopadotemachoselachogaleokranioleipsanodrimhypotrimmatosilphioparao melitokatakechymenokichlepikossyophattoperisteralektryonoptekephalliok igklopeleiolaoiosiraiobaphetraganopterygon.

Letter	Tally	Frequency
a	~~||||~~ ~~||||~~ ~~||||~~ |||	18
e	?	?
i	?	?
o	?	?
u	?	?

Source: The Second Kids World Almanac of Records and Facts

a. Copy and complete the frequency table.
b. Describe the data recorded in your frequency table.

8. Construct a frequency table from the line plot below.

```
                x
                x
 x              x
 x      x       x
 x      x       x       x
 x      x       x       x       x
 x      x       x       x       x
------------------------------------
1989   1990    1991    1992    1993
```

Chapter 1: Using Statistics to Analyze Data

Lesson 1-1 Objective 2: Make a line plot and find the range of data.

Dynamic Item

9. The numbers below represent the ages of the first ten people in line at the movie theater. Make a line plot and find the range of the data.
41, 38, 40, 41, 44, 37, 37, 45, 36, 41

[A] range= 45

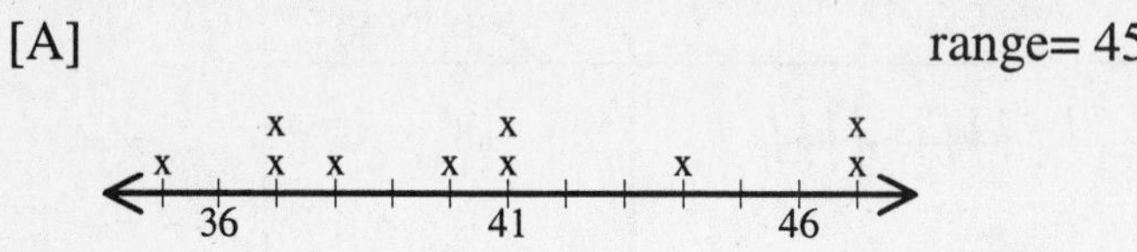

[B] range= 36

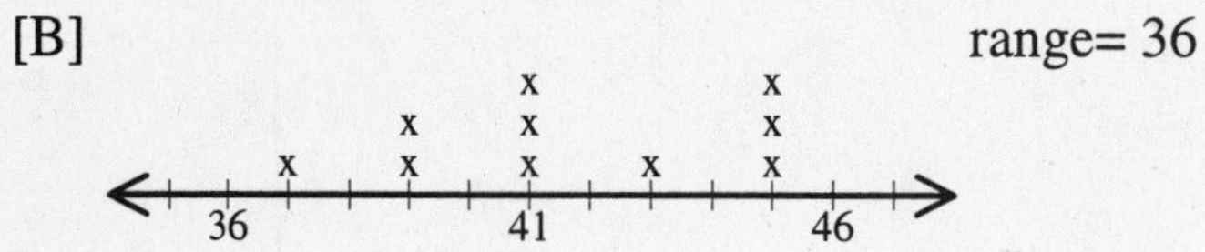

[C] range= 9

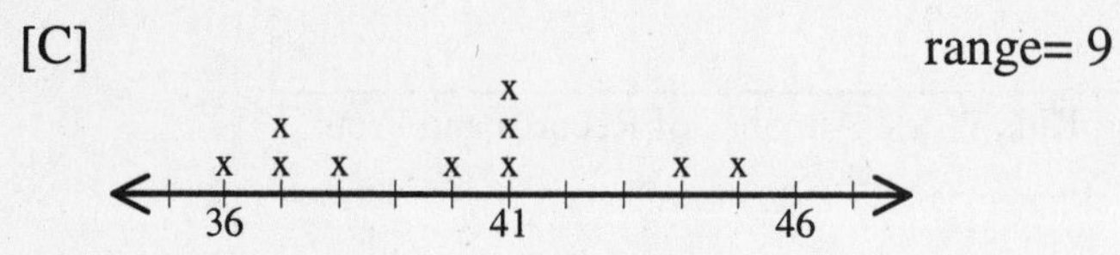

[D] range= 4

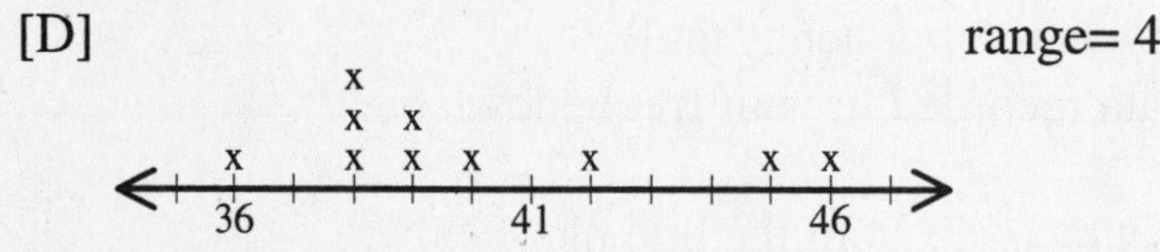

Dynamic Item

10. The numbers below represent the scores on a math test. Make a line plot and find the range of the data.
49, 49, 50, 50, 56, 46, 51, 56, 48, 51

11. Which question could NOT be answered by using the line plot below?

Ages of Students Who Volunteer at the Library

				X
				X
	X			X
	X		X	X
X	X		X	X
X	X	X	X	X
X	X	X	X	X
10	11	12	13	14

[A] How many more 13-year-old students volunteer at the library than 10-year-old students?

[B] How many 14-year-old students volunteer at the library?

[C] How many hours do the 12-year-old students volunteer at the library?

[D] How many students between the ages of 10 and 13 volunteer at the library?

12. Create a problem about birthdays using the information shown in the line plot below.

			X	
	X		X	
X	X		X	
X	X	X	X	
X	X	X	X	X
Mon.	Tues.	Weds.	Thurs.	Fri.

13. Use the following set of numbers: 39, 23.2, 18, 36.9, 45, 52
a. Add one more number to the data so that the range is 40.
b. Describe how you found the number.

14. The birth months of the 42 presidents of the United States are shown in the table below.

Month	Tally	Frequency
January	||||	4
February	||||	4
March	~~||||~~	5
April	||||	4
May	||	2
June	|	1
July	|||	3
August	|||	3
September	||	2
October	~~||||~~ |	6
November	~~||||~~	5
December	|||	3

Source: The Universal Almanac 1992

a. Make a line plot.
b. In which month were the most presidents born?

15. The favorite TV sports programs are shown below.

Sport	Frequency
Football	~~llll~~ ~~llll~~ llll
Soccer	llll
Baseball	~~llll~~ ~~llll~~ ll
Basketball	~~llll~~ llll
Other	ll

a. Make a line plot.
b. How many more people like football or basketball than baseball or soccer?
c. Can you find the range for this set of data? Explain.

Lesson 1-2 Objective 1: Solve problems by making a table.

16. Suppose you record the number of claps of thunder during a thunderstorm. The table below shows the pattern of claps over time. If the pattern continues, how many total claps will occur in 32 seconds?

Seconds	Total Claps
1	2
2	3
4	4
8	5

17. Mimo and Stan went to the ice cream parlor for some frozen yogurt. They wish to leave the waitress a tip. Mimo has 5 coins in his pocket: a penny, a nickel, a dime, a quarter, and a half-dollar. If he uses exactly three coins for the tip, how many different tips are possible?

[A] 15 [B] 10 [C] 5 [D] 20

18. John, Nick, and Brian are friends in college. They each play a sport. The football player and Brian are roommates. John has won an award for having the most runs batted in during a season. Who is the football player?

19. Find the smallest number that meets the following criteria:

    When you divide the number by 3, there is 1 left over.
    When you divide the number by 4, there is 2 left over.
    When you divide the number by 6, there is 4 left over.

Lesson 1-2 Objective 2: Solve problems using any strategy.

20. Crystal wants to put a fence around her vegetable garden. Her garden is 5 ft wide and 4 ft long. She plans to put a post at each corner and at every foot. How many fence posts will Crystal need?

    [A] 18 [B] 19 [C] 14 [D] 20

21. The numbers 1, 2, 3, and 4 are written on separate index cards. How many different numbers can be formed using one or more of the index cards?

22. The sales manager is printing out mailing labels for the annual sales flyer. There will be 175 customers receiving the flyer. The labels run 3 across and 10 down on each sheet. How many sheets of labels must the sales manager put into the printer?

23. The art teacher buys paints, paint brushes, and smocks for each student in her class. The paint can only be bought in tubes of 5. The paint brushes come in packs of 8, and the smocks in boxes of 6. The art teacher has 25 students in her class. What is the least amount of each item the art teacher can buy?

24. Together, Jim and Tony earned $18.50 raking leaves. Tony earned $3.00 less than Jim. How much money did Jim and Tony each earn?

Lesson 1-3 Objective 1: Find the mean.

Dynamic Item

25. Find the mean of 95, 88, 83, 91, and 83.

    [A] 88 [B] 83 [C] 89 [D] 96

Dynamic Item

26. Find the mean of 89, 38, 34, 70, and 34.

27. Would a frequency table be the most useful for finding the range, mode, or median of a set of data? Explain.

28. What is the best kind of average for the average height of the students on the basketball team? Explain.

29. If you were to predict the type of weather that Dallas, Texas, will have tomorrow, would you use the mean, median, or mode? Explain.

30. The mean of seven numbers in a set of data is 18. Six of the numbers are 15, 23, 8, 17, 20, and 36. Find the seventh number in the set of data.

31. The mean monthly rainfall for the first six months of the year was 4 in. For the last six months of the year, the mean rainfall was 2 in. per month. What was the mean monthly rainfall for the entire year?

Lesson 1-3 Objective 2: Find the median or mode.

Dynamic Item

32. Find the mode of 99, 29, 16, 98, and 16.

[A] 29 [B] 51.6 [C] 16 [D] 52.6

Dynamic Item

33. Find the mode of 98, 92, 60, 96, and 60.

34. The bar graph below shows the number of books read by students over the summer.

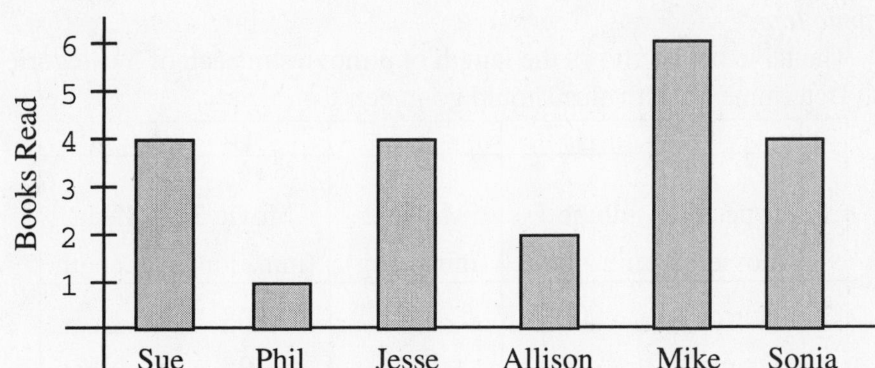

a. Find the mean and the mode.
b. Which one do you think better reflects the number of books read over the summer?

35. Explain how changing one or two numbers in a set of data can affect the mean.

36. Which can be most affected by the range of data: the mean, median, or mode? Explain.

37. A teacher allows her students to decide whether to use the mean, median, or mode to determine their test averages. One student determined that he will receive the highest average if he uses the mean. Which set of test scores are his?

    [A] 92, 83, 76, 76, 93　　[B] 72, 83, 95, 70, 85

    [C] 81, 85, 70, 72, 85　　[D] 81, 85, 73, 82, 76

38. Which pair of numbers, when included with the set of data, will raise the value of BOTH the mean and median?
    6, 8, 10, 14, 18

    [A] 14, 15　　[B] 1, 10　　[C] 8, 14　　[D] 7, 15

39. Which set of data is best described as having a mean of 6 and a mode of 5?

    [A] 10, 7, 5, 8, 5　　[B] 5, 12, 1, 5, 7

    [C] 2, 11, 5, 9, 3　　[D] 3, 8, 5, 9, 10

40. Write a sentence using the word median.

Lesson 1-4　Objective 1: Organize data in a spreadsheet.

Dynamic Item

41. The table below shows the length of 3 movies in each of 3 categories. Determine which value should go in cell C4.

	A	B	C	D	E
1	Type of Movie	Movie 1 (min. long)	Movie 2 (min. long)	Movie 3 (min. long)	Mean Length
2	Horror	90	93	108	
3	Drama		102	105	106
4	Action	96	???	99	103

    [A] 99　　[B] 114　　[C] 97　　[D] 111

Dynamic Item

42. What number goes in cell B5 in the spreadsheet below?

	A	B	C	D
1		Total	Males	Females
2	Southwest High School	1754	828	926
3	Marshall High School	1869		803
4	Washburn High School	1389	556	
5	Buena High School		640	453
6	Jefferson High School		776	836

43.

	A	B	C	D	E	F
1	Player	Game 1	Game 2	Game 3	Game 4	Mean
2	Rob	100	104	99	101	101
3	Jo Ann	96	97	100	103	99
4	Ed	105	107	101	99	103
5	Hector	89	90	88	93	

The spreadsheet above shows golf scores for each player in an amateur golf tournament.

a. Give the formula for cell F5. Calculate the value.

b. Hector said that if he scores 90 in Game 5 his average will decrease. Do you agree? Explain your reasoning.

44. Explain how you would set up the following information in a spreadsheet.

C. Jones	#1234	$7.00 per hour	35 hours worked
K. Smith	#1356	$5.00 per hour	30 hours worked
M. Chavez	#1567	$12.00 per hour	39 hours worked
D. Cuttoni	#1982	$15.00 per hour	40 hours worked

45. Russell's younger sister Paula asked him what he learned in math class today. Russell learned about computer spreadsheets. How would Russell explain to Paula what a computer spreadsheet is and how it is useful?

46. Below is a list of student test scores. Set up a spreadsheet from the data given. Explain how the spreadsheet is organized.

    Mark F. 90, 82, 95, 93
    Julie A. 92, 91, 85, 88
    Dimi C. 87, 84, 91, 90
    Raul R. 95, 73, 84, 88
    Patel H. 86, 87, 88, 91

Lesson 1-4 Objective 2: Create formulas for spreadsheets.

Dynamic Item

47. The spreadsheet below shows the length of 3 movies in each of 3 categories. Choose the formula that could be used in cell E2.

	A	B	C	D	E
1	Type of Movie	Movie 1 (min. long)	Movie 2 (min. long)	Movie 3 (min. long)	Mean Length
2	Animated	72	63	84	73
3	Drama	92	104	113	103
4	Action	119	84	109	104

[A] 3 * D2 – B2 + C2 [B] (B2 + C2 + D2) / 3

[C] B2 + C2 + D2 / 3 [D] 3 * D2 – (B2 + C2)

Dynamic Item

48. What formula could be used to solve for the cell B6 in the spreadsheet below?

	A	B	C	D
1		Total	Males	Females
2	Lincoln Middle School	1825	881	944
3	Lewisville Middle School	1772		855
4	Rindge Middle School	1369	582	
5	Watertown Middle School		622	479
6	Franklin Middle School		748	813

49.

	A	B	C	D	E	F
1	Player	Game 1	Game 2	Game 3	Game 4	Mean
2	Rob	100	104	99	101	101
3	Jo Ann	96	97	100	103	99
4	Ed	105	107	101	99	103
5	Hector	89	90	88	93	90

The spreadsheet above shows golf scores for each player in an amateur golf tournament. What is the mean golf score for Rob, Hector, and Ed for games 1 and 3?

[A] 99 [B] 97 [C] 98 [D] 96

50. Suppose a spreadsheet has six numbers in row 2. Write a formula that would be in cell G2 to find the mean of the six numbers.

51.

	A	B	C	D	E
1	School	Tuition 1991	Tuition 1992	Tuition 1993	Mean Tuition
2	Art Tech.	\$5000	\$6500	\$7199	\$6233
3	State Univ.	\$8500	\$8999	\$10,500	\$9333
4	Science Inst.	\$13,500	\$14,699	\$16,000	\$14,733
5	Comm. Coll.	\$4500	\$5600	\$6331	\$5477
6	Univ. of SNP	\$7000			

Above is a spreadsheet of tuition costs for several colleges and universities. In 1992 the tuition of the University of SNP increased \$1600 from the previous year. In 1993 the tuition was twice as much as it was in 1991. Fill in the missing information on the spreadsheet.

52. The spreadsheet below shows the windchill temperature for three days. Find the mean temperature for the three days for winds of 10 mph.

	A	B	C	D
1	Wind (mph)	Day 1 (temp.°F)	Day 2 (temp.°F)	Day 3 (temp.°F)
2	5	48	39	28
3	10	41	30	16
4	20	32	19	7
5	30	28	14	1

53. The spreadsheet shows golf scores for each player in an amateur golf tournament.

	A	B	C	D	E	F
1	Player	Game 1	Game 2	Game 3	Game 4	Mean
2	Rob	100	104	99	101	101
3	Jo Ann	96	97	100	103	99
4	Ed	105	107	101	99	103
5	Hector	89	90	88	93	90

Determine what will happen to the value in F5 if each of the following occurs:

a. the value in cell C5 gets larger
b. the value in cell B5 gets smaller
c. the value in cell B2 gets larger

Lesson 1-5 Objective 1: Read and understand bar and line graphs.

Dynamic Item

54. Which month had the least cloudy days?

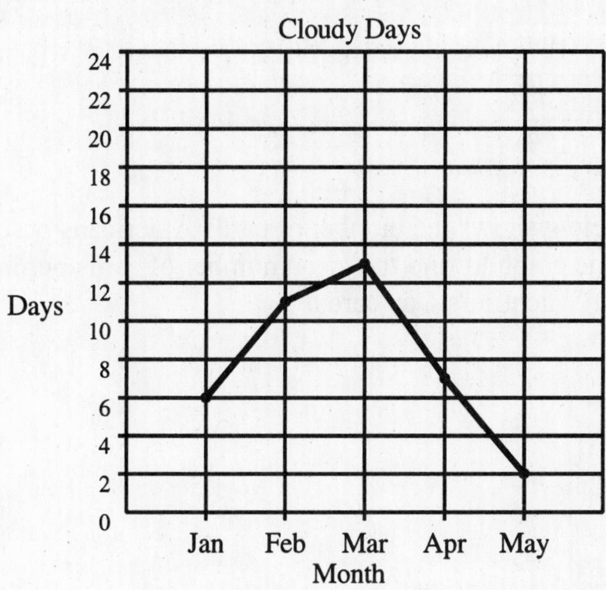

[A] January [B] May [C] April [D] February

Dynamic Item

55. The graph below shows the yearly rainfall in inches in Sagamore County for 1982-1987. Find the rainfall for 1982.

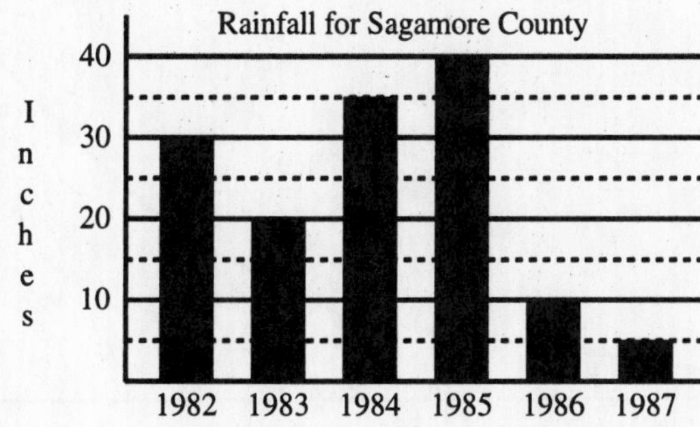

[A] 35 inches [B] 30 inches [C] 20 inches [D] 40 inches

56. Frederick claims that a line graph would be the most appropriate for displaying the data below. Do you agree? Explain.

Dairy	30%
Seafood	21%
Vegetables	18%
Fruits	20%
Chocolate	11%

57. The graph below shows the number of cards Americans purchased in 1990. Use the graph to find the mean number of cards purchased in 1990 that were not Valentine's Day cards.

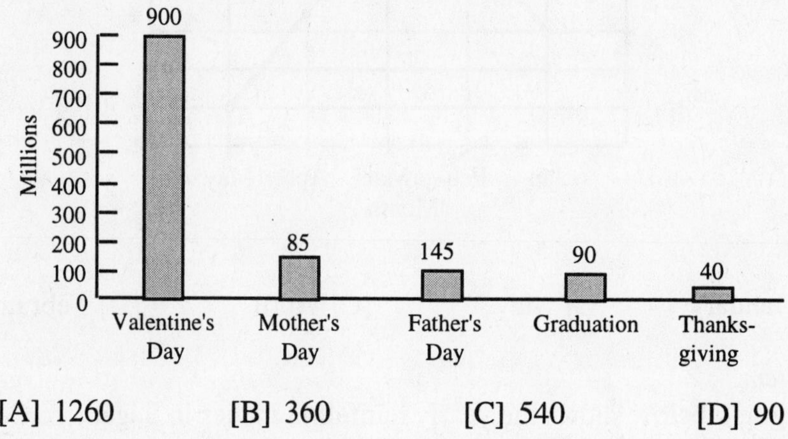

[A] 1260 [B] 360 [C] 540 [D] 90

58. Write two sentences describing the data displayed in the line graph below.

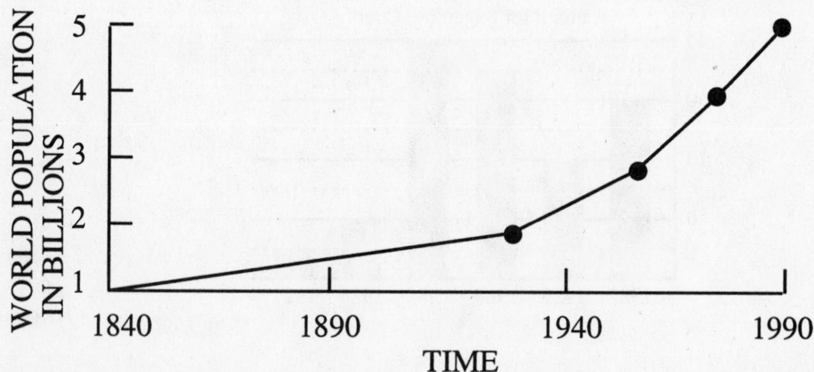

59. You are doing a report on heroic figures to kids. You have to write a paragraph summarizing the data on the bar graph shown below. What will you write?

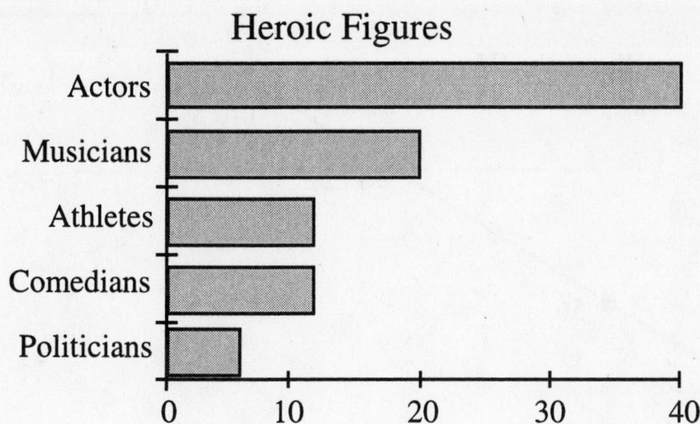

60. The graph below shows the cost to rent a car. Ann Marie can spend no more than $250 on a rental car. Use the graph to determine how many days Ann Marie can rent a car.

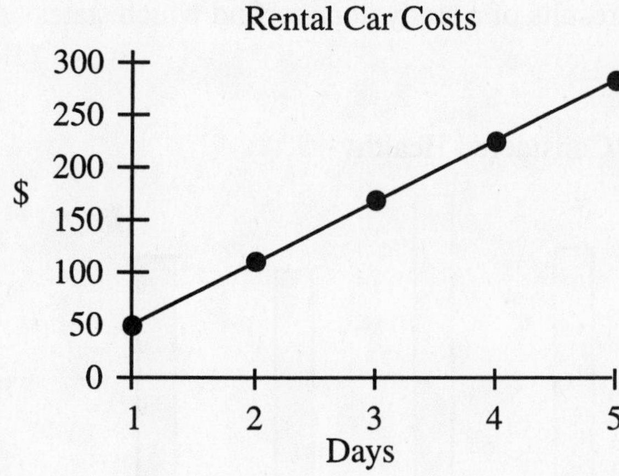

61. Sheryl is a junior accountant. The graph below shows the amount of money Sheryl earns for hours worked. Sheryl is a hard worker. To reward her, her boss decides to increase her hourly rate by $2. What is Sheryl's new hourly rate?

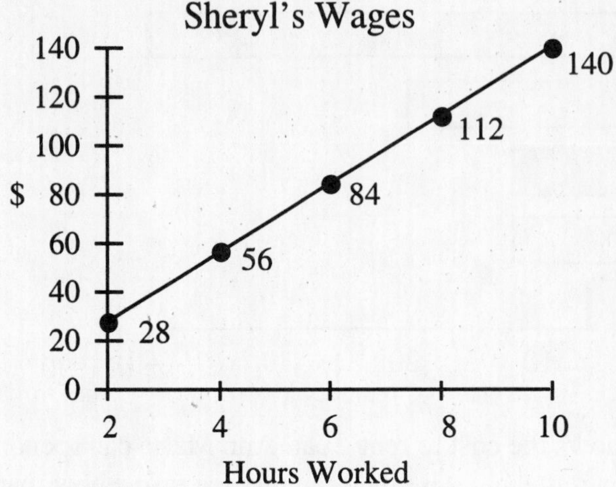

62. Certain states are healthier to live in than others. The bar graph below shows a portion of the results of a study done to find which states are healthier than others.

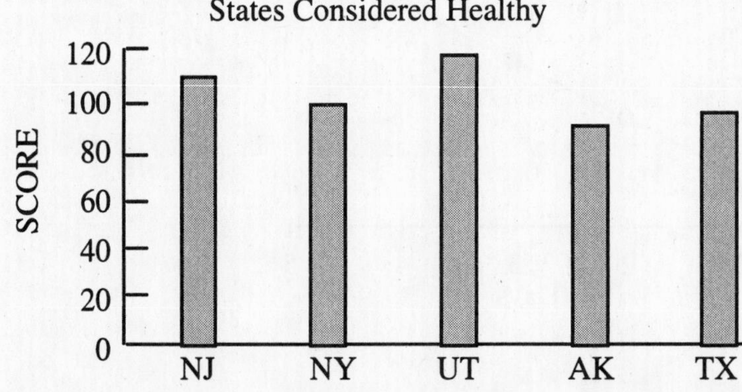

a. According to the graph, which state is the healthiest state to live in?
b. Explain how you would be able to determine the mode from this set of data.

63. Refer to the graph showing the number of games won.

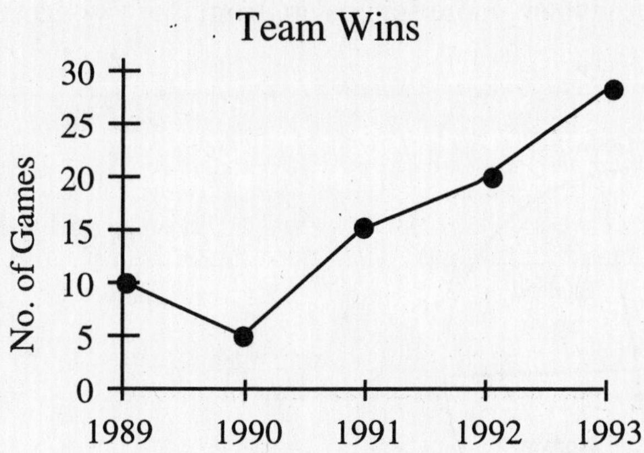

a. How many more games did the team win in 1993 than in 1990?
b. What conclusion can you make from the graph?

Lesson 1-5 Objective 2: Read and understand circle graphs.

Dynamic Item

64. Use the circle graph below to find out how many children are not playing baseball.

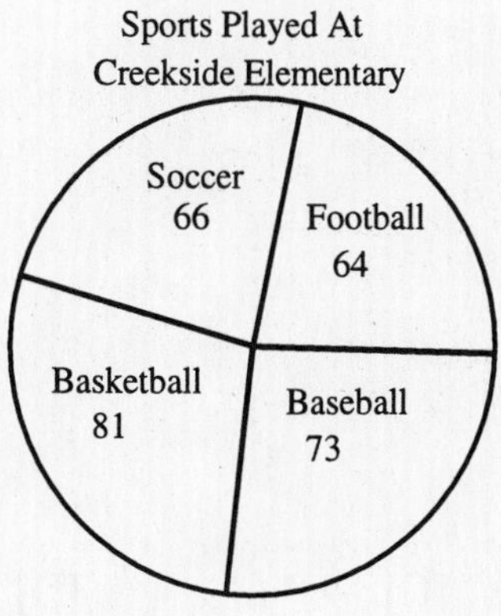

[A] 218 [B] 220 [C] 203 [D] 211

Dynamic Item

65. Erik has a stamp collection. The graph below shows how many stamps are from each country. How many more stamps are from Norway than from England?

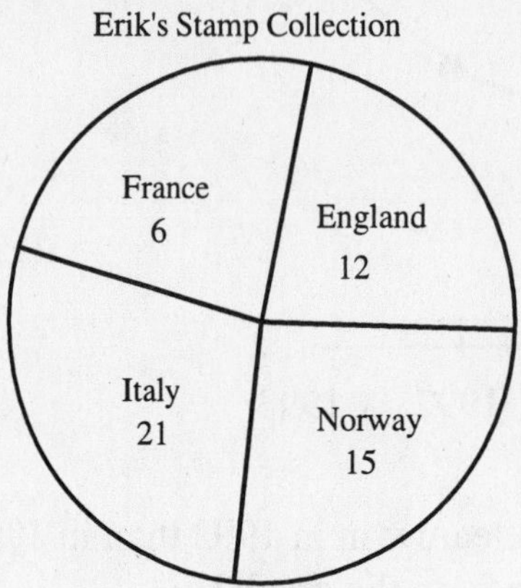

66. Describe the similarities and differences between a bar graph and a circle graph.

67. Estimate the fractional part of the monthly budget that goes into savings each month.

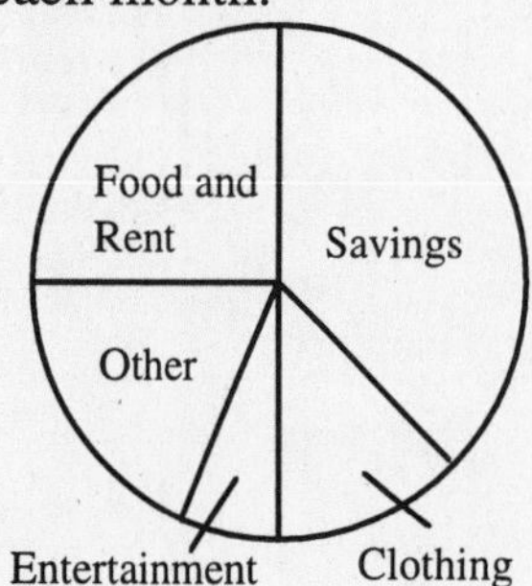

[A] $\frac{3}{8}$ [B] 1 [C] $\frac{3}{4}$ [D] $\frac{1}{2}$

68. Why would a circle graph NOT be appropriate for displaying the data below?

Foreign-Born Population of the United States
1950-1990

Year	Number
1950	10,095,000
1960	9,738,000
1970	9,619,000
1980	14,080,000
1990	19,767,000

(Source: SCOPE, No. 15, Summer 1993)

69. The circle graph below shows how the federal government spent an average tax dollar in 1990. What is the mean amount that the federal government spent on defense, income security, and education in 1990?

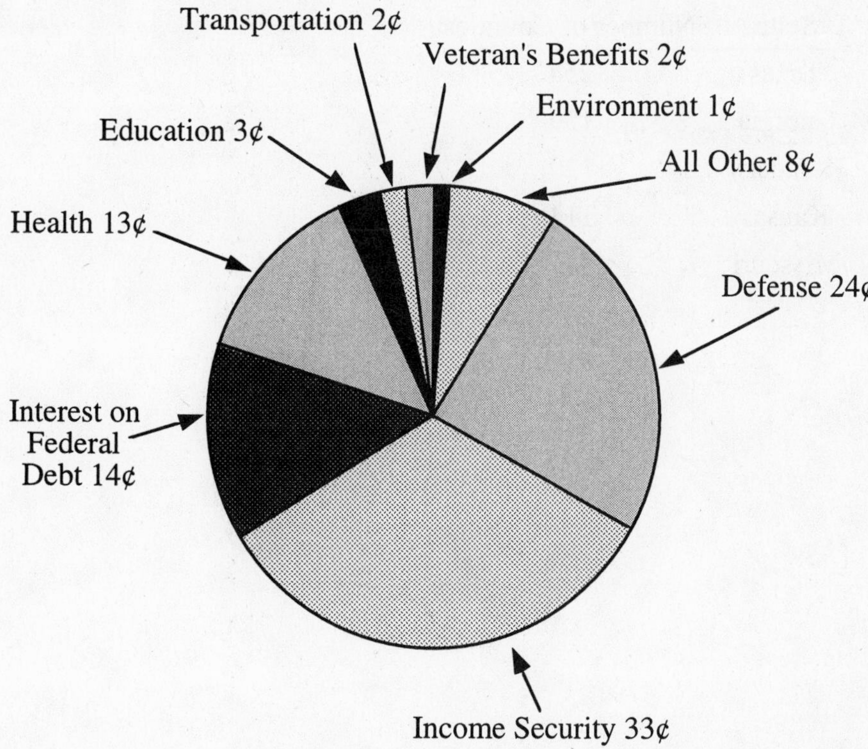

Lesson 1-6 Objective 1: Make bar graphs.

Dynamic Item

70. Use the following information to draw a bar graph showing the number of members of an athletic club who participate in various sports.

Tennis	55
Swimming	30
Aerobics	85
Volleyball	95
Track	70

71. Explain what the bars in a bar graph represent.

72. Why would a scale of 1 to 260 using intervals of 10 be inappropriate for graphing the data below? What scale and interval would be more appropriate for graphing the data?

State	Number of Counties
Texas	254
Georgia	159
Kentucky	120
Kansas	114
Missouri	105

73. Refer to the graph of Week 1 sales.

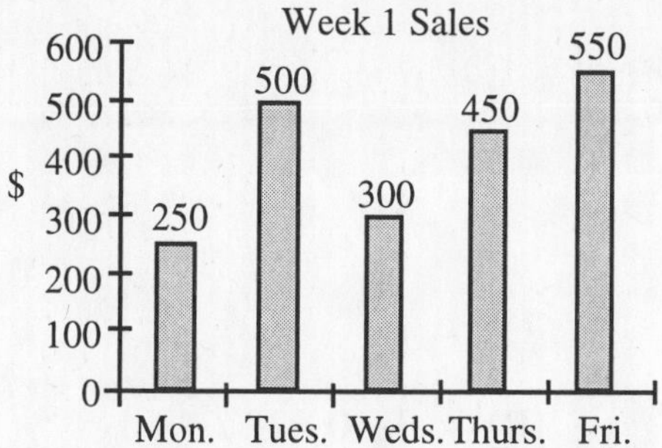

On Monday the sales for week 2 were $125 less than the sales for Monday of week 1. On Tuesday and Wednesday of week 2 the sales were $75 more than the sales for Thursday of week 1. The sales for Thursday were the same for both weeks. The sales for Friday of week 2 were $150 less than the sales for Friday of week 1. Which bar graph shows the amount of sales for week 2?

[A]

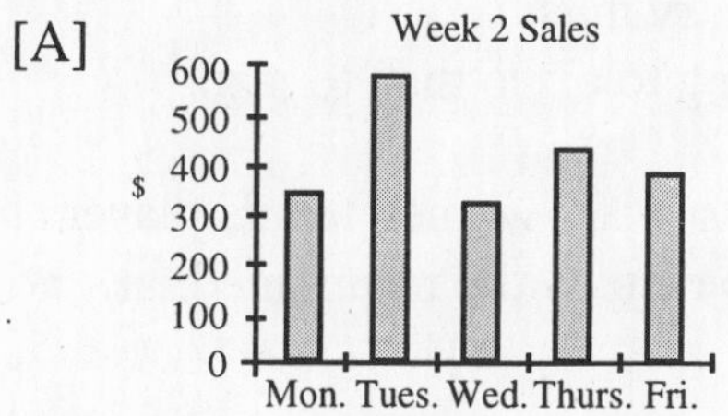

[B]

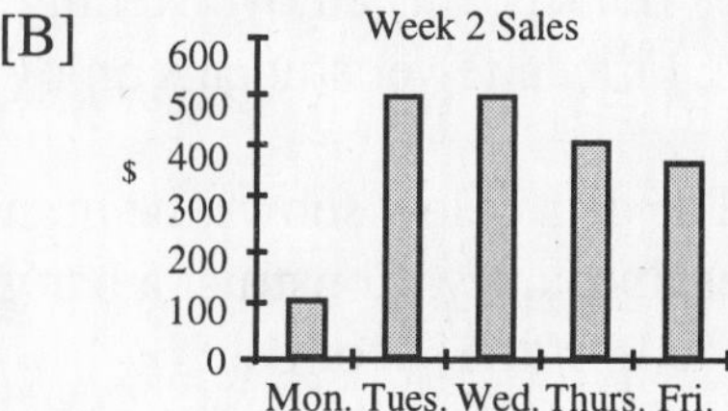

[C]

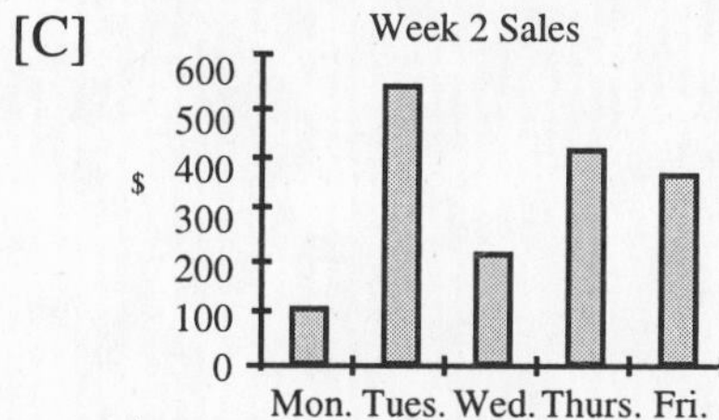

[D]

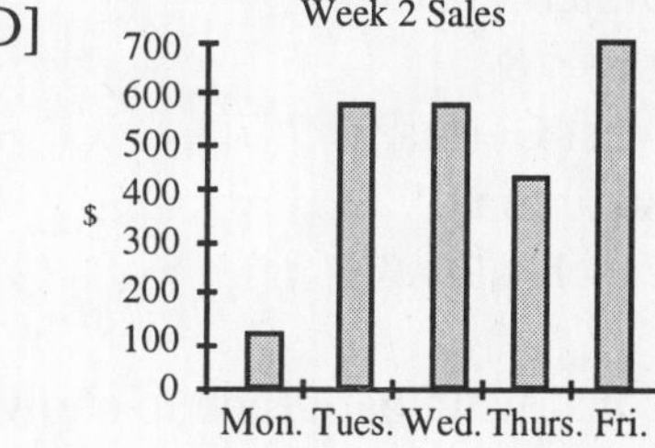

74. Which scale and interval would be the most appropriate for making a bar graph of the data?

Country	Area in Square Miles
Barbados	166
Dominica	290
Grenada	133
St. Lucia	238

[A] scale: 0 - 250
interval: 50

[B] scale: 0 - 300
interval: 50

[C] scale: 0 - 200
interval: 50

[D] scale: 0 - 240
interval: 10

75. Construct a bar graph using the information below.
a. Thirty-five students enjoy listening to rock-n-roll music.
b. Twenty more students enjoy listening to jazz than to rock-n-roll music.
c. Ten students enjoy listening to country music.
d. Fifteen fewer students enjoy listening to disco than to jazz.

76. The data below shows the number of top-100 women tennis players in each country. Construct a bar graph to display the mean, median, and mode of the set of data.

United States 31
Italy 8
West Germany 7
Australia 7
Czechoslovakia 6

77. Construct a bar graph to show the number of women in the state legislature in 1992 for each state in the table below. What was the mean number of women for the states listed?

State	Number of Women in 1992
New Hampshire	131
Maine	60
Washington	48
Nevada	9

Dynamic Item

78. The table below shows the number of games each team won last season. Choose the bar graph that best represents the data.

Team	Games Won
A	14
B	10
C	6

[A]

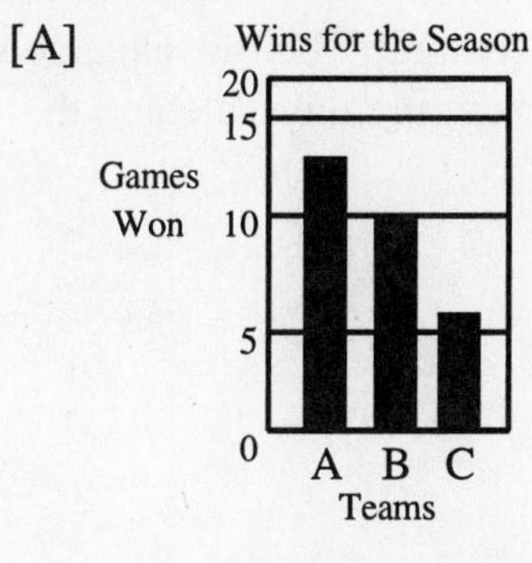

[B]

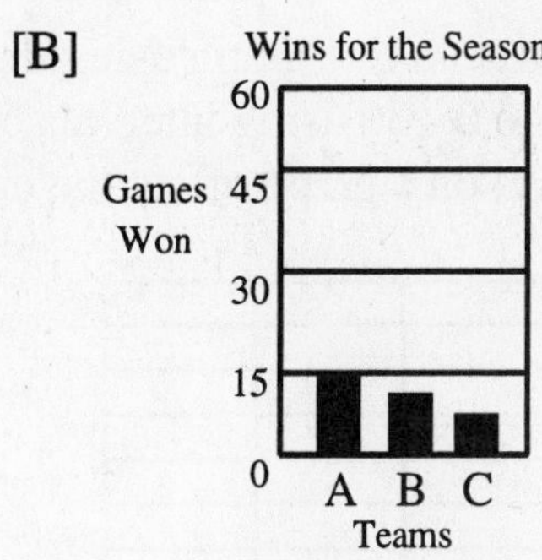

[C]

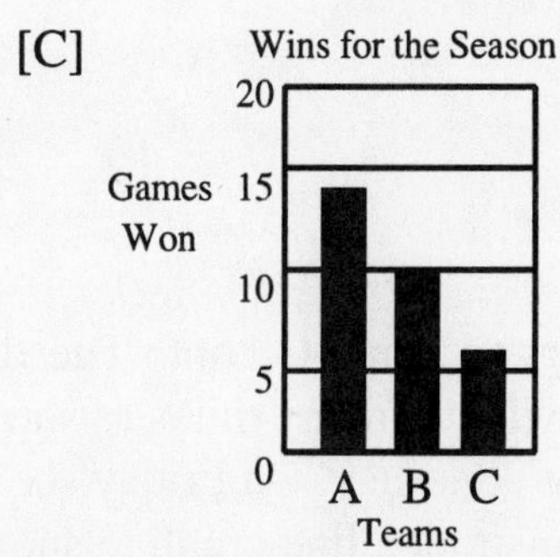

[D]

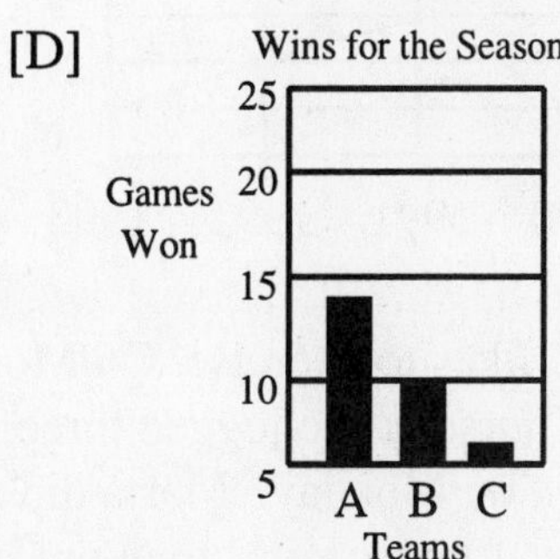

Lesson 1-6 Objective 2: Make line graphs.

Dynamic Item

79. The average price for a pair of shoes is shown for the years 1991 through 1995. Draw a line graph for this data. Which two year period had the greatest increase?

Year	1991	1992	1993	1994	1995
Price	$37.50	$39.70	$41.80	$45.50	$46.00

80. In your own words, explain how to construct a line graph.

81. Your classmate George is having trouble constructing a graph from a table below. Explain to George how to display the data in a graph.

Year	Salary
1990	$25,800.00
1991	$26,574.00
1992	$27,371.22
1993	$28,192.36

82. Construct a line graph using the data from the graph below. Change the scale to 0 - 30 using intervals of 5. Does changing the scale and the interval on a graph affect the data?

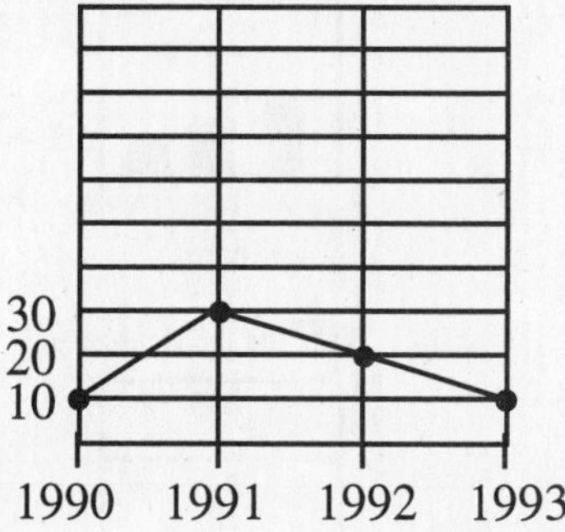

83. Marta likes to exercise. On Monday she jogged 5 mi. On both Tuesday and Thursday she jogged three more than twice as many miles as she jogged on Monday. Marta did not jog on Wednesday. On Friday she jogged 4 fewer miles than on Tuesday. Construct a line graph to show how many miles Marta jogged each day. What was the average number of miles per day?

Lesson 1-7 Objective 1: Recognize misleading line graphs.

Dynamic Item

84. Both graphs represent the number of clients signed up each year at Shadydeal Loans. Which graph is misleading? Why?

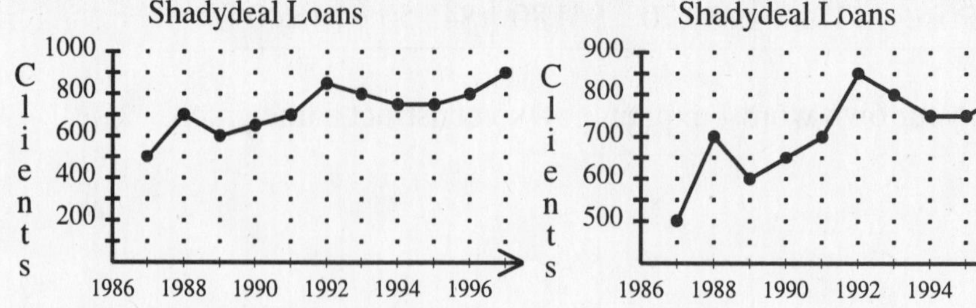

85. One graph below seems to show that the number of sit-ups Mark did in November was more than double the number of sit-ups he did in September. Which graph is it?

[A]

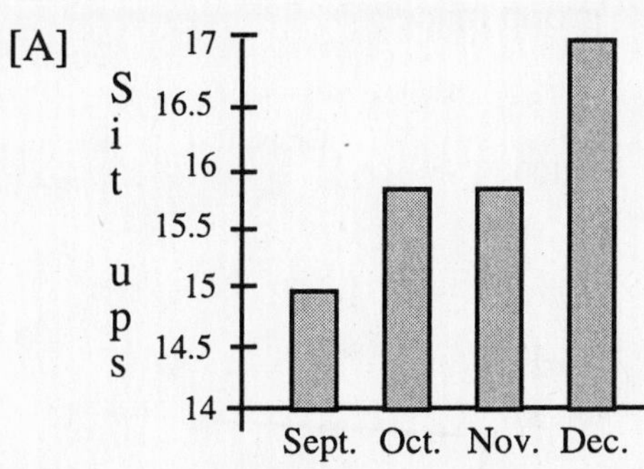

[B]

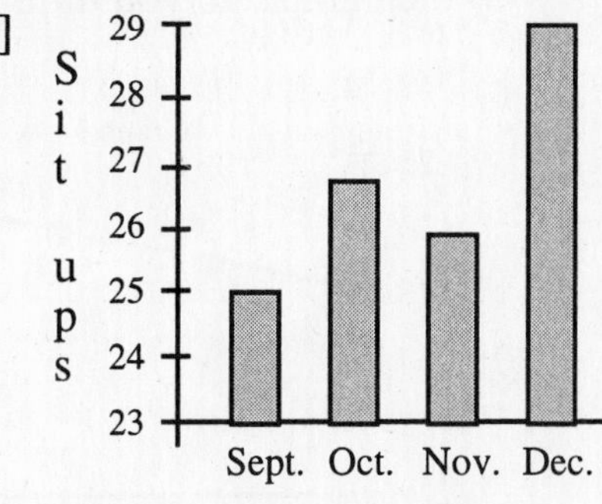

[C]

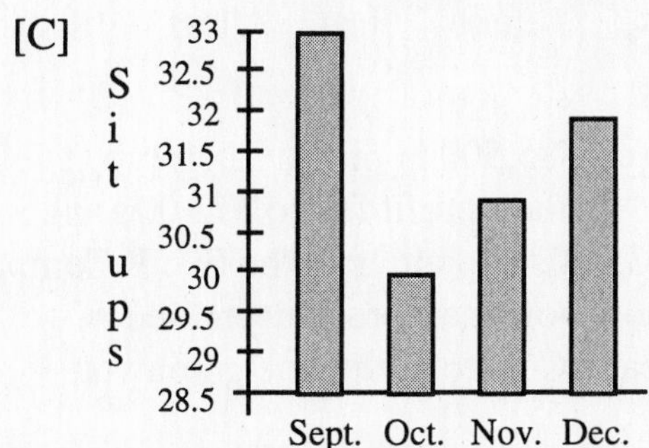

[D]

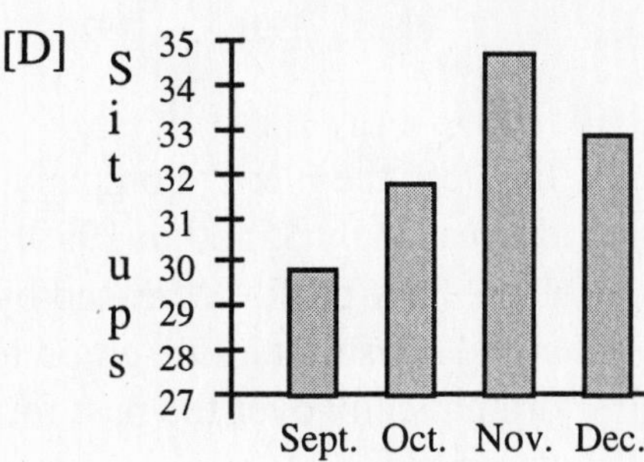

86. The sales for the Bicycle Company have decreased over the past five years. Use the table below. How would you construct a line graph to show a very small change in sales over the past five years?

Year	Sales
1989	$125,000
1990	$110,000
1991	$90,000
1992	$72,000
1993	$60,000

87. The fans of We Be Jam'in rock group are angry about the price of a concert ticket. They say that the price for concert tickets has been rising too sharply. The fans decided to make a line graph to support their claim. The rock group disagrees. They also made a line graph to support their claim. Which graph do you think the rock group made?

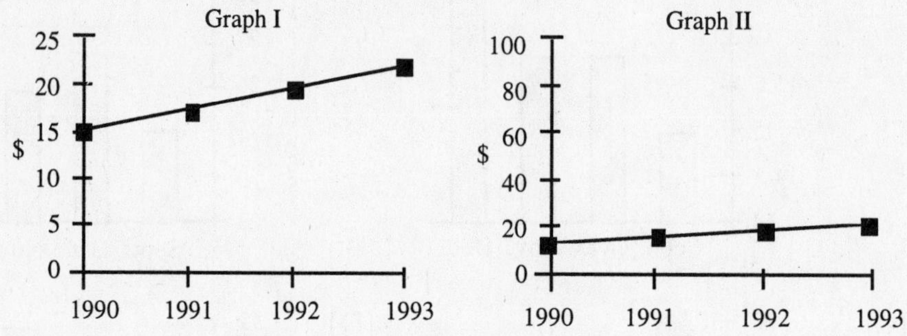

88. In 1989, the F & P Company earned $85,500 in profit. Their profit decreased by $5500 in 1990. In 1991 their profit fell to $73,000 and in 1992 their profit decreased by $13,000. Explain how the F & P Company could construct a line graph to show how their profit decreased dramatically over the past four years. Construct the line graph you described.

89. Explain how the horizontal scale on a line graph can be used to construct a misleading graph.

90. The line graph below suggests that there was a drastic decrease in the number of people who quit smoking within the last seven months. Give two reasons why the graph is misleading.

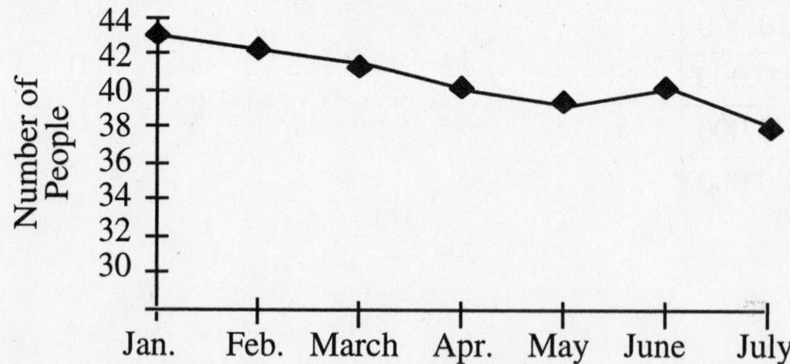

Lesson 1-7 Objective 2: Recognize misleading bar graphs.

Dynamic Item

91. Both graphs represent the number of new clients signed up each month at Excelsior Realty. Which graph is misleading? Why?

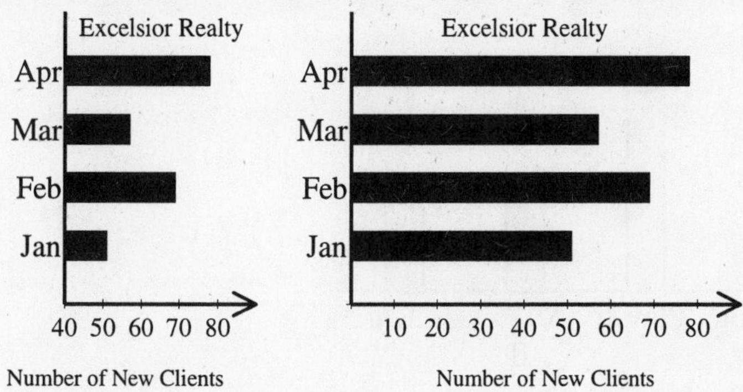

92. Use the graph below. Jeans-R-Us claims that the price of a pair of jeans in 1993 has decreased dramatically from the price of a pair of jeans in 1990. Do you agree with Jeans-R-Us? Explain.

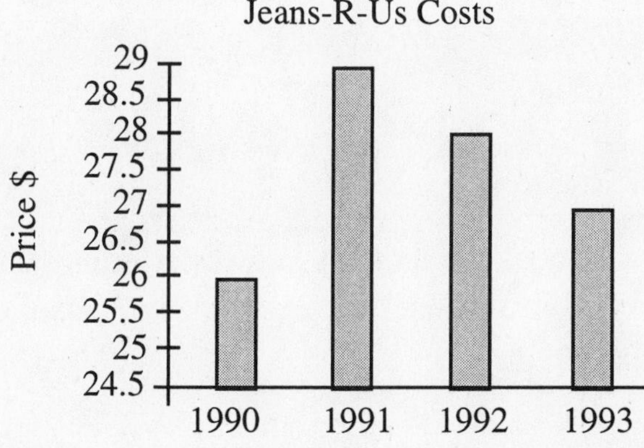

93. The bar graph in the advertisement about VCR's below is misleading. Explain why.

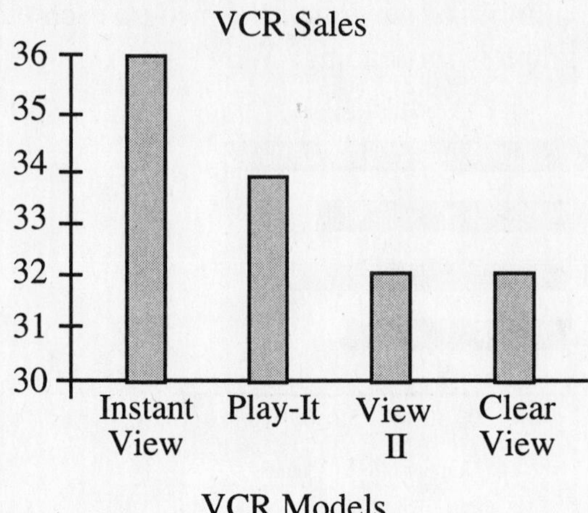

94. Explain why it is important to examine the scale on the axes before interpreting a graph.

95. Which graph below suggests that the number of helpers for the monthly fund-raisers decreased dramatically from September to October?

[A]

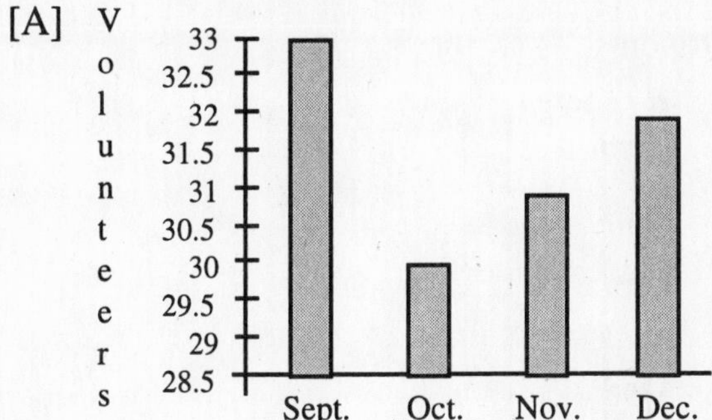

[B]

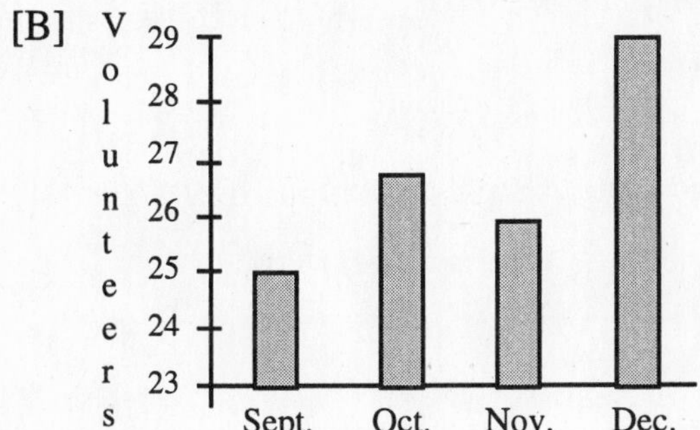

[C]

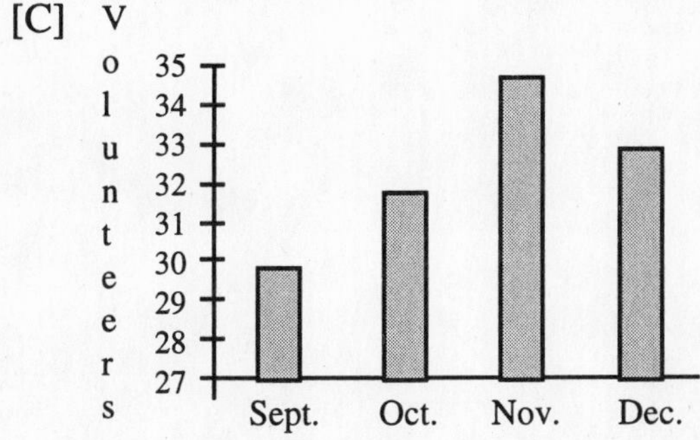

[D]

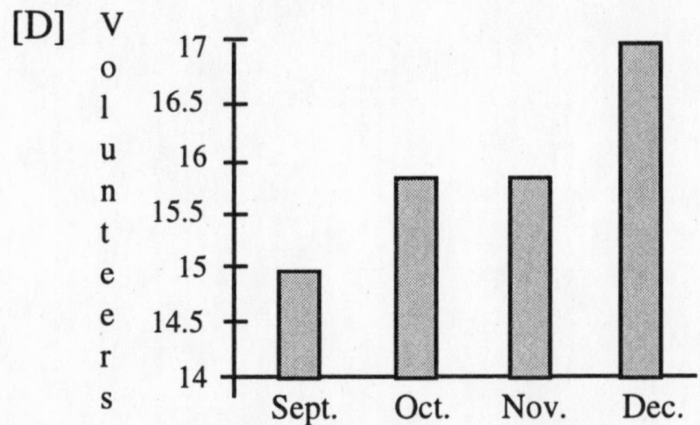

96. Explain how you can alter the graph below so that the graph misleads you about the number of miles driven by each car. Construct the new line graph.

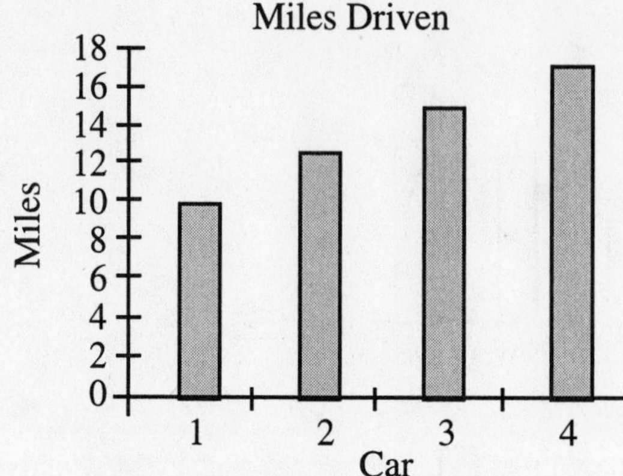

Chapter 2: Patterns and Algebraic Thinking

Lesson 2-1 Objective 1: Find the next term in a number pattern.

Dynamic Item

1. Assuming that the pattern continues, write the next 3 terms.
   10, 15, 20, ___, ___, ___

   [A] 30, 35, 40 [B] 26, 31, 36 [C] 24, 29, 34 [D] 25, 30, 35

Dynamic Item

2. Assuming that the pattern continues, write the next 3 terms.
   28, 25, 22, ___, ___, ___

3. a. Use graph paper to sketch the fourth design so that it continues the pattern below.
   b. How many small triangles are in the fourth design?
   c. Imagine the fifth triangle design. Describe the design in words.

4. Suppose there are 10 people at a business meeting. Everyone shakes hands with everyone else once. How many hand shakes would there be?

   [A] 55 [B] 45 [C] 100 [D] 36

5. Use the pattern of designs below to form a number pattern showing the total number of rectangles at each step in the pattern.

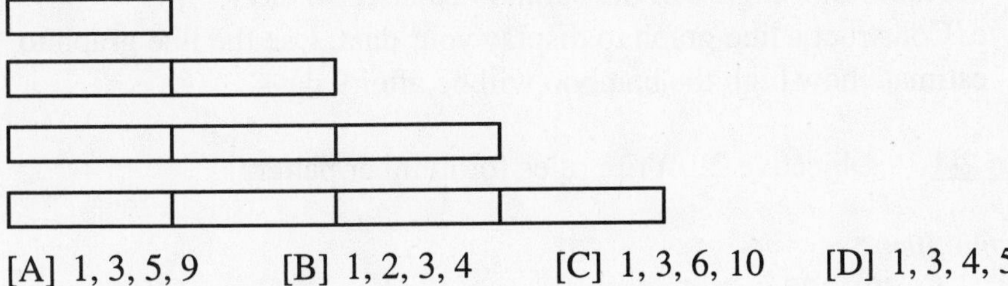

   [A] 1, 3, 5, 9 [B] 1, 2, 3, 4 [C] 1, 3, 6, 10 [D] 1, 3, 4, 5

6. Use graph paper to sketch the pattern: 2, 3, 5, 8, ...

7. Write the first five terms in the following number pattern: Start with the number 2 and add 3.5 repeatedly.

8. 0.57, 0.48, 0.39, 0.30, ...

 a. Find the next three terms in the number pattern.
 b. Write the rule to describe the number pattern.

9. Use graph paper to sketch the next two designs in the pattern below.

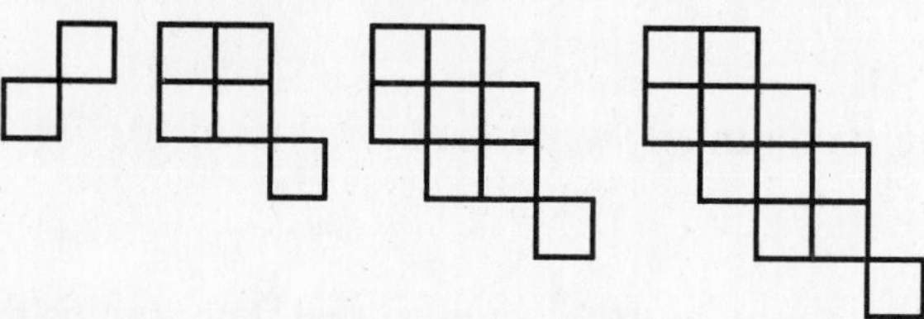

10. Complete the pattern.
 ‡ooo, o‡, ‡ooo, oo‡, ______, ______, ______

11. Most large trees grow at a steady rate year after year. Other types of plants grow either quickly or slowly and then stop. Bamboo, which is a grass, not a tree, grows as much as 3 ft high in one day.

Number of Days	Height of Plant
1	3
7	21
14	42
21	?
28	?

 a. Copy and complete the table above.
 b. About how high will the bamboo be after 30 days?
 c. Construct a line graph to display your data. Use the line graph to estimate how high the bamboo will be after 9 days.

Lesson 2-1 Objective 2: Write rules for number patterns.

Dynamic Item

12. 2, 8, 32, 128 ...
 a. Describe the pattern you see in the sequence.
 b. Predict the next four terms.

13. 3, 6, 12, 24, ...

a. Find the next three terms in the number pattern.
b. Write a rule to describe the number pattern.

14. In the table below, a cut is defined as a line from the center of the pie to the edge of the pie.

Number of Cuts	Number of Pieces of Pie	Number of Pies of Pie + Number of Cuts
2	2	4
3	3	6
4	?	?
5	?	?
6	?	?

a. Copy and complete the table.
b. Write a rule to describe the number pattern shown in Column III.

Lesson 2-2 Objective 1: Solve problems by looking for a pattern.

Dynamic Item

15. 5 bacteria are placed in a petri dish and then counted each hour. The first three bacteria counts were: 12, 26, 54. If this pattern continues, how many hours after the bacteria are placed in the dish will there be 222 bacteria?

[A] after 6 hours [B] after 5 hours

[C] after 3 hours [D] after 9 hours

Dynamic Item

16. Seven teams are playing in a tournament. In the first round, each team plays each of the other teams once. How many games are played in the first round of the tournament?

17. How many diagonals can be drawn from any ONE vertex of a polygon with eight sides? Five sides? Seven sides? Do you see a pattern?

18. Seventy-five students read books. Fifty-two students read non-fiction books. Twenty-eight students read adventure books. How many students read both non-fiction and adventure?

    [A] 23　　[B] 75　　[C] 5　　[D] 80

19. Kisha has five different marbles. How many different ways can she place the marbles into two bags so that at least one marble is in each bag?

    [A] 60　　[B] 15　　[C] 25　　[D] 30

20. The sum of the first two odd numbers is 4.
    The sum of the first three odd numbers is 9.
    The sum of the first five odd numbers is 25.
    What is the sum of the first eight odd numbers?

21. Given the following pattern, what would ______ be?
    $8 \times 6, 16 \times 3, 24 \times 2,$ ______ $\times 4$

22. You open a book and the product of the two facing page numbers is 240. Then you open the book and the product of those pages is 650. To what pages have you opened the book to? Describe how you found the answers.

23. Sarah has five brothers and sisters. Sarah's mom buys meat at the local butcher. The butcher is running a special on steaks. It costs $6.49 to purchase one steak. Each additional steak purchased thereafter is discounted by $0.50. How much money will Sarah's mom save if she purchases 8 steaks?

24. The numbers in the third column follow a pattern from the first two columns. What number goes in the empty space?

1	5	8
2	6	12
3	7	16
4	8	

Lesson 2-2 Objective 2: Solve problems using any strategy.

25. Use the table below. What is the total number of squares for a 5×5 grid?

Number of Different Size Squares

Size of Grid	1×1	2×2	3×3	4×4	Total
1×1	1	0	0	0	1
2×2	4	1	0	0	5
3×3	9	4	1	0	14
4×4	16	9	4	1	30

26. Use the table below. Determine the total number of letters that would be delivered by Sunday if the mail came every day.

Day of Week	Number of Letters Delivered	Total Number of Letters Delivered
Monday	1	1
Tuesday	3	4
Wednesday	5	9
Thursday	7	16
Friday	9	25

Lesson 2-3 Objective 1: Find the value of expressions using the order of operations.

Dynamic Item

27. $(9 \times 8) - 3 \times 6 + 9 =$

[A] 27 [B] 45 [C] 423 [D] 63

Dynamic Item

28. Simplify. $((25 \div 5) \times 10) + 8 - 2$

29. What is the order of operations?

30. Which operation would you perform first? Why? $16 - 5 \times 3$

31. Felicia was asked to find the value of the expression $6 + 3 \times 1 \times 4$. The answer she got was 36. Explain to her the correct way to evaluate the expression. What is the correct value? Suggest what mistakes she might have made.

32. Place parentheses so that the expression $133 \div 2 + 1 = 6$ is true. How could the parentheses be placed differently so that the value of the equation changes? What would the new value be?

33. Write another expression that has the same value as $(184) \times 2 + 6$.

Lesson 2-3 Objective 2: Compare values of expressions.

Dynamic Item

34. Write <, >, or = between the two expressions to make a true statement.
$(2 \times 2) \div (4 + 3 - 2)$ _____ $2 \times 2 \div 4 + 3 - 2$

[A] < [B] = [C] >

Dynamic Item

35. Write <, >, or = between the two expressions to make a true statement.
$(5 + 1) \times 2 \div (5 - 1)$ _____ $5 + 1 \times 2 \div 5 - 1$

36. Which of the following expressions has a value of 28?

[A] $3 \times 5 + 6 \times (2 + 1)$ [B] $3 \times (5 + 6) \times 2 + 1$

[C] $(3 \times 5) + 6 \times (2 + 1)$ [D] $(3 \times 5) + (6 \times 2) + 1$

37. The value of $2 \times (12 - 3) + 1$ is the SAME as

[A] $9 + 1 \times 2$ [B] $4 \times 2 + 6 - 12$

[C] $(2 \times 12) - 3 + 1$ [D] $1 + (5 + 4) \times 2$

38. Write an expression that has the same value as $10 \times (7 + 2) \div (9 \times 5)$.

39. Caroline was rewriting her class notes when she realized that she was missing part of an equation. Would you replace the ______ with <, >, or = ? Explain how you got your answer.
$(7 + 3) \times 4 + 1$ ______ $7 + 3 \times 4 + 1$

40. Use the numbers 1, 2, 4, 6 and the order of operations to write an expression that equals 13.

41. Write an expression containing all four operations that has a value of 12.

Lesson 2-4 Objective 1: Model variable expressions.

42. Model the variable expression $5x + 3$.

43. Choose the variable and write a variable expression for the model shown below.

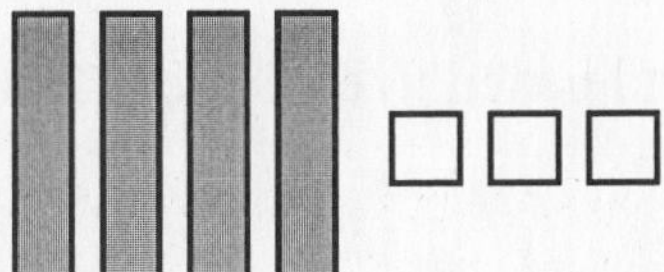

Lesson 2-4 Objective 2: Evaluate variable expressions.

Dynamic Item

44. Evaluate $46 - (2 \times x)$ for $x = 3$.

[A] 89 [B] 132 [C] 43 [D] 40

Dynamic Item

45. Evaluate: $18 - y$ for $y = 13$

46. a. Multiply each entry in the magic square below by 5 and then add 2. Draw the new magic square.
b. Is your result a magic square? Explain.
c. Write a variable expression to show how the second magic square was formed.
d. Use the original magic square to create another magic square. Write a variable expression to show how you created your magic square.

8	1	6
3	5	7
4	9	2

47. Explain how you would evaluate the expression: $a^2 + 3b$ for $a = 5$ and $b = 2$.

48. Use a calculator, mental math, or paper and pencil to evaluate $4x^3 - 3$ for $x = 2$.

[A] 21 [B] 9 [C] 32 [D] 29

49. Which numerical expression has a value closest to 60?

[A] $38.5+5\times4$ [B] $5^2+(3.5\times2)^2$

[C] $(4.5)^2+3\times(3.5)^2$ [D] $11\times4+5$

50. If $3a-b=13$, find three pairs of possible values for a and b.

51. Use a calculator, mental math, or paper and pencil to evaluate $a(27.07+b)$ for $a=0.25$ and $b=0.93$.

52. Copy and complete the magic square shown below. Find the values of a, b, and c.

a	1	b
3	5	7
4	c	2

53. Use mental math to evaluate the expression $3x+1$ for $x=5$.

Lesson 2-5 Objective 1: Describe variable expressions with word phrases.

Dynamic Item

54. Write the word phrase that describes the expression. $r + 11$

[A] a number r multiplied by eleven

[B] a number r increased by eleven [C] a number r divided by eleven

[D] eleven times a number r increased by fifteen

Dynamic Item

55. Write the word phrase that describes the expression. $10p$

56. Do the word phrases, "the quotient of 21 and x" and "x divided by 21," result in the same variable expression? Explain.

57. Name two word phrases to describe the variable expression $x+10$.

Lesson 2-5 Objective 2: Write variable expressions.

Dynamic Item

58. Which variable expression below means the quotient of 4 times a number and 23?

[A] $4x \div 23$ [B] $27x \div 19$ [C] $19x \div 27$ [D] $23x \div 4$

Dynamic Item

59. Write a variable expression for each word phrase.
a) 2 times a number
b) seven less than a number
c) a number increased by three
d) forty-four divided by a number

60. Suppose x is an even number. Write a variable expression to show what the next greater even number is. Explain how you arrived at your expression.

61. Marcus is 12 years old. Arlene is 8 years old. Write a variable expression for Arlene's age using Marcus' age as M.

[A] $M - 4$ [B] $M + 8$ [C] $M - 12$ [D] $M + 4$

62. Which variable expression describes the area of the shaded region in the diagram shown below?

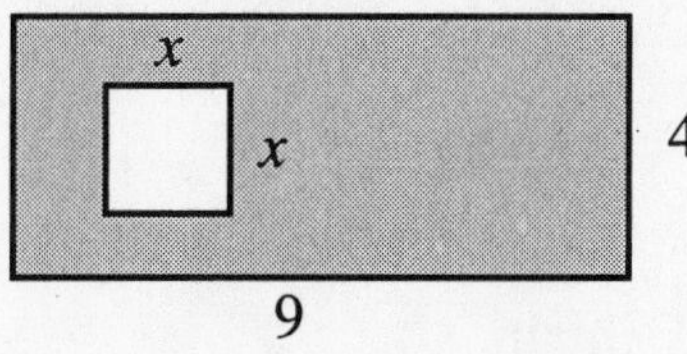

[A] $36 - x^2$ [B] $36 - 2x$ [C] $x^2 + 13$ [D] $x^2 - 36$

63. Write a variable expression for the word phrase below.
The difference between some number and 5

64. Write a variable expression for the perimeter of the rectangle below.

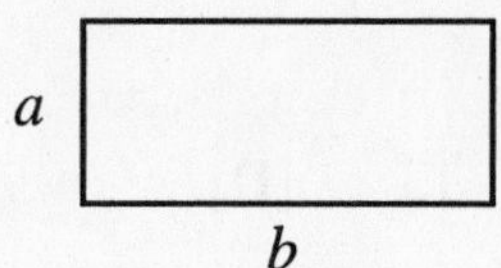

65. Write a variable expression to describe the table below.

x	?
2	4
3	9
4	16
5	25

66. Write a variable expression for the word phrase "five more than the cube of a number x." Then evaluate the expression for $x = 2$.

67. Carmen is two years older than twice as old as her brother Jesse. Write a variable expression to show how old Carmen is.

68. Reggie bought four items at the supermarket. How much did the lemon, eggs, and noodles cost?

Item	Expression	Price
Cereal	$2x$	$2.10
Lemon	$x \div 3$	?
Eggs	x	?
Noodles	$x + 0.2$	?

69. Alice has x marbles in a bag. She gives them all to five friends. Each gets the same number of marbles. Write a variable expression to show how many marbles each friend receives.

Lesson 2-6 Objective 1: Define equations.

70. Is the equation 5 + 12 = 17 true or false? Explain.

71. What is the difference between an expression and an equation? Give an example of each.

Lesson 2-6 Objective 2: Solve equations.

Dynamic Item

72. Which of the following makes the equation true?
$2 = 11 - x$

[A] $x = -9$ [B] $x = 13$ [C] $x = -13$ [D] $x = 9$

Dynamic Item

73. Solve: $17 = m - 7$

74. In which equation does $x = 14$?

[A] $x + 6 = 8$ [B] $x - 6 = 8$ [C] $10 - x = 4$ [D] $8 + x = 14$

75. What number is represented by ______ in the problem:
$522 - 129 =$ ______ $+ 93$

[A] 200 [B] 400 [C] 300 [D] 600

76. What equation is modeled below?

▯ □□□□ = □□□□□□□

77. Use tiles to solve each addition equation.
a. $7 + x = 12$
b. $a + 9 = 15$
c. $z + 3 = 10$

78. Complete. If $x + a = b$, then $x =$ ______.

79. Write an equation for each variable in the magic square below. Solve each equation.

a	1	6
3	5	b
4	9	2

80. Solve each subtraction equation.
a. $x - 236 = 338$
b. $15{,}430 = y - 763$
c. $129.06 = z - 335.04$

81. The chart below shows the total cost of buying soda. Write an expression for the cost of soda including deposit. How much would it cost for 10 bottles?

Bottles of Soda	Cost + Deposit
1	\$0.99 + \$0.05
2	\$1.98 + \$0.10
3	\$2.97 + \$0.15
4	\$3.96 + \$0.20

82. Use tiles, mental math, or a calculator to solve the equation: $28.9 + x = 34.4$

83. Solve the equation shown in the model.

Lesson 2-7 Objective 1: Solve equations using models.

84. Use tiles to solve each equation.
a. $3x = 6$
b. $4y = 12$
c. $5z = 15$

85. What equation is modeled below? Solve the equation.

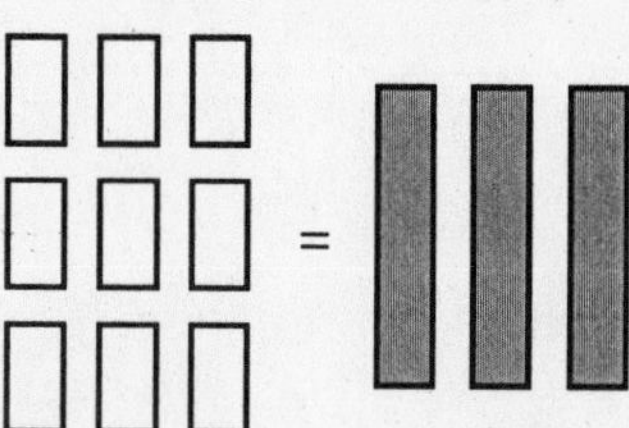

Lesson -7 Objective 2: Solve equations using a calculator or mental math.

Dynamic Item

86. Solve: $3 = 15 \div y$

[A] 18 [B] 12 [C] 6 [D] 5

Dynamic Item

87. Solve: $160 = 32m$

88. Explain how the procedures used to solve $4x = 16$ and $x + 6 = 12$ are similar.

89. Without solving the equation $\frac{1}{2}x = 3$, state whether the value of x is greater than or less than 3. Explain.

90. Anita was selling Girl Scout cookies for the local Girl Scout Troop. Each box of cookies cost $2.95. Mrs. Brown's purchase of Girl Scout cookies totaled $14.75. Choose the equation to determine how many boxes of Girl Scout cookies were purchased by Mrs. Brown.

    [A] $2.95 + c = 14.95$ [B] $2.95 = 14.75(c)$

    [C] $2.95(14.75) = c$ [D] $2.95(c) = 14.95$

91. Write an equation that has a solution of 12 and uses division to solve the equation.

92. Solve each division equation.

    a. $276 \div x = 23$
    b. $y \div 0.02 = 80$
    c. $3056 \div z = 764$

93. The CN tower in Toronto, Canada, which is 1,822 feet high, is the world's tallest free standing tower. This is 1.85 times higher than the Eiffel Tower. Let x represent the height of the Eiffel Tower. Write and solve an equation to determine the height of the Eiffel Tower. Round your answer to the nearest hundredth; nearest foot.

94. Jonathan works part-time for a department store in the county mall. Last week Jonathan worked 15 hours and received a check for $63.75. Write and solve an equation to determine how much money Jonathan earns in 1 hour.

95. Use the table below. How many complete orchestras can be formed?

ORCHESTRA

Instrument	Number of Musicians Needed	Number of Musicians Available
Flute	5	15
Clarinet	6	13
Drums	1	7
Violin	8	24
Trumpet	4	11
Cymbals	1	3
Saxophone	3	5

96. Use mental math or a calculator to solve.
$17a = 340$

97. Use mental math or a calculator to solve.
$504 \div x = 56$

Chapter 3: Adding and Subtracting Decimals

Lesson 3-1 Objective 1: Model decimals.

Dynamic Item

1. What decimal does the figure represent?

[A] 0.6 [B] 0.06 [C] 6.4 [D] 6

Dynamic Item

2. Draw a model for 0.06.

3. Write a sentence using the decimal 0.3 in words.

4. Draw a model and explain why three tenths is equivalent to thirty hundredths.

5. John's friend is visiting the U.S. He is from another country. How would you explain to him that 10 dimes is equal to 1 dollar? You may use a model.

6. Choose the decimal that is modeled below.

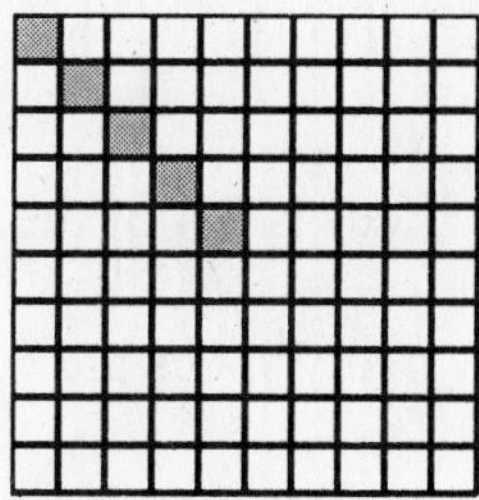

[A] 0.50 [B] 5.0 [C] 0.05 [D] 0.005

7. Choose a word expression that represents the decimal 0.85.

[A] eighty-five hundredths [B] eighty-five hundred

[C] eight and five hundredths [D] eighty-five tenths

8. How many tenths are in 0.35?

[A] five [B] three [C] thirty-five [D] thirty

9. Draw a model to represent the decimal 0.48.

CHAPTER 3

Lesson 3-1 Objective 2: Explore equivalent decimals.

Dynamic Item

10. Tell whether the statement is true or false. Explain your reasoning.
100 thousandths = 100 tenths

11. Which model below represents 0.4?

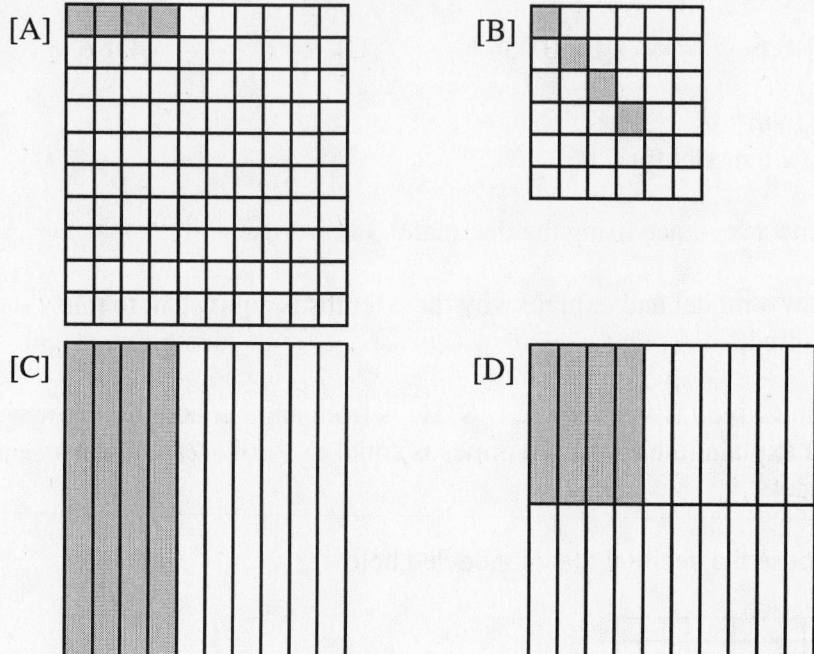

12. A pizza pie is cut into 10 equal slices. How many slices is 0.4 of the pie?

13. Suppose a pizza pie is cut into 5 equal slices. How many slices are 0.5 of the pie?

Lesson 3-2 Objective 1: Read and write whole numbers.

Dynamic Item

14. Write 200,239,508 in words.

    [A] two hundred billion, two hundred thirty-nine million five hundred eight thousand

    [B] two hundred million, and two hundred thirty-nine thousand, and five hundred eight

    [C] two hundred thousand, two hundred thirty-nine thousand, five hundred eight

    [D] two hundred million, two hundred thirty-nine thousand, five hundred eight

Dynamic Item

15. Write two billion, two hundred eight million, nine hundred fifteen thousand, four hundred eighteen in standard form.

16. Explain how the values increase or decrease as you move from right to left in the place value chart.

17. In your own words explain the difference between a number in standard form and a number in expanded form.

Lesson 3-2 Objective 2: Read and write decimals in standard and expanded forms.

Dynamic Item

18. Write one thousand two hundred nine and sixty-eight thousandths in standard notation.

    [A] 1209.068 [B] 10,209.068 [C] 1209.0068 [D] 1029.068

Dynamic Item

19. Write 92.427 in expanded form.

20. Choose the expanded form of the number twenty-two and 5 thousandths.

    [A] 22.05 [B] 22.005 [C] 20 + 2 + 0.05 [D] 20 + 2 + 0.005

21. Study the decimals shown. Choose the next decimal in the pattern.
    0.51, 0.54, 0.57

    [A] 0.060 [B] 0.06 [C] 0.006 [D] 0.60

22. Write any two decimal numbers in standard and expanded forms.

23. What is the value of the digit 7 in the number 5.387?

24. Write the decimal for four hundred sixty-two hundredths.

25. Draw a model for two and fifteen hundredths.

26. In spite of the large amount of water on Earth, its total weight is only twenty-two thousandths percent of that of the Earth. Write this number in standard form.

27. Draw a place value chart using one dollar as the unit to show $3.52.

28. Fill in the names for each place in the place value chart below.

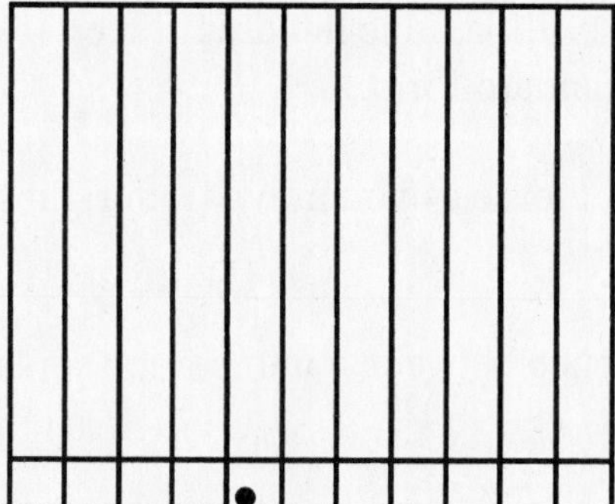

29. Use the table below. Write the expanded form and the word name for each weight given.

Elements in a 150-pound Individual

Element	Weight (lb)
Oxygen	97.5
Sodium	0.165
Phosphorus	1.8
Cobalt	0.00024

Source: The Universal Almanac

Lesson 3-3 Objective 1: Compare decimals using models.

30. Write three statements about the batting averages given in the chart below.

PLAYER	TEAM	BATTING AVERAGE
Rickey Henderson	Oakland Athletics	0.283
Frank Thomas	Chicago White Sox	0.323
George Brett	Kansas City Royals	0.285
Barry Bonds	San Francisco Giants	0.311
Wade Boggs	New York Yankees	0.259

31. Points X, Y, and Z are decimals graphed on a number line. Read each statement I-IV. Which two statements give exactly the same information?

I. $X < Y$ and $Y > Z$
II. Y is greater than X and Z
III. $X < Z$ and $Z < Y$
IV. $X < Y$ and $Y < Z$

[A] II and III [B] II and IV [C] I and II [D] III and IV

32. What decimal numbers are at points A, B, and C?

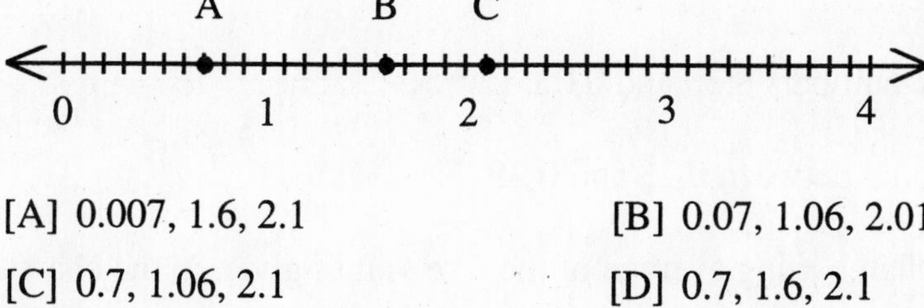

[A] 0.007, 1.6, 2.1 [B] 0.07, 1.06, 2.01
[C] 0.7, 1.06, 2.1 [D] 0.7, 1.6, 2.1

33. Draw models for 0.32 and 0.51. How do the models show which number is greater?

34. Graph 3.3 on a number line.

35. Graph 0.23, 0.4, 0.32, and 0.1 on a number line.

36. Write two statements to compare the numbers graphed on the number line below.

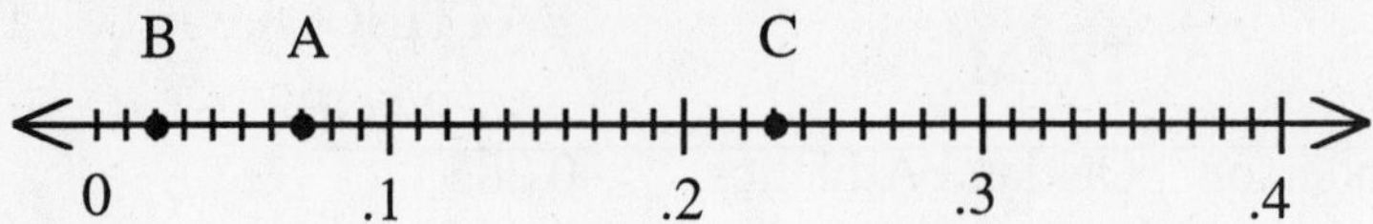

Lesson 3-3 Objective 2: Order decimals using place value.

Dynamic Item

37. Arrange from smallest to largest:
6.003 6.03 6.038

[A] 6.038 , 6.03 , 6.003 [B] 6.003 , 6.038 , 6.03

[C] 6.003 , 6.03 , 6.038 [D] 6.038 , 6.003 , 6.03

Dynamic Item

38. Insert <, >, or = to form a true statement:
3.419 _______ 3.419000

39. Explain how you would compare two decimals.

40. Describe two situations where you might need to compare and order decimals.

41. Compare the numbers 0.30 and 0.03. Use >, <, or =.

42. Write a decimal between 0.25 and 0.35.

43. Find the median batting average of the five values given in the chart below.

PLAYER	TEAM	BATTING AVERAGE
Rickey Henderson	Oakland Athletics	0.283
Frank Thomas	Chicago White Sox	0.323
George Brett	Kansas City Royals	0.285
Barry Bonds	San Francisco Giants	0.311
Wade Boggs	New York Yankees	0.259

Lesson 3-4 Objective 1: Solve problems by using Guess and Test.

44. The local library had a sale to get rid of books that were slightly damaged. It sold paperback books for $2.00 and hard-cover books for $5.00. The library raised $271 and sold 89 books. How many hard-cover books were sold?

 [A] 155 [B] 58 [C] 70 [D] 31

45. Veronica saves quarters and nickels. She has 92 coins adding up to $11.00. How many quarters does she have?

 [A] 60 [B] 8 [C] 3 [D] 32

46. The sum of two numbers is 27 and the product of these numbers is 182. One of the numbers is ______.

 [A] 16 [B] 10 [C] 12 [D] 13

47. Two numbers have a sum of 25 and a product of 114. What are the two numbers?

48. Soo Lee is 11 years old and has one brother and one sister. The ages of the three children add up to 24. When the three ages are multiplied together, the answer is 440. How old are Soo Lee's brother and sister?

49. Write the numbers 1 – 9 in each of the boxes shown so that the numbers in each of the diagonals add up to the same amount. Do not place any consecutive numbers next to each other.

 □ □
 □ □
 □
 □ □
 □ □

50. There are 138 people visiting the aquarium. The entrance fee is $5.00 for students and $8.00 for adults. The total cost is $717. How many students and how many adults went to the aquarium?

51. Apples are priced at 5 for $1.00. Oranges are priced at 4 for $1.20. Ariel spent $3.80 and bought between 10 and 16 pieces of fruit. How many of each fruit did she buy?

Lesson 3-4 Objective 2: Solve problems using any strategy.

52.

U	V	W	X	Y
P	Q	R	S	T
K	L	M	N	O
F	G	H	I	J
A	B	C	D	E

C ↑ ← The answer is G. Find

a. L → → ↑

b. K → ↑

c. R ↑ → → ↓

53. Rank the cities in size order using the information given.
San Diego is larger than Detroit but smaller than Philadelphia. New York is larger than Los Angeles. Chicago is larger than Houston but smaller than Los Angeles. Philadelphia is larger than Dallas but smaller than Houston. Detroit is smaller than San Diego but larger than Dallas.

Lesson 3-5 Objective 1: Model addition of decimals.

Dynamic Item

54. 1.3 + 1.2 =

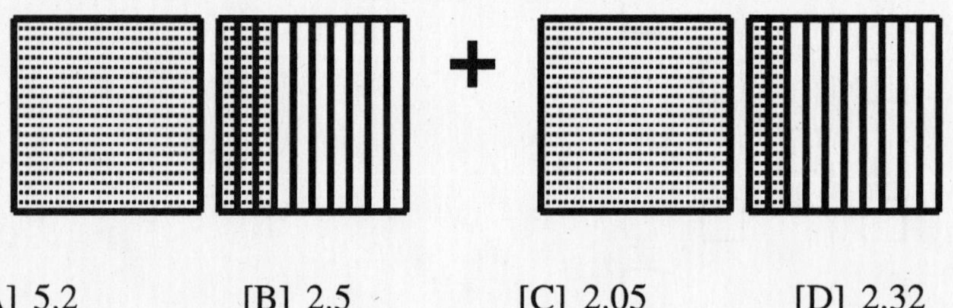

[A] 5.2 [B] 2.5 [C] 2.05 [D] 2.32

55. Choose the sum shown by the model below.

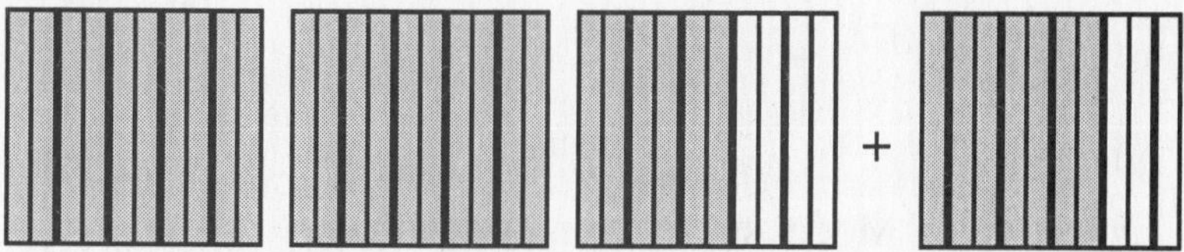

[A] three and three hundredths
[B] three and three tenths
[C] three and three tens
[D] three and thirteen tenths

56. Choose the model below that shows the sum of 2.8 and 0.7.

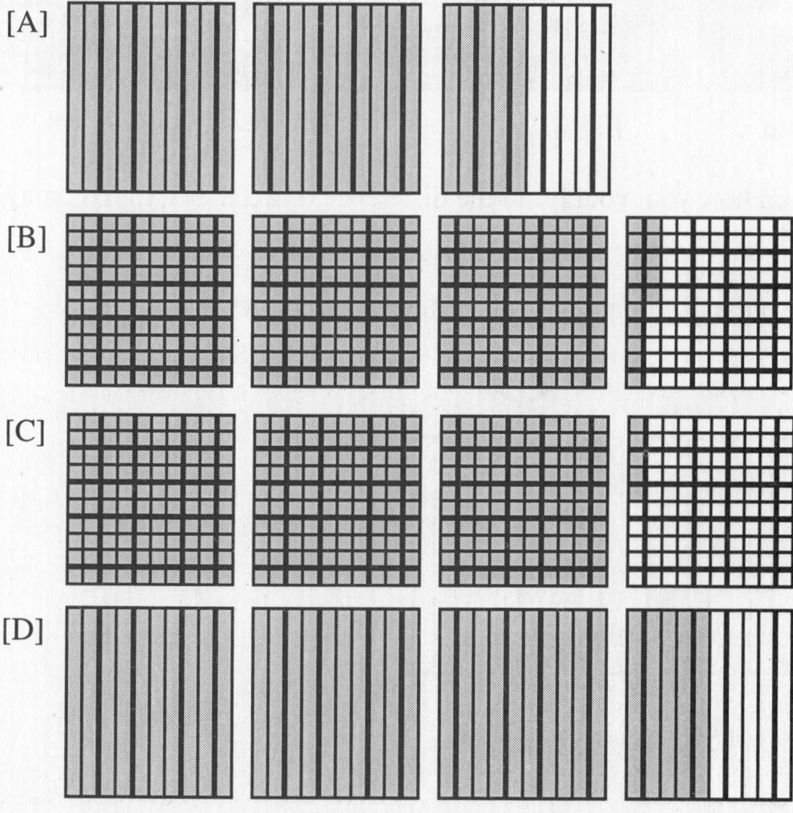

57. Draw a model showing 0.5 + 0.3. What is the sum?

58. Draw a model showing 1.5 – 0.3. What is the difference?

59. Express the number 0.63 in words without using the words "six" or "sixty."

60. Add. Use a model to help you.

$$\begin{array}{r} 5.36 \\ +\ 0.25 \\ \hline \end{array}$$

Lesson 3-5 Objective 2: Model subtraction of decimals.

Dynamic Item

61. Choose the difference the model shows.

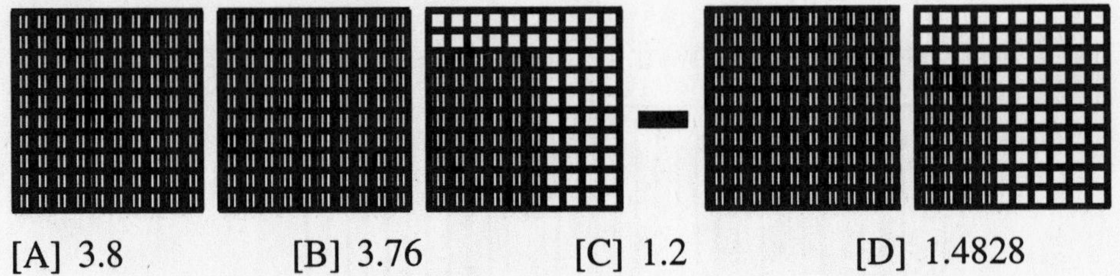

[A] 3.8 [B] 3.76 [C] 1.2 [D] 1.4828

62. Explain how you would find the difference of 2.2 and 1.1. You may use a model.

63. What is the difference shown by the model below?

64. Subtract. Use a model to help you.

$$\begin{array}{r} 1.56 \\ -\ 0.94 \\ \hline \end{array}$$

SPORTS ETC. SALE	
Baseball Jersey	$23.95
Baseball Glove	$35.95
Batting Glove	$6.99
Baseball Cap	$15.99

65. Use the data in the chart above. What is the total cost for 2 baseball jerseys, 1 baseball cap, and 2 batting gloves?

66. Use the data in the chart above. Suppose you have $85 to spend at Sports Etc. List the quantity of each item you would buy. What is the total cost of your purchase?

67. Explain how you would use mental math to find the sum $1.85 + $3.99.

Lesson 3-6 Objective 1: Round data.

Dynamic Item

68. What is 20.438 rounded to the nearest tenth?

[A] 20.44 [B] 20.5 [C] 20 [D] 20.4

Dynamic Item

69. Round 349.851 to the nearest ten.

70. Use the data in the chart below. How much more sugar is in $\frac{1}{2}$ c of sherbet than in one 4-oz. glass of orange juice? Estimate your answer to the nearest tenth.

FOOD	SUGAR CONTENT
Orange Juice (4 oz)	0.417 oz
Plain Granola Bar	0.333 oz
Raisins (7 oz)	0.75 oz
Sherbet $\left(\frac{1}{2}\text{ cup}\right)$	1.166 oz
Yogurt (8 oz)	1 oz

[A] 1.917 [B] 1.9 [C] 1.1 [D] 1.083

71. Round 0.52 to the nearest tenth.

72. Round 6.9997 to the nearest thousandth.

Lesson 3-6 Objective 2: Estimate sums and differences.

Dynamic Item

73. Estimate: \$13.43 + \$12.59

[A] \$30 [B] \$26 [C] \$20 [D] \$24

Dynamic Item

74. Estimate the difference using front-end estimation. 42.42 – 14.56

[A] 35 [B] 40 [C] 20 [D] 30

75. In your own words, explain how to estimate a sum using front-end estimation.

76. A low estimate of \$16 and a high estimate of \$18 is a good range for which of the following sums?

[A] \$12.56 + \$4.91 + \$0.98 [B] \$3.52 + \$10.31 + \$5.01

[C] \$8.56 + \$2.25 + \$6.50 [D] \$2.81 + \$8.05 + \$6.98

77. Describe three situations in which you might need to estimate.

78. Use the numbers 15.08, 3.211, 7.09, 9.75, and 2.31.
a. Which pair of numbers has an estimated sum of 13?
b. Which pair of numbers has an estimated difference of 5?

79. Use front-end estimation to find the sum of \$0.95 + \$3.46 + \$8.41.

80. Use the data in the chart below. Suppose you have to limit your sugar intake to 2.5 oz per day. Make a list of the different combinations of food that can be taken in one day.

FOOD	SUGAR CONTENT
Orange Juice (4 oz)	0.417 oz
Plain Granola Bar	0.333 oz
Raisins (7 oz)	0.75 oz
Sherbet $\left(\frac{1}{2}\text{ cup}\right)$	1.166 oz
Yogurt (8 oz)	1 oz

81. Explain how you would estimate the sum of $5.35 and $2.89.

82. Round to the nearest dollar to estimate.
$$\begin{array}{r} \$15.39 \\ -\ 8.05 \\ \hline \end{array}$$

83. Round to the nearest dollar to estimate.
$$\begin{array}{r} \$6.89 \\ -\ 4.56 \\ \hline \end{array}$$

Lesson 3-7 Objective 1: Add decimals.

Dynamic Item

84.
$$\begin{array}{r} 17.26 \\ 3.17 \\ +\ 2.6 \\ \hline \end{array}$$

[A] 5.77 [B] 20.43 [C] 19.86 [D] 23.03

Dynamic Item

85. Add: 76.854 + 7.69

86. Read each statement. Explain why each statement is true or false. You may use a model to help you. Correct all false statements.
a. The difference of two decimals less than 1 is always less than one.
b. The sum of two decimals less than 1 is always less than one.

87. Suppose you want to add 1.52, 3.48, and 9.59. Choose the answer that shows an estimate and the exact answer.

[A] Estimate: 23; Actual 14.59 [B] Estimate: 13; Actual: 14.59

[C] Estimate: 13; Actual: 24.59 [D] Estimate: 20; Actual: 24.59

88. If you place the digits 1–7 in these boxes □ □ .□ □ +□ □ .□ to give the greatest possible sum, the digit in the second box must be:

[A] 4 [B] 5 [C] 6 [D] 4 or 5

89. At the local deli, you order a ham, salami, and cheese sandwich for \$3.25, a soft drink for \$1.05, and a quarter pound of potato salad for \$0.56. You pay with a \$10 bill. How much change will you get?

90. Anthony had the following bills to pay for the month of September: \$89.12, \$1,714.32; and \$307.98. What was the total amount of money he spent on bills?

91. Find the missing number. Use mental math.

$(5.87 + 0.31) + 1.9 = 5.87 + (0.01 + \_\_ + 1.9)$

Lesson 3-7 Objective 2: Subtract decimals.

Dynamic Item

92. Subtract: 13.54 – 1.635

[A] 11.419 [B] 11.905 [C] 10.905 [D] 12.905

Dynamic Item

93. Subtract: 743.22 – 14.6

94. Suppose you want to subtract 2.5 from 13.98. Choose the answer that shows an estimate and the exact answer.

[A] Estimate: 16; Actual: 16.48 [B] Estimate: 15; Actual: 16.48

[C] Estimate: 11; Actual: 11.48 [D] Estimate: 8; Actual: 11.48

FIRST CLASS MAIL	
Weight (oz)	Rate
1	$0.32
2	$0.55
3	$0.78
4	$1.01
5	$1.24
6	$1.47
7	$1.70
8	$1.93
9	$2.16
10	$2.39
11	$2.62

95. Use the data in the table above. What is the difference in rate between a 2 oz letter and a 9 oz letter?

96. Study the postage rates in the table above. Look for a pattern. Describe the pattern you find.

97. Use the data in the table above. Estimate the amount it would cost to mail one 2 oz letter, two 4 oz letters, one 10 oz letter and one 11 oz letter.

98. You use a $50 bill to pay for a pair of jeans costing $26.99. How much change will you get?

99. Juan used a calculator to find the following difference. Estimate to see if his answer is reasonable. If it is not, explain what Juan did wrong.
3.56 – 0.98 = 4.54

Lesson 3-8 Objective 1: Use metric units of length.

Dynamic Item

100. The segment is how many centimeters long?

[A] 1.5 cm [B] 0.15 cm [C] 1.6 cm [D] 15 cm

Dynamic Item

101. The segment is how many centimeters long?

102. Suppose the length of your foot is about 25 cm. How can you estimate the length of a room by using your feet?

103. Suppose each step you take is 0.5 m. How many steps will it take you to walk around a square room with a side of 4 m?

[A] 32 steps [B] 4 steps [C] 20 steps [D] 16 steps

104. Suppose you had to measure the length of your pencil using a centimeter ruler. Explain how you would find the measurement.

105. Draw a figure that has a perimeter of 100 mm.

106. Suppose one side of a regular octagon measures 5 cm. What is its perimeter?

107. Draw a line segment 93 mm long.

108. Find the perimeter for the figure below.

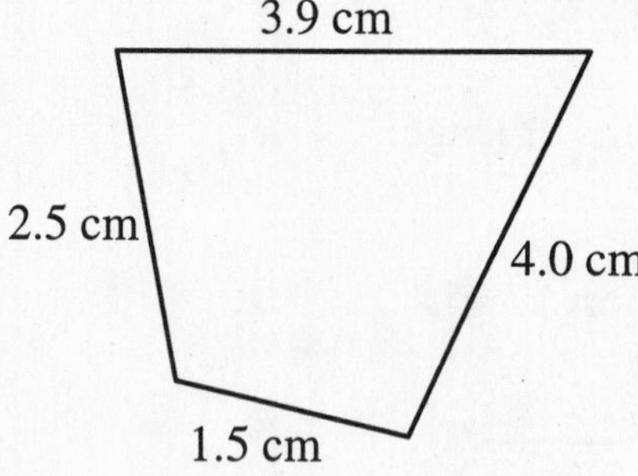

Lesson 3-8 Objective 2: Choose appropriate units of measurement.

Dynamic Item

109. A _______ would be about one meter tall.

[A] desk [B] basketball player [C] mouse [D] two-story building

Dynamic Item

110. What metric unit would you most likely use to measure the thickness of a finger?

111. Explain why it would not be appropriate to measure a football field in centimeters.

112. Which unit of measure would be appropriate to measure each item?
a. the length of a swimming pool
b. the length of your foot
c. the distance between two states
d. the size of a pinhead

113. Explain why you could use either meters or centimeters to measure the length of your classroom. Which do you think would be better?

114. Tell which measure makes sense for the length of a swimming pool.

[A] 800 cm [B] 1 km [C] 80 m

Lesson 3-9 Objective 1: Choose metric units of mass.

Dynamic Item

115. A ______ would weigh about 910 kg.

[A] grown hippopotamus [B] hamburger

[C] 5-year-old cat [D] professional football player

Dynamic Item

116. A ten-year-old girl could weigh about 32 kg. True or false?

Lesson 3-9 Objective 2: Choose metric units of capacity.

Dynamic Item

117. Choose the best answer. 3 1/2 L describes the amount of ______.

[A] water in a home aquarium [B] milk in a full jug

[C] water a car-washing bucket will hold [D] salt in a pot of soup

Dynamic Item

118. 3 1/2 L is the amount of milk in a full jug. True or false?

119. Would it be sensible to use grams to find the mass of a horse? Explain your answer.

120. You want to find the mass of your math book. Which unit is most appropriate?

[A] meter [B] kilogram [C] liter [D] milligram

121. One cubic centimeter of water has a mass of 1 gram. A fish tank holds 3,000 cubic centimeters of water. What is the mass of the water in kilograms?

122. Choose the best estimate of the mass of a basketball.

[A] 550 g [B] 5 L [C] 5 kg [D] 550 m

123. Marty sent 4 packages. Their masses were 3 kg, 500 gm, 660 g, and 5 kg. What was the approximate average mass of the packages?

[A] 3 kg [B] 6500 g [C] 5 kg [D] 2300 g

124. Choose a sensible unit to measure the mass of a serving of dry cereal. Explain your answer.

125. Which unit of capacity - liter, milliliter, or kiloliter - would you use to express the capacity of a bathtub?

126. Give an example of something that would be measured in milliliters. Explain why.

127. Which measure below is the most sensible for the capacity of a car's gas tank?

[A] 70 kg [B] 700 mL [C] 7 L [D] 70 L

128. If you are comparing the capacity of several containers, which system of measurement, metric or Customary, do you think would be easier to use? Explain why.

129. Gina has 3 glass beakers in her chemistry set. They hold 2 L, 750 mL, and 1500 mL. Which one holds the most? How do you know?

Lesson 3-10 Objective 1: Add and subtract measures of time.

Dynamic Item

130. If it is evening, what time will it be in 4 hours and 25 minutes ?

[A] 1:00 p.m. [B] 9:25 p.m. [C] 2:25 a.m. [D] 1:25 a.m.

Dynamic Item

131. If it is afternoon, what time was it 5 hours and 20 minutes ago?

[A] 1:10 p.m. [B] 9:30 a.m. [C] 8:30 a.m. [D] 8:10 p.m.

132. In your own words, explain the meaning of elapsed time.

133. Write a description of what you do during the time after you wake up in the morning and before you leave. Include the elapsed time for each activity and the total elapsed time.

134. A Broadway play begins at 8:00 p.m. It takes 45 minutes to get there. When should you leave for the play if you want to arrive one hour early?

[A] 6:15 p.m. [B] 7:00 p.m. [C] 6:45 p.m. [D] 7:15 p.m.

135. A football game began at 1:05 p.m. and ended at 4:15 p.m. Find the elapsed time.

136. Flight #528 leaves the airport at 6:15 a.m. and arrives at its destination at 1:50 p.m. Find the elapsed time.

137. On December 9, at 5:30 p.m. the Chengs arrived home from a vacation in the mountains. This was 75 hours 30 minutes after they left their home for vacation. What was the date and time the Chengs left for their vacation?

138. Anne Marie began to study for a history exam at 6:15 p.m. She studied until her bedtime at 9:00 p.m. Find the elapsed time.

139. You have to meet your sister in New York for dinner at 8:30 p.m. At 3:30 p.m. you have an appointment to get your hair cut at home. Which is the best route below for you to take?

To New York	Leave	Arrive
Route 1	3:45 P.M.	6:30 P.M.
Route 2	5:50 P.M.	8:15 P.M.
Route 3	3:55 P.M.	7:25 P.M.
Route 4	6:50 P.M.	8:55 P.M.

140. At 1:30 p.m. Patel decided to do his chores. He told his friends that he will meet them at the park when he is finished with his chores. It takes Patel 1 hour 45 minutes to clean his room, 8 minutes to walk the dog, 20 minutes to return books to the library, and 14 minutes to walk to the park. At about what time should Patel meet his friends?

Lesson 3-10 Objective 2: Read, use, and make tables.

Dynamic Item

141.

		Open	Close
Liberty Bell Pavilion	Daily	9:00 a.m.	5:30 p.m.
Philadelphia Art Museum	M – F	9:30 a.m.	5:15 p.m.
	Sa – Su	10:30 a.m.	6:15 p.m.
Betsy Ross House	M – Sa	9:00 a.m.	5:00 p.m.
	Sun	10:00 a.m.	5:00 p.m.
Independence Hall	Daily	9:30 a.m.	5:30 p.m.

If Heidi worked at Independence Hall from opening until 11:30 a.m. how long did she work?

[A] Five hours [B] Two hours

[C] Three hours and thirty minutes [D] Three hours

Dynamic Item

142. Below is the exhibit judging schedule for the Sweetwater County Fair. Which animals are judged from ten to quarter to four?

Exhibit Judging

Food	Livestock	Begin (a.m.)	End (p.m.)
Pies	Cows	10:00	2:15
Cakes	Sheep	10:00	3:45
Jellies	Llamas	10:00	3:15
Chili	Horses	10:00	3:30

143. Shown below is a bus schedule to New York from your town. You want to spend the least amount of time on the bus. Which is the best route for you to take to New York?

To New York	Leave	Arrive
Route 1	3:45 P.M.	6:30 P.M.
Route 2	5:50 P.M.	8:15 P.M.
Route 3	3:55 P.M.	7:25 P.M.
Route 4	6:50 P.M.	8:55 P.M.

[A] Route 3 [B] Route 2 [C] Route 4 [D] Route 1

144. Make a schedule for a typical day in school.

145. Joanne plans to do the activities given below after school but before dance class at 5:30 p.m. School is out at 3:00 p.m. Make a schedule of Joanne's afternoon.

Walk home from school	15 minutes
Have a snack	15 minutes
Walk the dog	10 minutes
Do homework	1 hour
Eat dinner	25 minutes
Change into dance uniform	10 minutes
Walk to dance class	15 minutes

Lesson 4-1 Objective 1: Estimate products of numbers containing decimals.

Dynamic Item

1. Estimate the product by rounding. 2.08 × 9.96

   [A] 22 [B] 20 [C] 32 [D] 10

Dynamic Item

2. Estimate: 38.31 × 32.4

3. What are compatible numbers?

4. Each student in Ethan's craft class received a box of supplies containing the items listed in the chart below. Estimate the mass of 4.75 boxes of supplies.

Item	Mass (g)
Scissors	81.6
Markers	22.3
Tape measure	34.8
Paper	57.9

   [A] 200 g [B] 40 g [C] 400 g [D] 1000 g

5. Explain to Brad whether it is easier to estimate the product 13.72 × 47.28 by using compatible numbers or rounding each factor to the nearest whole number.

6. Caterina estimated the product 26.8 × 11.73 by rounding the factors to the nearest whole numbers. Dennis estimated the product by using compatible numbers. Whose estimate do you think will be closer to the actual product? Why?

CHAPTER 4

7. Estimate the cost of each purchase. Assume there are no additional charges such as sales tax.

Item	Cost ($)
Notebook	2.29
Folder	1.11
Pencils (Pkg.)	1.71
Pens (Pkg.)	1.95
Writing Pad	1.02
Book Cover	0.43

a. 2 packages of pencils and 3 folders
b. 2 notebooks and 2 packages of pens
c. 1 book cover, 2 writing pads, and 2 folders

8. The chart below shows the lengths of 6 different bridges. Use the information to estimate how long a bridge would be if it was:
a. 4 times as long as the Lake Washington Bridge.
b. 3 times as long as the difference in length between the Quebec Bridge and the Lake Washington Bridge.
c. $\frac{1}{2}$ as long as the Rockville Bridge.

Year Completed	Name of Bridge	Length (km)
1981	Humber Estuary Bridge (UK)	1.4
1964	Verrazano – Narrows Bridge (USA)	1.3
1917	Quebec Bridge (CDA)	0.9
1977	New River Gorge Bridge (USA)	0.52
1963	Lake Washington Bridge (USA)	3.8
1901	Rockville Bridge (USA)	1.2

9. There are 5.7 grams of fat in one of Aunt Amelia's big cookies. Estimate how many grams of fat are in 3.2 cookies. How did you get your answer?

10. Jackie completed a scientific experiment in which she had to monitor the growth of plants for 68.82 hours each week. The experiment lasted 2.76 weeks. Estimate the total number of hours included in the experiment.

Lesson 4-1 Objective 2: Estimate quotients of numbers containing decimals.

Dynamic Item

11. Estimate: 49.1 ÷ 5.92

    [A] 8 [B] 9 [C] 80 [D] 42

Dynamic Item

12. Estimate: 64.05 ÷ 3.5

13. How can compatible numbers be used to estimate products and quotients?

14. Which of these estimates is CLOSEST to the actual quotient 22.7 ÷ 2.48?

    [A] 7 [B] 8 [C] 6.67 [D] 12.5

15. If you saved $147.32 in one year, estimate how much you saved each month.

16. A box of books at a book store weighs 33.92 lb. Each book in the box weighs 2.65 lb. Estimate the number of books in the box.

Lesson 4-2 Objective 1: Use exponents.

Dynamic Item

17. Write as a power: $5 \times 5 \times 5 \times 5$

    [A] 5^4 [B] $(4)^5$ [C] 5^5 [D] 5^{-4}

Dynamic Item

18. Write using exponents: $8 \times 8 \times 8$

19. Explain the order of operations you would use to evaluate:
    $3 + (5 + 18 - 2^3)$

20. a. Find the next number in the pattern: 4, 16, 64, 256, ...
    b. Write a rule to describe the number pattern.

21. Does the expression $(2^2 + 3^2)$ equal the expression $(2 + 3)^2$? Explain your answer.

22. Name the base and the exponent in 5^9 .

23. Express the product of $4 \times 4 \times 4 \times 4 \times 4 \times 4$ using an exponent.

24. Express 128 as a power of 2.

25. Use a calculator to find a pattern in the last digits of the first 8 powers of 7.

26. Use an exponent to express the area of a square whose side measures 18 cm.

Lesson 4-2 Objective 2: Apply the order of operations to simplify powers and expressions.

Dynamic Item

27. Simplify. $5^6 \div 5^4 \div 5$

[A] $\frac{1}{5}^1$ [B] 5 [C] $\frac{1}{5}^9$ [D] 5^9

Dynamic Item

28. Calculate. $36 \div 3 - 3^4$

29. Find the measure of each side of a cube if the volume of the cube is 64 cm^3.

[A] 32 [B] 8 [C] 16 [D] 4

30. Use a calculator, mental math, or paper and pencil to evaluate:
$5^3 - 2 \times 3 + 2^2 - (6 - 4)$

[A] 121 [B] 371 [C] 109 [D] 11

31. Use a calculator, mental math, or paper and pencil to evaluate:
$15 + (6^2 + 5)$

Lesson 4-3 Objective 1: Find areas of rectangles.

Dynamic Item

32. Which expression does not describe the total area of the rectangle?

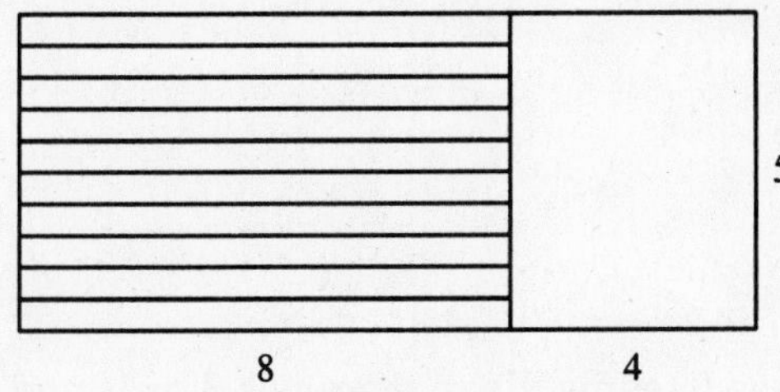

[A] $(8 \times 5) + (4 \times 5)$ [B] $5 \times (8 + 4)$

[C] $(5 \times 4) + (5 \times 8)$ [D] $8 \times (4 + 5)$

Dynamic Item

33. Write two expressions to describe the total area.

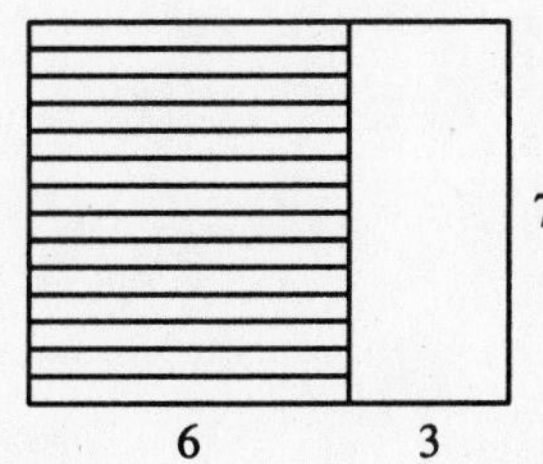

34. The swimming pool in Lian's town is 50 ft wide and has an area of 5,000 ft^2. What is the length of the pool? Explain how you found your answer.

35. Explain what is meant by a number that is given as the area of a rectangle.

36. The total area of the two rectangles in the figure below is ______ square units.

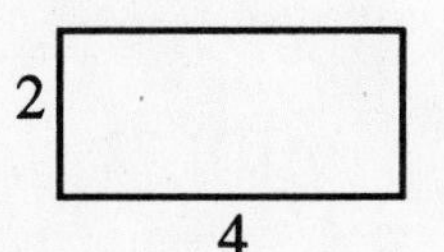

[A] 14 [B] 22 [C] 8 [D] 44

37. How would you write two different expressions that each find the total area of the rectangles shown below? Use your expressions to find the total area of the rectangles.

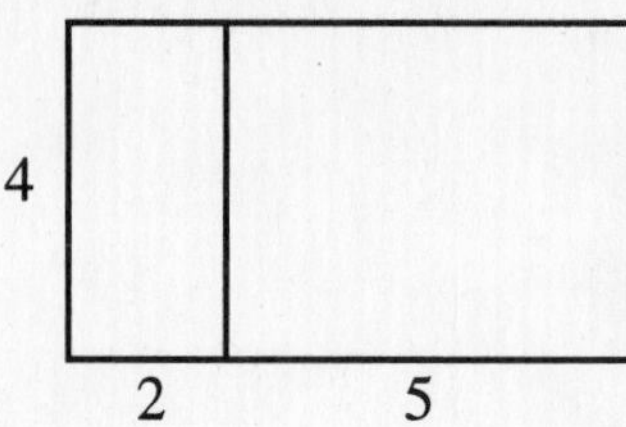

38. The local baseball league has 5 teams. Each team has 3 girls and 9 boys. Write the expression to find the total number of players in the league. Draw a rectangular model for the expression. Use the model to evaluate the expression.

39. A local theater is divided into 2 smaller theaters by a wall as shown below. The more popular movies are shown in the larger section. What would the area of the entire theater be if the wall was removed? Explain how you got your answer.

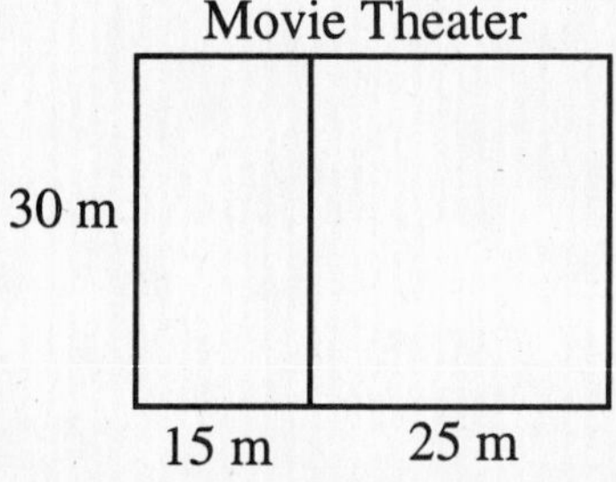

40. The largest television screen ever made was featured at the Tsukuba International Exposition near Tokyo, Japan in 1985. The screen was called the Sony JUMBOtron and measured 40 m by 25 m. Use the distributive property to find the area of the screen.

Lesson 4-3 Objective 2: Use the distributive property.

Dynamic Item

41. Simplify: $8 \times (6 + 3)$

[A] 144 [B] 17 [C] 51 [D] 72

Dynamic Item

42. Simplify: $6 \times (8 - 4)$

43. Use the distributive property to write in the missing numbers. Explain how you found the answer.

 $5\times(\_\_ +13)=(\_\_\times4)+(5\times\_\_)$

44. Explain the distributive property in your own words.

45. 19×50 is the SAME as

 [A] $50+(9\times50)$ [B] $(1\times50)+(9\times50)$

 [C] $500+(9\times50)$ [D] $(1\times25)+(9\times25)$

46. The auditorium at the School for the Arts has 102 rows of seats and each row has 7 seats in it. Use the distributive property to figure out how many seats are in the auditorium.

Lesson 4-4 Objective 1: Model the multiplication of a decimal and a whole number.

47. Describe the similarities and differences between the models showing the products of the following expressions: 0.2×0.3 and 2×0.3

48. Which of the following is represented by the model below?

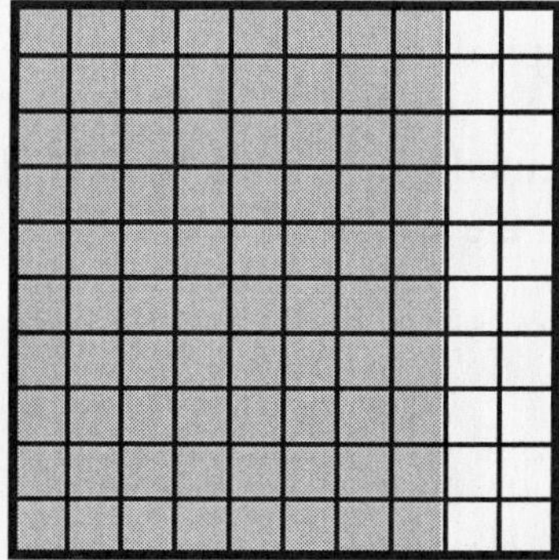

 [A] The total weight of 10 books that each weigh 0.8 lb.

 [B] The total cost of 1 shirt that costs $8.

 [C] The total weight of 8 calculators that each weigh 0.1 lb.

 [D] The total cost of 8 magazines that each cost $1.

49. Which question can be answered by using the model below?

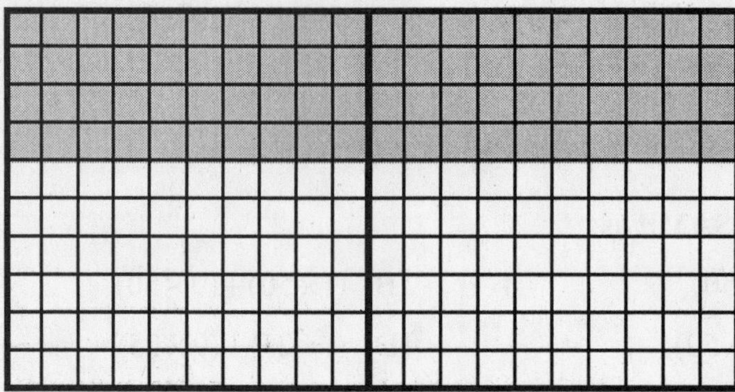

[A] A cabinet is 2 ft by 4 ft. What is the area of the cabinet?

[B] A rectangular painting is 2 ft long and 0.4 ft wide. What is the area covered by the painting?

[C] A shelf is 0.2 m by 0.4 m. How many square meters is the shelf?

[D] A flower box is 0.2 m by 4 m. What is the area of the flower box?

50. Nancy walks 1.3 miles each day. Use a model to determine how far Nancy walks in 4 days.

Lesson 4-4 Objective 2: Model the multiplication of two decimals.

51. Explain how to draw a model to find the product 0.5×0.2.

52. Describe a situation that might be represented by the model below. Then write a multiplication sentence to go with the model.

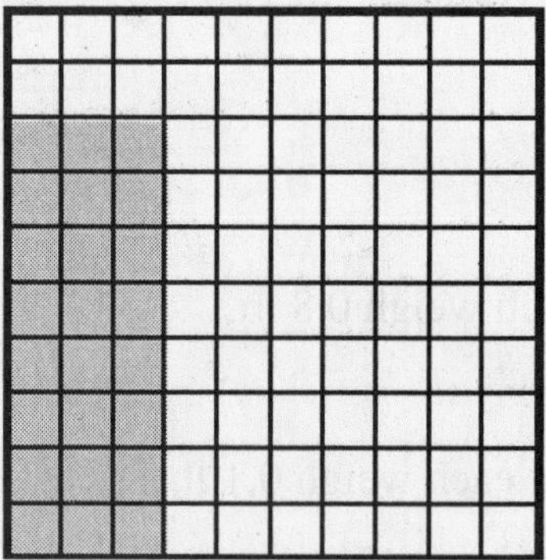

53. Your parents have never seen models used to find the product of two decimal numbers. Prepare an explanation describing why you use models to find products. Make sure you consider some of the drawbacks of using models each time you find a product as well.

54. Draw a model to find the product 0.6×0.3.

55. One kilogram is equal to 2.2 pounds. Draw a model that shows how many pounds are equal to 0.6 kg.

56. Draw a model to find the product 1.3×0.4.

57. Alex was drawing a model to find the product of two numbers when he lost his place and forgot which question he was up to in his homework problems. The figure below shows how far along he was. Which question or questions might he have been answering? How do you know?

(a) 0.3×0.9 (d) 1.7×0.7
(b) 2.3×0.9 (e) 0.6×0.8
(c) 1.3×0.2 (f) 2.6×0.5

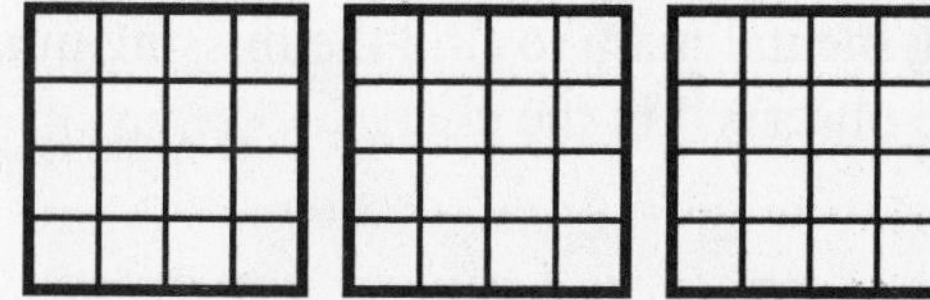

Lesson 4-5 Objective 1: Multiply decimals and whole numbers.

Dynamic Item

58. $$\begin{array}{r} 1.25 \\ \times\ 4 \\ \hline \end{array}$$

[A] 0.5 [B] 0.47 [C] 5 [D] 4.7

Dynamic Item

59. Multiply: $$\begin{array}{r} 0.4 \\ \times\ 4 \\ \hline \end{array}$$

60. Use a calculator to find each product.

23×48 23×4.8 2.3×4.8 2.3×48

Relate the number of decimal places in each product to the number of decimal places in the factors of each expression.

61. The Green Street School ordered 1,000 book covers at $0.42 each. How much did the covers cost all together?

62. What is the value of 215 quarters? Write the equation you used to find your answer.

63. The speed at which trees grow depends on the environmental conditions around the tree. A certain species of tree in Mexico, however, was found to be the slowest-growing tree under even the best conditions. The tree grows an average of 0.03 inches per year. How many inches does the tree grow in 15 years?

64. When you drop an object, it travels faster and faster as it falls. Each second the object falls, its speed increases by 9.8 m/sec. By how much does an object's speed increase after it falls for 4 seconds?

65. Complete the chart below using mental math to find the missing numbers. Describe the pattern that can be observed in the chart.

Factor 1	Factor 2	Factor 3
2.4	10	---
2.4	---	240
2.4	1000	---
0.24	---	2.4
0.24	100	---
0.24	---	240

Lesson 4-5 Objective 2: Multiply two decimals.

Dynamic Item

66. Multiply: 0.84×0.4

[A] 0.336 [B] 3.36 [C] 3.46 [D] 0.346

Dynamic Item

67. Multiply:

$$\begin{array}{r} 0.85 \\ \times\ 0.6 \\ \hline \end{array}$$

68. Explain why the product 0.05×0.28 has only 3 decimal places when computed on a calculator.

69. Explain how you can determine how many decimal places are needed in the product of 2 decimal numbers.

70. Which of the products has the same value as the product of 0.37×0.2?

    [A] 3.7×2. [B] 0.037×0.02. [C] 3.7×0.02. [D] 37×20.

71. Gwen is having trouble figuring out how many decimal places belong in the product of two decimal numbers such as 3.2×12.4. Explain to her how she can use estimates to help her.

72. It takes an average of 270 days (9 months) for humans to develop before they are born. It takes a rhinoceros about 2.4 times longer. How long does it take for a rhinoceros to develop? It takes a swan 0.16 times as long as it does for a human to develop. How long does it take for a swan to develop?

73. A dolphin can swim up to 30 mi/h. A cheetah can run up to 2.33 times as fast as a dolphin can swim. How fast can a cheetah run? A spider can crawl 0.039 times as fast as a dolphin can swim. How fast can a spider crawl?

Lesson 4-6 Objective 1: Model dividing by tenths.

74. Explain how the model below can be used to show the quotient

    $0.6 \div 0.3$.

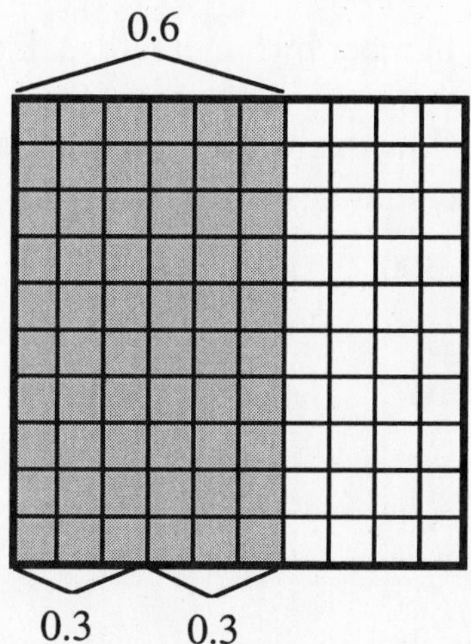

75. At Jeff's auto shop, it takes 0.2 h to have a car's oil changed. On how many cars can Jeff change the oil if he works for 4 h? Use a model to find your answer.

[A] 200 [B] 20 [C] 2 [D] 0.2

76. The model below is unfinished. Complete the division sentence and the model.

0.4 ÷ ____ = ____

77. The fastest type of centipede in the world lives in southern Europe and can travel 0.3 mi in 0.2 h. At how many mi/h does the centipede travel? You may want to draw a model to find your answer.

Lesson 4-6 Objective 2: Model dividing by hundredths.

78. Can you use a model to divide a decimal number by hundredths? Explain.

79. Raven ran 0.9 mile. Andy ran 0.03 mile. How many times farther than Andy did Raven run? Use a model to find your answer.

[A] 3 [B] 0.03 [C] 300 [D] 30

80. Write a mathematical sentence that describes the model shown below. Then write a problem that can be solved using the model.

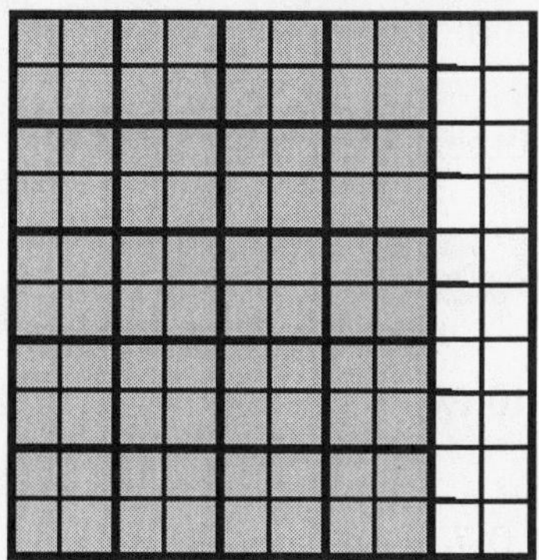

81. Robin bought peaches that cost $0.30 each. She spent $1.20. How many peaches did she buy? Draw a model to find the answer.

82. Anthony has 0.6 L of water to give to the plants in his classroom. If each plant needs 0.12 L of water, how many plants can he water? Draw a model to find the answer.

83. Jean has 0.8 lb. of apples. An apple dessert requires 0.16 lb. of apples. Draw a model to show how many apple desserts Jean can make. Write a sentence describing the model and explain what each part of the sentence represents.

84. In 1900, the Kentucky Derby was won by a horse named Lt. Gibson. The length of the race was about 2 km. Lt. Gibson finished in about 0.04 h. At how many km/h did Lt. Gibson run? You may want to draw a model to find your answer.

Lesson 4-7 Objective: Divide decimals by whole numbers.

**Dynamic Item*

85. $1.55 \div 5 =$

[A] 3.1 [B] 0.31 [C] 0.301 [D] 3.01

**Dynamic Item*

86. Divide. $5\overline{)3.5}$

87. Danny spent $0.90 at the stationery store. If he bought 6 identical pencils, how much did each pencil cost? You may want to draw a model to help you find the answer.

88. Explain how you would divide 4.68 by 3.

89. Explain what happens when you move the decimal point in 0.8 to the right one place. What about two places? Three places?

90. Four boxes are stacked one on top of the other. The entire stack is 8.96 ft tall. How many feet tall is each box?

    [A] 22.4 [B] 24 [C] 0.224 [D] 2.24

91. Judy divided 15.46 gal of water evenly into two fish tanks. How many gallons of water went into each tank?

    [A] 7.73 [B] 773 [C] 0.773 [D] 77.3

92. Three T-shirts cost $22.65. If all three shirts have the same price, how much does each shirt cost?

93. In a gymnastics competition, the highest mark is a 10. One gymnast was in 5 events. He scored a total of 48.75 points. What was his average per event?

94. Write a division of a decimal by a whole number that has a quotient of 0.065.

95. Would you use a model, calculator, pencil and paper, or mental math to find 0.045 ÷ 15? Explain.

96. The weight of the element potassium in a human who weighs 150 lb is 1.8 lb. The weight of the element phosphorus in a 150-lb person is 1/6 of the amount of potassium. How many pounds is that?

Lesson 4-8 Objective: Divide decimals by decimals.

Dynamic Item

97. Divide: 5.95 ÷ 0.07

    [A] 0.0085 [B] 85 [C] 0.85 [D] 8.5

Dynamic Item

98. Divide: 60.52 ÷ 7.12

99. How are the numbers in each expression alike and how are they different? Use a calculator to find each quotient. Compare each quotient. What do you notice?

    0.48 ÷ 0.06   4.8 ÷ 0.6   48 ÷ 6

100. Explain how you would divide 8.25 ÷ 0.5.

101. Mai reads one page in 0.7 min. How many pages does she read in 14.28 min?

    [A] 204   [B] 2.04   [C] 2040   [D] 20.4

102. Would you use a model, calculator, pencil and paper, or mental math to find 0.045 ÷ 0.15? Explain.

103. A stack of 40 quarters measures 6.6 cm tall. Find the thickness of one quarter.

104. Ashley Brophy of Australia walked 7.175 miles on a tightrope in 3.5 h. At what average speed (mi/h) did he walk?

105. Which number below is the quotient of 2.016 ÷ 0.03?

    [A] 6.72   [B] 0.672   [C] 672   [D] 67.2

106. Suppose that your family traveled 275.75 miles on 12.5 gallons of gas. Was the average mileage more or less than 20 miles per gallon? Explain how you know.

107. Write an exercise dividing a decimal by a decimal that has a quotient of 0.25. Explain how you decided.

108. When you divide a number by a decimal in tenths, what is the first step? Explain why.

Lesson 4-9 Objective: Solve problems that have too much or too little information.

Dynamic Item

109. Eric is purchasing prizes for the 4 races at the class picnic. There are 33 students in his class. He wants to have a first, second, and third place prize for each category. The prizes must cost less than $11 each. What information is **not** needed to find out how much Eric will spend?

CHAPTER 4

Dynamic Item

110. Barbara weighs 5 pounds less than Stephanie. What more do you need to know to find Barbara's weight?

Dynamic Item

111. The average life span of an elk is 15 years. The average speed of an elk is 45 miles per hour. The longest that an elk has lived is 27 years. How much longer did the oldest elk live than average? Is there any information you did not need to solve this problem?

Dynamic Item

112. Tanya worked 7 hours more than Hercules during the month of May. What more do you need to know to find how many hours Tanya worked in May?

    [A] the number of hours Hercules worked in June

    [B] the number of hours Tanya worked in June

    [C] the number of hours Hercules worked in May

    [D] the number of hours Tanya worked in April

113. The average of 3 numbers is 6. The sum of those three numbers is 18. The second number is 3 times the first number. The third number is 5 times the first number. Find one of the numbers.

    [A] 3 [B] 9 [C] 10 [D] 7

114. Solve the following problem if possible. If it is not possible, tell what information is needed. The bookstore sells 12-month calendars for $8 and 16-month calendars for $10. Last weekend, the store sold $192 worth of calendars. How many 16-month calendars were sold?

115. Abdul rents some videos at a local store. He gives the cashier $10 and receives $0.40 in change. Each video has the same rental price. How much does each video cost to rent? What information is given to help you find the cost? What information is missing?

116. When Bart was 7 years old, his parents gave him and his sister money to open savings accounts. Every year since then, Bart has put more money into the account than the year before. The chart below show the amount he put in each year. If the pattern continues, how much will Bart put in the account in Year 5?

Year	Amount ($)
1	20
2	28
3	39.2

[A] $76.83 [B] $60 [C] $107.56 [D] $150.60

117. The sixth grade held a car wash to raise money for a class trip. They raised $438. They charged $6 for each car. Their expenses totaled $54. Thirty-six students were involved and washed 73 cars. It took 15 minutes to wash each car. How much money did they earn for the trip? Which information is not needed?

118. Timmy is painting the walls in some rooms in his house. There are 10 rooms in his house. He needs 1 gallon of paint for every 50 sq. ft. A coat of paint needs 6 hours to dry. Each wall is a different color as shown in the table below. The prices of 1 gallon of each color paint are shown in the second table. How much will it cost to paint the three rooms?

Room	Area (sq. ft)	Color
1	80	Blue
2	96	Yellow
3	120	White

Color	Price / Gal ($)
Blue	9
Green	7
Yellow	8
Red	6
White	7

119. Maxwell bought a pair of roller skates for $59.99. Each skate has red wheels and black shoelaces. The pair of skates weighs 5.6 lb. How much does each skate weigh? Is there any information that is not necessary?

120. Mrs. Turtle brought in 126 crayons to give out to the students in her kindergarten class. She divided them evenly among the students. Do you have too much or too little information to figure out how many crayons each student got? What information is extra or missing?

121. Bernadette works at a card store for a total of 8 hours per week. She works Saturday, Sunday, and after school on Tuesday and Thursday. She earns $5 per hour. Bernadette's sister Sara also works there 5 hours per week. How many weeks must Bernadette work to buy a new stereo that costs $200? What information is not necessary?

122. Solve the following problem if possible. If it is not possible, tell what information is needed. Melony had to pay to mail a letter. Postage costs $0.32 for the first ounce and $0.23 for each additional ounce. How many ounces did Melony's letter weigh?

Lesson 4-10 Objective 1: Change metric units.

Dynamic Item

123. How many meters are there in 500 millimeters?

[A] 0.05 m [B] 50 m [C] 0.5 m [D] 5 m

124. A dime is 1.25 mm thick. How many meters high would a stack of dimes worth $100 be?

125. Which measure below is the greatest? Explain how you know.
70 mg 6,900 g 7×10 kg 68.1 kg

126. The mass of 1 cubic centimeter of copper is about 8.9 g. About how many kilograms is the mass of 100 cubic centimeters of copper?

127. The mass of 1 cubic centimeter of silver is about 10.5 g. Sterling silver is 0.95 silver and 0.05 copper. How many kilograms of silver are in 250 g of sterling?

128. The Great Pyramid in Egypt has a square base that is 230 m on each side. What is the perimeter of the base in kilometers?

129. Soup brand A contains 0.23 g of sodium per serving. Brand B contains 25 mg per serving. Which brand of soup has more sodium per serving? How much more?

130. Which of the following statements is not true? Explain how you got your answer.
3.6 kg = 3600 g 300 mL < 2L 3.7 cm > 45 mm 1.5 g > 50 mg

131. The table below shows the amount of fat in various soups. Suppose you are on a low-fat diet. Which soup should you choose? Explain how you decided.

Soup A	Soup B	Soup C
750 mg	3 g	0.004 kg

132. Marty is giving a party and has asked some of her friends to bring soda. Alana brings 750 mL, Harry brings 2 L, and Jane brings 1500 mL. Who brings the most?

133. Suppose you are going to fence in a garden that has the dimensions shown below:

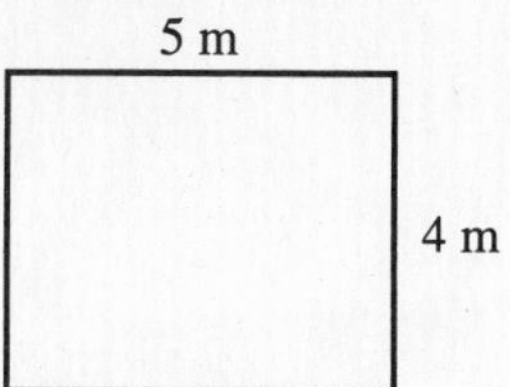

Fencing comes in rolls that contain 275 cm each. How many rolls do you need to buy?

Lesson 4-10 Objective 2: Use mental math to change units.

**Dynamic Item*
134. Complete: 0.984 mL = _____ L

[A] 0.000984 [B] 0.00984 [C] 984 [D] 98.4

**Dynamic Item*
135. Complete: 42 cm = ____ mm

Lesson 5-1 Objective 1: Find divisibility by 1, 2, 5, and 10.

Dynamic Item

1. Given the following numbers, identify the list below in which all the numbers are divisible by 5.
   459, 60, 204, 14, 375, 480

   [A] 204, 14, 60, 480 [B] 480, 459, 204, 375, 60

   [C] 60, 459, 375, 480 [D] 60, 375, 480

Dynamic Item

2. Given the following list of numbers, identify the numbers that are divisible by 5.
   90, 406, 386, 266, 170, 295

3. What is divisibility and what rules exist for divisibility?

4. The Swift Bus Company has 140 buses. Each night all of the buses are parked in a lot. How many buses could be in each row if all of the buses fit evenly into rows?

   [A] 8 [B] 11 [C] 9 [D] 10

5. The Liberty Bell in Philadelphia first rang on July 8, 1776 to celebrate the adoption of the Declaration of Independence. It was rung every year thereafter on the Fourth of July until 1835 when it cracked. The number of times the Liberty Bell was rung is divisible by all of the following except ______.

   [A] 3 [B] 7 [C] 4 [D] 6

6. The chart below shows several numbers that are divisible by 4 and several numbers that are not. Use the information to determine a rule for divisibility by 4. Test your rule with additional examples.

Number	Divisible by 4	Number	Divisible by 4
124	Yes	102	No
188	Yes	135	No
216	Yes	219	No
240	Yes	241	No
1260	Yes	2457	No
5928	Yes	4438	No

7. Mrs. Cloud is organizing a fund-raising luncheon and needs to assign seats to all of the guests. There are 192 people attending. If she wants to have the same number of people at every table, can she assign 10 people to each table? Explain.

8. Tony and his four brothers and sisters chipped in to buy their parents a gift. If the gift cost $85, did they each contribute the same amount to the gift? How do you know?

9. The chart below shows several numbers and tells whether they are divisible by 2, 3, 4, 5, and 6. Use the information to determine a rule for divisibility by 6. Give additional examples to test your rule.

	Divisibility by				
Number	2	3	4	5	6
6	yes	yes	no	no	yes
12	yes	yes	yes	no	yes
15	no	yes	no	yes	no
20	yes	no	yes	yes	no
24	yes	yes	yes	no	yes
36	yes	yes	yes	no	yes
42	yes	yes	no	no	yes

10. Jamie and Carmela are playing a board game in which they buy property and place hotels on the properties. Jamie owns 9 properties and 135 hotels, while Carmela owns 10 properties and 93 hotels. Can they each divide their hotels evenly among their properties ? Explain.

11. Tony and his four brothers and sisters chipped in to buy their parents a gift. If the gift cost $87, could they each have contributed the same amount? How do you know?

Lesson 5-1 Objective 2: Find divisibility by 3 and 9.

Dynamic Item

12. Which of the following numbers is divisible by 9?

[A] 4,901 [B] 18,473 [C] 7,371 [D] 1,183

Dynamic Item

13. Which of the following numbers is divisible by 9?
    5,265 7,475 3,887 845

14. The number 1,524 is divisible by 3 because the sum of the digits is divisible by 3. Is it always true that a number is divisible by another number if the sum of its digits is divisible by that number? Explain and give examples.

15. Why is a number that is divisible by 9 also divisible by 3 ? Can you give another example of two such numbers?

16. Marisa has a beautiful doll collection. She is purchasing shelves on which to display her dolls and is trying to decide how many shelves to get. The number depends on how many dolls will be placed on each shelf. If Marisa has 140 dolls, will all of the dolls fit evenly if 9 dolls are placed on each shelf? If not, how many dolls should she put on each shelf so that they all fit evenly?

17. The length of the Boston Marathon is 138,435 ft. Each stride, or step, by a particular runner is 3 ft long. Does the number of strides the runner takes fit evenly into the length of the race? How do you know?

Lesson 5-2 Objective 1: Identify prime and composite numbers.

Dynamic Item

18. Which of the following is a prime number?
    [A] 0 [B] 27 [C] 2 [D] 15

Dynamic Item

19. Write the composite numbers from the list below.
    2, 3, 5, 8, 10, 13, 19, 12, 26

20. What is the difference between a prime number and a composite number?

21. Explain why zero is neither prime nor composite.

22. Fill in the missing number in the pattern.

    157, 163, 167, ______, 179, 181

    [A] 175 [B] 177 [C] 171 [D] 173

23. Both A and B are prime numbers. Determine if $A \times B$ is prime. Explain and give an example.

24. Mac's clothing store is having a prime number sale. The cost of everything that is on sale is a prime number. Arnold bought two pairs of socks, one T-shirt, and one pair of sweat pants for $24. Sweat pants cost $11 during the sale. Sweatshirts, which are not on sale, cost twice as much as T-shirts, which are on sale. How much does a sweatshirt cost?

25. Today is Ashley's birthday. Her age is a prime number. Two years ago, her age was not a prime number. But in two, six, eight, eighteen, and twenty years from now, her age will be a prime number again. Ashley is younger than 50 years old. How old is she?

Lesson 5-2 Objective 2: Find the prime factorization of a composite number.

Dynamic Item

26. Which factor tree is correct?

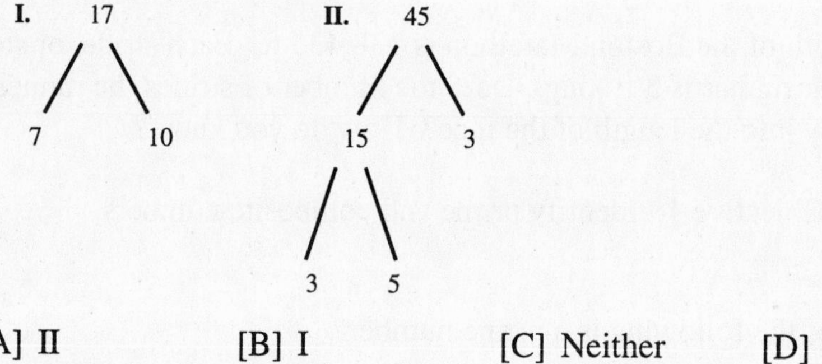

[A] II [B] I [C] Neither [D] I & II

Dynamic Item

27. Make a factor tree of 650.

28. Sketch all the different shaped rectangles that can be formed using exactly 7 tiles. Do the same with exactly 18 tiles. Explain how you can use the dimensions of the rectangles to determine whether a number is prime or composite.

29. How many numbers between 64 and 76 have a prime factorization that has two factors?

[A] 3 [B] 0 [C] 2 [D] 1

30. Mr. Tindell divided the 6th grade class of 80 students into equal groups. The number of students in each group was a prime number. How many groups did he make? How many were in each group?

31. How many different shaped rectangles can you construct using exactly 20 square units? Draw them and give their dimensions.

32. The numbers 2, 5, and 7 are prime factors of *n*. What are four other factors of *n*?

33. Miss Gold asked her class groups to make posters for the bulletin board. She told them to draw, color, or paste 42 stars on poster board. The only rule was that the stars had to be in equal groups and the number of stars in each group had to be prime. How many groups of stars might be on a poster and how many stars are in each group?

Lesson 5-3 Objective 1: Find the greatest common factor by listing factors.

Dynamic Item

34. What is the greatest common factor of 24 and 60?

    [A] 30 [B] 3 [C] 12 [D] 7

Dynamic Item

35. What is the greatest common factor of 30 and 60?

36. What is a greatest common factor? Give an example.

37. Your classmate is confused as to how to find the greatest common factor of two numbers. Explain how it can be found.

38. You bought some pencils for $.78. Your friend bought some of the same pencils for $1.17. What is the most that each pencil could cost?

39. Suppose your teacher has a rectangular sheet of poster board 90 cm × 120 cm. He wants to divide it evenly into squares. What are the dimensions of the largest possible squares?

40. Two numbers whose GCF is 1 are called relatively prime. Which pair of numbers below are relatively prime?

    [A] 42, 93 [B] 105, 69 [C] 27, 95 [D] 64, 74

Lesson 5-3 Objective 2: Find the greatest common factor using prime factorization.

Dynamic Item

41. Find the greatest common factor of 18 and 8.

[A] 1 [B] 3 [C] 2 [D] 4

Dynamic Item

42. What is the greatest common factor of 36 and 12?

43. Explain the pattern presented in the chart below.

First number	Second number	GCF
3	5	1
5	7	1
11	13	1
17	19	1

44. The greatest common factor of 52 and another number is 13. The unknown number could be

[A] 91. [B] 104. [C] 31. [D] 78.

45. The chart below shows the average length of time several items last. In Tommy's family, some things are passed down to a younger child after they are outgrown by an older child. If a baseball glove, a bicycle, a television set, and a suitcase are shared evenly among the boys in the family during the lifetimes of each object, what is the greatest number of brothers Tommy can have?

Item	How Long It Lasts (yr)
Automatic Washing Machine	8
Baseball Glove	10
Piano	25
Bicycle	10
Toaster	10
Suitcase	20
Television Set	12

[A] 4 [B] 3 [C] 1 [D] 2

46. Eloise knows that the greatest common factor of 16 and some number y is 4. List three possible values for the number y.

47. Sandra is making a holiday decoration using ribbon for the trim. She has three pieces of ribbon with lengths of 42 cm, 78 cm, and 108 cm. What is the length of the longest strips of equal length that Sandra can cut from the ribbon without wasting any? How do you know?

48. Alejandro and Jean are distributing erasers and pencils to the art class. If there are 24 erasers and 36 pencils each being divided evenly among the students in the class, what is the greatest number of students in the class?

49. Sierra High School has a marching band. The band is made up of 30 musicians. At some performances, the cheerleading squad marches with the band. There are 15 cheerleaders. The band is known for its stunning entrances during which it marches onto the field in a long procession. What is the greatest number of rows into which the marchers can be arranged so that the number of rows remains the same whether or not the cheerleaders march? Explain how you found your answer.

50. Angela is helping out on her uncle's farm. She has to divide 50 golden apples and 75 red apples equally among several baskets. What is the largest number of baskets she can use?

51. Erica, Ariel, and Jaclyn each picked flowers in a meadow. Erica picked 15 flowers, Ariel picked 18 flowers, and Jaclyn picked 24 flowers. If the girls are going to divide each group of flowers evenly among some vases, what is the greatest number of vases they can fill?

52. The table below shows the ages at which several U.S. presidents were elected to office. Find the greatest common factor of the ages of George Washington, Theodore Roosevelt, and Dwight D. Eisenhower.

President	Year Elected	Year Born	Age at election
George Washington	1788	1732	56
Ulysses S. Grant	1868	1822	46
Theodore Roosevelt	1900	1858	42
Herbert Hoover	1928	1874	54
Franklin D. Roosevelt	1932	1882	50
Dwight D. Eisenhower	1952	1890	62
Ronald Reagan	1980	1911	69

Lesson 5-4 Objective 1: Model fractions.

Dynamic Item

53. What fraction does the diagram represent?

[A] $\frac{3}{5}$ [B] $\frac{3}{2}$ [C] $\frac{2}{5}$ [D] $\frac{1}{5}$

Dynamic Item

54. Draw a diagram to show $\frac{7}{10}$ as part of a whole.

55. What is a fraction bar and how can one be used to model a fraction?

56. What are equivalent fractions? Give an example of two fractions using fraction bars or pattern blocks.

57. Carla's class is made up of 8 boys and 16 girls. What fraction of the class is made up of boys? Draw a model to find your answer.

58. There are three positions on a basketball team: center, guard, and forward. Five people from one team play on the basketball court at any time. Two people play forwards, two people play guards, and one person plays center. Draw a model to show the fraction of players on the court from each team that play guard. What is the fraction?

59. Radnish bought fruit at a corner stand. He bought four peaches, three apples, and two kiwis. Draw a model to show what fraction of the fruit was made up of peaches. What is the fraction?

60. Hal made a list of his top ten favorite movies. Two of the movies on the list were horror movies, five were comedies, and three were adventures. Draw a fraction bar to show the fraction of the movies that were comedies. Then use the model to find a fraction that is equivalent to your answer.

61. Use the table below. Draw a model that shows what fraction of the top classical albums are by Vladimir Horowitz.

Best-Selling Classical Albums

Title	Artist
Horowitz at Home	Vladimir Horowitz
Horowitz: The Last Recording	Vladimir Horowitz
Horowitz in Moscow	Vladimir Horowitz
Beethoven: Symphony No. 9	Leonard Bernstein
Tutto Pavarotti	Luciano Pavarotti
Handel: Arias	Kathleen Battle
Verdi & Puccini: Arias	Kiri Te Kanawa
Black Angels	Kronos Quartet
Beethoven: 9 Symphonies	Arturo Toscanini

62. The noise level of sound is measured in decibels. The louder the sound, the greater the number of decibels. Use the information in the chart below to determine what fraction of the sounds listed have noise levels greater than 50 decibels. Model the fraction using fraction bars.

Noise Levels

Sound	Decibels
Rustling Leaves	20
Whispering	25
Normal Conversation	60
Screaming Baby	90
Jackhammer	100
Jet Engine	140

63. Which fraction below is closest to 1/2? Draw a model.

$\frac{3}{5}$ $\frac{8}{12}$ $\frac{6}{15}$ $\frac{11}{20}$

Lesson 5-4 Objective 2: Round fractions.

Dynamic Item

64. Round to the nearest half-unit.

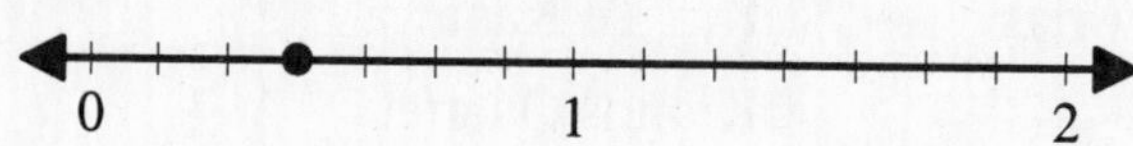

65. Which fraction is CLOSEST to 1?

[A] $\frac{89}{90}$ [B] $\frac{50}{100}$ [C] $\frac{34}{47}$ [D] $\frac{1}{100}$

66. Monique's teacher gave her the fractions below and asked her to classify each fraction as being closest to zero, one-half, or one. How should she classify each fraction?

$\frac{2}{45}$ $\frac{76}{80}$ $\frac{15}{38}$ $\frac{4}{56}$
$\frac{9}{10}$ $\frac{45}{100}$ $\frac{7}{60}$ $\frac{32}{35}$

67. Use each numerator in the box once. Complete each fraction so that it is close to 1/2.

24, 8, 12, 6

a. $\frac{p}{25}$ b. $\frac{p}{13}$ c. $\frac{p}{14}$ d. $\frac{p}{50}$

Lesson 5-5 Objective 1: Find equivalent fractions.

Dynamic Item

68. Find the missing number to make the fractions equivalent. $\frac{7}{10} = \frac{?}{20}$

[A] 14 [B] 13 [C] 20 [D] 16

Dynamic Item

69. Which three fractions are equivalent?
$\frac{36}{40}, \frac{20}{20}, \frac{9}{10}, \frac{18}{20}$

70. Explain how you can form equivalent fractions.

71. Use the numbers 3, 6, 12, and 24 to write three pairs of equivalent fractions.

72. Jenny and some of her friends had a pizza party. They got two pizzas, each of which had eight slices. Jenny ate two slices of pizza. Write two fractions describing what fraction of the total amount of pizza Jenny ate.

Rain Fall in Sun City			
Month	Rain (in.)	Month	Rain (in.)
January	4	July	7
February	3	August	6
March	4	September	7
April	6	October	5
May	5	November	4
June	6	December	3

73. The amount of rain Sun City received last year is shown in the chart above. Write three fractions describing what fraction of the rain fell in April.

74. Use the chart above to find the answer. Write two fractions that describe the amount of rain that fell in the first half of the year.

Lesson 5-5 Objective 2: Write fractions in simplest form.

Dynamic Item

75. Write $\frac{12}{18}$ in simplest form.

[A] $\frac{2}{3}$ [B] $\frac{5}{6}$ [C] $\frac{1}{3}$ [D] $\frac{6}{9}$

Dynamic Item

76. Write $\frac{8}{12}$ in simplest form.

77. What does it mean for a fraction to be in simplest form? How can you find the simplest form of a fraction?

78. Use mental math to determine which fraction is not in simplest form.

[A] $\frac{3}{18}$ [B] $\frac{8}{17}$ [C] $\frac{23}{3}$ [D] $\frac{7}{15}$

79. Johnny took a poll among his classmates and found that 18 out of 30 students prefer carrots to spinach. The simplest form of the fraction describing the number of students who prefer carrots is ______.

[A] $\frac{3}{5}$ [B] $\frac{5}{3}$ [C] $\frac{6}{10}$ [D] $\frac{18}{30}$

80. Because rhinoceroses are hunted for their horns, they are in danger of becoming extinct. Today there are only about 10,000 rhinoceroses left in the world. Africa's black rhinoceros population accounts for roughly 2,500 of those rhinoceroses. Write the fraction of rhinoceroses made up by Africa's black rhinoceros population. Then write the fraction in simplest form.

81. Write a fraction that describes what fraction of $100 each of the following is: $10, $20, and $50. Then express each fraction in simplest form.

82.

AVERAGE LIFE SPAN

Animal	Years	Animal	Years
Beaver	5	Gorilla	20
Camel	12	Kangaroo	7
Chicken	7	Lion	12
Cow	11	Elephant	35
Duck	10	Tiger	16
Goat	12		

The table above gives the average life span for several animals. Name two animals, one whose life span is $\frac{3}{4}$ of the other's life span.

83. From the circle graph below, estimate the fraction of the world's land made up by Antarctica. Write the fraction in simplest form.

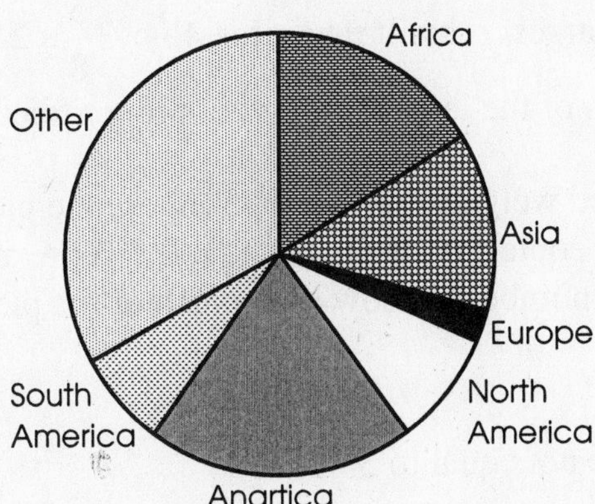

Lesson 5-6 Objective 1: Write improper fractions.

Dynamic Item

84. Write $8\frac{1}{3}$ as an improper fraction.

    [A] $\frac{23}{3}$ [B] $\frac{81}{3}$ [C] $\frac{24}{3}$ [D] $\frac{25}{3}$

85. Christopher is having trouble expressing a mixed number as an improper fraction. Explain to Christopher how to express a mixed number as an improper fraction.

86. Robert served a 12-ft hero sandwich at his birthday party. Six feet of the sandwich was left over. Robert divided the leftovers equally among his friends to take home. If each friend took home $1\frac{1}{2}$ ft of the sandwich, how many friends were at Robert's birthday party?

    [A] 4 [B] 3 [C] 5 [D] 2

87. Draw models to show the relationship between a mixed number and an improper fraction.

88. Write 6 as three different improper fractions.

89. Sarah is making her own Halloween costume. The costume requires $2\frac{3}{4}$ yards of materials. Write the number of yards needed for Sarah's Halloween costume as an improper fraction.

90. The eminent Star Ruby is the largest ruby. It measures $4\frac{1}{4} \times 3\frac{5}{8} \times 2\frac{1}{4}$ inches. Express the dimensions of the largest ruby as improper fractions.

91. The largest apple pie ever baked weighed 30,115 lb. Suppose the pie was divided into 52 pieces and 14 people shared the pie equally. Write an improper fraction and a mixed number to show how much of the pie each person received.

92. Which of the numbers below is not equal to $3\frac{2}{5}$?

    [A] $\frac{34}{10}$ [B] $\frac{90}{25}$ [C] $\frac{17}{5}$ [D] $\frac{340}{100}$

Lesson 5-6 Objective 2: Write mixed numbers.

Dynamic Item

93. Write $\frac{15}{2}$ as a mixed number.

94. Model the fraction $\frac{11}{4}$.

95. Jane's favorite recipe is for cheese calzones. She decided to triple the recipe and determined that she needed $\frac{39}{4}$ cups of flour. Express this as a mixed number.

96. Jonathon added four mixed numbers and found a sum of $7\frac{23}{4}$. Express the sum as a mixed number in simplest form.

97. Suppose you bought 3 pizzas for a party. Each pizza was cut into 8 pieces. Twenty pieces were eaten. How many pizzas is that? Give your answer as a mixed number.

Lesson 5-7 Objective 1: Find the least common multiple by listing multiples.

Dynamic Item

98. Find the least common multiple of 30 and 18.

[A] 90 [B] 540 [C] 270 [D] 36

Dynamic Item

99. Find the least common multiple of 22, 26, and 117.

100. Mike works in the shipping department for a toy store. Every six weeks he receives a shipment of games. Every nine weeks he receives a shipment of bicycles. Mike determined that since he received a shipment today of both games and bicycles, the next time he will receive a shipment of both will be in 54 days. Do you agree with Mike? Explain your reasoning.

101. Joseph mows the lawn every two weeks and weeds the garden every three weeks. Joseph stops his schedule on November 1st. How many days from June to October did Joseph mow the lawn and weed the garden? Assume that there are four weeks in one month.

[A] 4 [B] 6 [C] 3 [D] 5

CHAPTER 5

102. Anita owns a beauty supply store. Every two weeks she receives a supply of shampoo. Every four weeks she receives a carton of nail polishes. Every eight weeks she receives a box of combs, and every twelve weeks she receives a box of hair dyes. If Anita received a shipment of all these supplies today, when is the next time all four supplies will arrive on the same day?

    [A] In 48 weeks [B] In 24 weeks [C] In 12 weeks [D] In 32 weeks

103. The LCM of a number and 8 is 40. Find the number.

104. One hundred people volunteered to clean up the beaches in Sunnyside Township. Matt Roth was the chairman of the "Clean up Sunnyside" committee. He decided that every third person would be chosen to clean up the beach and every tenth person would be chosen to clean up the boardwalk. Which people were chosen to clean up both the beach and the boardwalk?

105. Donato was born on February 29, 1968. He was born on a leap year. A leap year occurs every fourth year. Donato is 25 years old. List the years from 1968 that were leap years. How many leap years will have occurred when Donato is 40 years old?

106. A group of students collects rocks. They decide to put all their rocks together and divide each type of rock equally among themselves. The collection of rocks consists of 102 metamorphic rocks, 90 igneous rocks and 72 sedimentary rocks. What is the greatest possible number of students?

107. Name four numbers that have 10 and 12 as factors. What is the smallest number that has 10 and 12 as factors?

108. Refer to the September calendar below. Corrine joined ceramics and aerobics to occupy her free time after school. Ceramics meets at 3:30 p.m. on days that are multiples of 2. Aerobics meets at 5:00 p.m. on days that are multiples of 3. On which days do both ceramics and aerobics meet?

SEPTEMBER

Sunday	Monday	Tuesday	Wednesday	Thursday	Friday	Saturday
	1	2	3	4	5	6
7	8	9	10	11	12	13
14	15	16	17	18	19	20
21	22	23	24	25	26	27
28	29	30				

Lesson 5-7 Objective 2: Find the least common multiple using prime factorization.

Dynamic Item

109. Use prime factorization to find the least common multiple of 30 and 90.

[A] 450 [B] 30 [C] 60 [D] 90

Dynamic Item

110. Use prime factorization to find the least common multiple of 24 and 72.

111. Explain the difference in the procedures for finding the GCF and LCM of two numbers.

112. Wendy has a cold and an ear infection. The doctor told Wendy to take 1 teaspoon of her medicine every four hours and an aspirin every eight hours. Wendy's mother gave her both the medicine and an aspirin at 6:00 a.m. Monday morning. List the times that Wendy will take both the medicine and the aspirin at the same time on Monday.

[A] 6 a.m., 10 a.m., 12 a.m., 4 p.m.

[B] 6 a.m., 10 a.m., 2 p.m., 6 p.m., 10 p.m.

[C] 6 p.m., 2 a.m., 10 a.m. [D] 6 a.m., 2 p.m., 10 p.m.

113. The arrow on the diagram below points to a column containing multiples of 4. Copy the diagram below. Draw diagonals through the multiples of seven. Explain how you could use the diagram to find the least common multiple of 4 and 7.

			↓		
1	2	3	4	5	6
7	8	9	10	11	12
13	14	15	16	17	18
19	20	21	22	23	24
25	26	27	28	29	30
31	32	33	34	35	36
37	38	39	40	41	42
43	44	45	46	47	48
49	50	51	52	53	54
55	56	57	58	59	60
61	62	63	64	65	66
67	68	69	70	71	72
73	74	75	76	77	78
79	80	81	82	83	84
85	86	87	88	89	90
91	92	93	94	95	96
97	98	99	100		

Lesson 5-8 Objective 1: Compare fractions.

Dynamic Item

114. Insert =, <, or > to make a true statement: $\frac{7}{9}$ ____ $\frac{4}{15}$

115. Study the table of fractions below. Do you observe a pattern? Explain.

$\frac{3}{8}$	$\frac{3}{10}$	$\frac{3}{10} < \frac{3}{8}$
$\frac{5}{7}$	$\frac{5}{11}$	$\frac{5}{11} < \frac{5}{7}$
$\frac{9}{17}$	$\frac{9}{21}$	$\frac{9}{21} < \frac{9}{17}$
$\frac{1}{3}$	$\frac{1}{4}$	$\frac{1}{4} < \frac{1}{3}$
$\frac{7}{9}$	$\frac{7}{12}$	$\frac{7}{12} < \frac{7}{9}$

116. Explain how you would compare three or more fractions.

117. Complete $\frac{1}{3} < \frac{}{8} < \frac{5}{12}$.

[A] 9 [B] 3 [C] 4 [D] 2

118. Draw a model to show which fraction is greater, $\frac{12}{5}$ or $2\frac{3}{4}$.

119. Carla drew a rectangle and a square on grid paper for Geometry class. The width of the rectangle is $\frac{2}{3}$ ft and the length is 1 foot. The side of the square is $\frac{1}{6}$ ft. Compare the area of each figure. Which figure has the greatest area?

120. On an exam, Harry answered $\frac{4}{5}$ of the questions correctly. Celma answered $\frac{9}{10}$ of the questions correctly. Moira and Jean both answered $\frac{9}{15}$ of the questions correctly. What is the least number of questions that could be on the exam? Explain.

CHAPTER 5

Lesson 5-8 Objective 2: Order fractions.

Dynamic Item

121. If $\frac{12}{5}$, $\frac{20}{6}$, $\frac{10}{4}$, and $\frac{20}{8}$ are placed in order from smallest to largest which would be first?

[A] $\frac{12}{5}$ [B] $\frac{20}{8}$ [C] $\frac{10}{4}$ [D] $\frac{20}{6}$

Dynamic Item

122. Order these fractions from smallest to largest: $\frac{3}{4}, \frac{1}{2}, \frac{1}{4}$

123. A recipe calls for $1\frac{2}{3}$ cups of water, $1\frac{1}{2}$ cups of sour cream, and $1\frac{5}{8}$ cups of flour. Order the amounts from least to greatest.

124. Use the numbers in the box below to write four fractions that are greater than $\frac{1}{3}$ but less than $\frac{4}{7}$. Use one number for the numerator and one number for the denominator.

1	2	3
4	5	
6	7	8

125. Write the largest fraction, less than 1, that can be formed using the numbers in the box below.

1	2	3
4	5	
6	7	8

126. Kisha lives $\frac{7}{12}$ of a mile from school. Enrico lives $\frac{5}{8}$ of a mile away. Juan lives $\frac{1}{4}$ of a mile and Greg lives $\frac{2}{3}$ of a mile from school. Who lives the farthest away from school? Who lives the closest to school?

CHAPTER 5

127. The chart below shows Phillip's list of his favorite songs and the length of time that each song plays. Which song plays the longest? Which song plays the shortest?

Song	Length of time (min.)
The Rain Song	$4\frac{11}{30}$
Yellow Rainbow	$4\frac{14}{15}$
Loving You	$4\frac{13}{60}$
Going to LA	$4\frac{19}{30}$
1234	$4\frac{1}{3}$

Lesson 5-9 Objective 1: Write decimals as fractions.

Dynamic Item

128. Write 2.2 as a fraction in simplest form.

[A] $\frac{12}{5}$ [B] $\frac{220}{100}$ [C] $\frac{11}{5}$ [D] $\frac{1}{5}$

Dynamic Item

129. Write 0.45 as a fraction in simplest form.

130. Write a paragraph describing terminating and repeating decimals.

131. Edward and Gary run 5 miles every day after school. It takes Edward $5\frac{3}{8}$ minutes to run 1 mile. Gary can run 1 mile in 5.4 minutes. Who runs faster?

132. Felicia has a stamp collection. She has over 150 stamps in the collection. When Felicia researched the stamps, she learned that the smallest stamp has dimensions of 0.31×0.37 in. Express the dimensions of the smallest stamp as fractions.

133. Draw a decimal square to show 0.54. Write the decimal as a fraction in lowest terms.

134. Marietta is selling cheeses for the holiday fund-raiser. On Monday she sold $\frac{7}{9}$ of the boxes of cheeses. On Tuesday she restocked her supply and sold 0.85 of the boxes of cheeses. On which day did Marietta sell more boxes?

135. Use the chart below to find a pattern. Then, write the decimal 0.81 as a fraction.

Fraction	Decimal
$\frac{1}{11}$	0.09
$\frac{2}{11}$	0.18
$\frac{3}{11}$	0.27
$\frac{4}{11}$	0.36

Lesson 5-9 Objective 2: Write fractions as decimals.

Dynamic Item

136. Write $3\frac{7}{8}$ as a decimal.

[A] 0.307 [B] 3.14 [C] 3.875 [D] 3.07

Dynamic Item

137. Write $2\frac{9}{20}$ in decimal form.

138. Study the chart below. Look for a pattern. Describe the pattern.

Fraction	Decimal
$\frac{1}{11}$	0.09
$\frac{2}{11}$	0.18
$\frac{3}{11}$	0.27
$\frac{4}{11}$	0.36

139. Vivian is making cupcakes for the school bake sale. The recipe calls for $2\frac{3}{4}$ cups of flour. Vivian has 4.35 cups of flour in a bowl. After Vivian completes the recipe, how much flour is left in the bowl? Express your answer as an improper fraction.

    [A] $1\frac{3}{5}$ cups [B] $\frac{11}{42}$ cups [C] $\frac{8}{5}$ cups [D] $4\frac{7}{20}$ cups

140. On March 15 and 16, 1952, a record of $\frac{7331}{50}$ inches of rain fell in 24 hours in Cilaos, LaReunion, Indian Ocean. Express the amount of rainfall as a decimal.

    [A] 7331.50 in. [B] 73.31 in. [C] 0.7362 in. [D] 146.62 in.

141. Describe three real-world situations where you would use fractions and decimals.

142. Monday night Sheila's mother baked a carrot cake. By Tuesday night $\frac{1}{6}$ of the cake was eaten. Express the amount of cake eaten as a decimal.

143. If each square below represents 0.125, what fraction is shown in the figure?

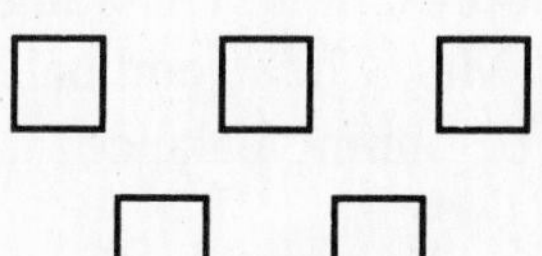

Lesson 5-10 Objective: Solve a problem by working backward.

Dynamic Item

144. Davonne gave Paul half of her tennis balls plus 1 more. Then, Davonne gave Anna half of her remaining balls and 2 more. Finally, she gave Farah half of the balls she had left and 4 more. By then Davonne had one ball for herself. How many tennis balls did she have to begin with?

Dynamic Item

145. Rose had $94.82 in her account at the end of the month. During the month, she wrote checks for $79.00, $227.28, and $32.08. She also withdrew $50 at a banking machine and deposited $100 from her pay check. How much was in her account at the beginning of the month?

146. Mr. Siegel measures the distance around each tree in his backyard every year. This year the distance around the smallest tree is 44 inches. The radius of the tree is approximately how many inches?

[A] 21 [B] 22 [C] 14 [D] 7

147. Mr. Christie is laying new carpet in the family room. The area of the family room is 270 square feet. How many square yards are needed to carpet the family room?

[A] 2430 [B] 90 [C] 810 [D] 30

148. The largest dome is the Louisiana Superdome, in New Orleans. The Superdome has a circumference of 2,135.2 feet. What is the diameter of the Louisiana Superdome?

149. The least common multiple of some number and 18 is 36. Find the number.

150. Ashley needs to have a mean score of 92 on her math exams to become a member of the National Honor Society. She has received grades of 88, 90, 93, 89, and 95. What grade must Ashley earn on her next exam to make the average?

151. Mrs. Chez withdrew $101.75, $65.50, and $98.00 from her checking account. On May 28, she deposited $250.00. If Mrs. Chez's end balance in her checking account is $289.99, what was her beginning balance?

152. If you divide some number by nine and then subtract 8, the result is 4. What is the number?

153. Lynn takes her children to visit their grandparents every two weeks. Every three weeks she takes them to the movies. List the first five weeks that Lynn will take the children to visit their grandparents and take them to a movie.

154. The area of a rectangle is 195 in.^{2} and one side is 13 in. What is the perimeter of the rectangle?

155. The width of a rectangle is 13 in. and the length is 14 in. Suppose a circle with a radius of 5 in. is inscribed within the rectangle. What is the area outside of the circle? Round your answer to the nearest tenth.

Lesson 6-1 Objective 1: Estimate sums and differences by rounding fractions.

Dynamic Item

1. Estimate by first rounding to the nearest half. $\frac{12}{16} + \frac{9}{20} =$

Dynamic Item

2. Estimate by first rounding to the nearest half. $\frac{16}{20} - \frac{1}{16} =$

3. Your are cutting vegetables for a stew. You have $\frac{7}{8}$ cup carrots, $\frac{1}{3}$ cup onions, and $\frac{1}{2}$ cup peppers. About how many cups of vegetables do you have in all?

4. Explain how you round a measurement to the nearest half inch. How can this help you estimate the sum of or difference between two fractions?

5. Write four fractions with a sum of about 2. Explain how you determined your answer.

Lesson 6-1 Objective 2: Estimate sums and differences by rounding mixed numbers.

Dynamic Item

6. Estimate: $8\frac{5}{9} + 3\frac{1}{4}$

   [A] 1 [B] 12 [C] 8 [D] 13

Dynamic Item

7. Estimate by first rounding to the nearest whole number: $5\frac{5}{8} - 4\frac{9}{13}$

8. Describe how to estimate the difference between $31\frac{6}{7}$ and $10\frac{1}{8}$.

9. Vincent's computer printer takes $1\frac{1}{4}$ minutes to print a page. A page with a chart on it takes $1\frac{7}{8}$ minutes to print. A page with a graph on it takes $2\frac{2}{3}$ minutes. A report takes about 11 minutes to print. How many pages is the report and what type pages are in it? Explain how you found your answer.

CHAPTER 6

10. Which number is closest to 8?

[A] $7\frac{3}{4}$ [B] $7\frac{1}{6}$ [C] $7\frac{6}{9}$ [D] $7\frac{2}{5}$

11. Susan's grandmother is knitting a blanket. She works on it each night after dinner. The chart below shows the number of inches she added to the blanket each night. About how many inches did she add to the blanket over the weekend?

Mon	Tues	Wed	Thurs	Fri	Sat	Sun
$1\frac{3}{5}$	$1\frac{4}{6}$	$1\frac{3}{4}$	$2\frac{1}{4}$	$1\frac{1}{8}$	$2\frac{7}{9}$	$3\frac{2}{3}$

[A] 1 [B] 7 [C] 5 [D] 6

12. Mr. Tanner ordered some items from a catalog. The shipping fee is \$0.80 per pound. The first item weighs $2\frac{1}{3}$ lb, the second item weighs $4\frac{3}{12}$ lb, and the third item weighs $3\frac{4}{5}$ lb. Estimate the total fee Mr. Tanner will pay for shipping.

13. Danny's puppy is growing very quickly. The veterinarian has kept a record of the puppy's weight during his first few months. Use the table below. About how much weight did the puppy gain between his first and last visit? Between its second and third?

Visit 1	Visit 2	Visit 3	Visit 4
$7\frac{2}{8}$ lb	$18\frac{2}{3}$ lb	$25\frac{4}{5}$ lb	$36\frac{1}{9}$ lb

14. Milo completed a laboratory investigation in which he recorded the temperature of a liquid at various times. His data table is shown below. Fill in the second row of his table to estimate about how much the temperature increased from the previous time. The original temperature of the liquid was 0° C.

Time 1	Time 2	Time 3	Time 4	Time 5
$16\frac{1}{8}$° C	$18\frac{2}{3}$° C	$21\frac{3}{4}$° C	$24\frac{3}{7}$° C	$28\frac{7}{12}$° C

Lesson 6-2 Objective 1: Add fractions with like denominators.

Dynamic Item

15. Add: $\frac{9}{16}+\frac{6}{16}$

[A] $\frac{15}{32}$ [B] $\frac{16}{15}$ [C] $\frac{21}{32}$ [D] $\frac{15}{16}$

Dynamic Item

16. Add: $\frac{9}{10} + \frac{5}{10}$

17. Explain how you can use fraction bars to model addition problems.

18. Describe how you can explain how to add $\frac{2}{9}$ and $\frac{4}{9}$ without using a model.

19. Jackie bought $\frac{1}{4}$ lb of turkey and $\frac{3}{4}$ lb of potato salad. Draw a model that shows the weight of Jackie's total purchase. Explain why you chose to draw the model you did.

20. The chart below shows three types of animals and the weight of the smallest of each type ever found. What is the weight of all three animals combined?

Animal	Bat	Mouse	Bird
Specific Name	Kitti' s hog nosed bat	Pygmy Mouse	Hummingbird
Weight	$\frac{6}{100}$ oz	$\frac{28}{100}$ oz	$\frac{6}{100}$ oz

[A] $\frac{2}{5}$ oz [B] $\frac{48}{100}$ oz [C] $\frac{4}{30}$ oz [D] $\frac{4}{100}$ oz

21. Phyllis was practicing free throws. Eight out of 12 tries went into the basket. What fraction of her throws did not go into the basket? Write your answer in simplest form.

22. Gerri spent $\frac{5}{24}$ of her money on pencils and $\frac{7}{24}$ on paper. What fraction of her money did she spend? Give the answer in simplest form.

CHAPTER 6

Lesson 6-2 Objective 2: Subtract fractions with like denominators.

Dynamic Item

23. Subtract: $\frac{13}{20} - \frac{9}{20}$

[A] $\frac{1}{5}$ [B] $\frac{1}{10}$ [C] $\frac{3}{40}$ [D] $\frac{3}{10}$

Dynamic Item

24. Find the difference. $\frac{19}{30} - \frac{13}{30}$

25. Eleven of the twenty students in the mathematics class are also in the mathematics club. Four of those eleven students are also in the science club. What fraction of the class is in the mathematics club but not in the science club?

[A] $\frac{7}{20}$ [B] $\frac{11}{20}$ [C] $\frac{5}{20}$ [D] $\frac{15}{20}$

26. Cliff bowled one strike and three spares out of ten frames. In what fraction of the frames did he bowl neither a strike nor a spare? Write an equation that describes the problem.

27. Sam's father brought home a dozen apples. Throughout the week, Sam ate 4 apples and his sister ate three. What portion of the apples were eaten by the end of the week? Write the equation you used to find your answer.

28. Arlo wants to try out for the track team. Every day he tries to run a little farther than the day before in order to prepare. He has been keeping the record shown below to chart his progress. On what day did he run the greatest distance over the previous day?

Day 1	Day 2	Day 3	Day 4	Day 5
4 miles	$4\frac{1}{8}$ miles	$4\frac{3}{8}$ miles	$4\frac{6}{8}$ miles	$4\frac{7}{8}$ miles

29. It took Nadia $\frac{3}{5}$ h to complete her Language Arts homework and $\frac{4}{5}$ h to complete her Mathematics homework. Which took longer? How much longer?

30.

	Mon	Tues	Wed	Thrus	Fri
Distance (miles)	$\frac{7}{8}$	$\frac{5}{8}$	$\frac{3}{8}$	$\frac{7}{8}$	$\frac{6}{8}$

The table above shows the distances a runner covered one week. How much farther did she run on Thursday than on Friday?

Lesson 6-3 Objective 1: Use fraction models to add and subtract fractions with unlike denominators.

31. Write a subtraction sentence for the given model below. Write a problem that can be solved using the subtraction sentence.

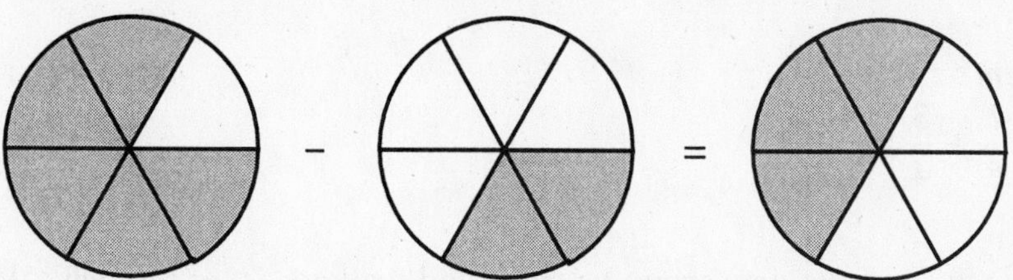

32. Describe two ways in which you can use fraction bars to add or subtract fractions with unlike denominators.

33. Why is it important to know how to estimate the sum of or difference between two fractions even when you are looking for an exact answer?

34. Sal painted a wall in his art classroom. He used $\frac{2}{3}$ gallon of blue paint and $\frac{1}{5}$ gallon of white paint. Use any method to determine how much paint he used.

[A] $\frac{3}{8}$ gallon [B] 1 gallon [C] $\frac{7}{15}$ gallon [D] $\frac{13}{15}$ gallon

35. Maya's school held an aluminum collection program in which they collected aluminum and brought it to be recycled. In the first week, Maya collected $\frac{6}{10}$ lb of aluminum and her friend Abigail collected $\frac{3}{4}$ lb. How much aluminum did the two girls collect?

CHAPTER 6

36. Karl drank $\frac{2}{8}$ of the gallon of milk his mother brought home. His brother Pierre drank $\frac{1}{4}$ of the gallon. How much milk is left?

Lesson 6-3 Objective 2: Use equivalent fractions to add and subtract fractions with unlike denominators.

Dynamic Item

37. Subtract: $\frac{3}{4} - \frac{1}{2}$

[A] $\frac{2}{6}$ [B] $\frac{1}{4}$ [C] 1 [D] $\frac{2}{3}$

Dynamic Item

38. Add: $\frac{2}{5} + \frac{3}{4} =$

39. Cindy ran $\frac{2}{5}$ of the way around a track and walked $\frac{3}{10}$ of the way. What portion of a 3-mile track is left for her to travel? How much farther does she have to go?

40. Mishkel's fish tank can hold 20 gallons of water. He added $\frac{5}{6}$ gallon to the tank on Monday and $\frac{1}{8}$ gallon on Tuesday to fill it. How many gallons of water were in the tank before he added any water?

41. Jared is scheduled to work for $\frac{3}{4}$ of an hour at the school fair. He has already worked $\frac{1}{3}$ of an hour. How much longer does he have to work?

42. A recipe calls for $\frac{3}{4}$ cup of applesauce. Jean has $\frac{1}{8}$ cup. How much more does she need?

43. Meritza has made a scale model of Earth based on the width of each section inside the planet. Use the table and figure below. What is the total length from the center of Meritza's model to the edge of the model?

Earth' s Dimensions	
Solid core	1300 km
Liquid outer core	2250 km
Mantle	2900 km

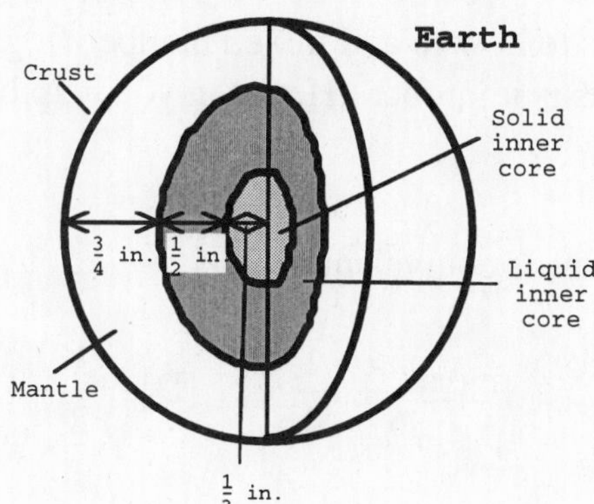

44. The chart below shows the number of games won and tied by each hockey team. Write a subtraction equation for each team showing the fraction of games that were lost. All the teams played 80 games during the season. Which team had the smallest fraction of lost games? The largest? Are these the teams you would have predicted? Explain.

Team	Games Won	Games Tied
Boston Bruins	44	12
Pittsburgh Penquins	41	6
Calgary Flames	46	8
Hartford Whalers	11	31

CHAPTER 6

Lesson 6-4 Objective 1: Add mixed numbers mentally.

Dynamic Item

45. Add: $5\frac{6}{13} + 1\frac{4}{13}$

 [A] $6\frac{10}{13}$ [B] $4\frac{1}{13}$ [C] $5\frac{2}{13}$ [D] $\frac{2}{13}$

Dynamic Item

46. Add: $\frac{1}{20} + \frac{1}{8}$

47. Your friend Alison is confused as to how to add mixed numbers together when the sum of the fraction parts is improper. How can you help her? Use an example in your explanation.

48. Which of the following expressions is equivalent to $5\frac{2}{3}$?

 [A] $8\frac{7}{9} - 3\frac{1}{6}$ [B] $2\frac{2}{4} + 3\frac{1}{6}$ [C] $3\frac{5}{6} + 1\frac{1}{4}$ [D] $9\frac{1}{2} - 4\frac{2}{5}$

49. Mrs. Peters bought $7\frac{2}{3}$ yards of fabric. She needs another $3\frac{1}{6}$ yards. How many yards of fabric does she need all together?

50. Eliza and Jamie are making cupcakes for a bake sale at school. Eliza needs $2\frac{1}{3}$ c of flour for her recipe and Jamie needs $1\frac{3}{4}$ c for her recipe. They have 4 c of flour. Do they have enough flour for both recipes? Explain.

51. Explain how you can mentally find the sum of $3\frac{2}{3} + 4\frac{1}{5} + 1\frac{1}{3} + 2\frac{3}{5}$.

52. Last year it rained $2\frac{1}{2}$ in. in April, $1\frac{1}{3}$ in. in May. Which number below is the total rainfall for the two months?

 [A] $2\frac{10}{12}$ in. [B] $3\frac{1}{2}$ in. [C] $3\frac{2}{5}$ in. [D] $3\frac{5}{6}$ in.

53. Use the diagram below. What is the total height of the bookcase?

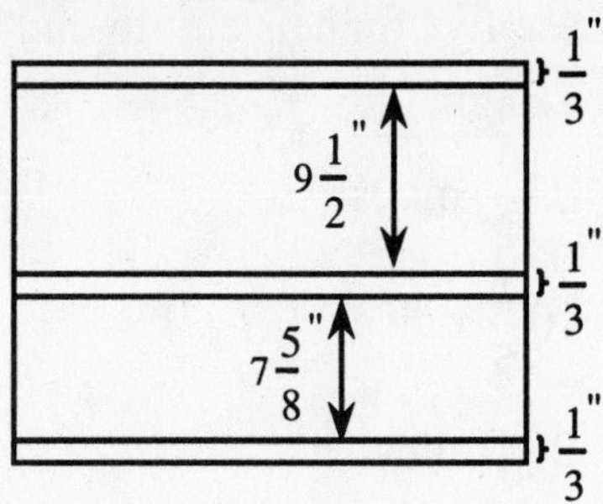

Lesson 6-4 Objective 2: Add mixed numbers by renaming.

Dynamic Item

54. Add. $10\frac{2}{3} + 10\frac{2}{7}$

[A] $14\frac{2}{5}$ [B] $6\frac{1}{7}$ [C] $20\frac{20}{21}$ [D] $20\frac{2}{5}$

Dynamic Item

55. Find the sum. $5\frac{9}{13} + 4\frac{12}{13}$

56. Mr. Friendly plans to put hedges around three sides of his parking lot as shown below. If hedging can be ordered only in three-foot sections, how many feet must he order? Explain.

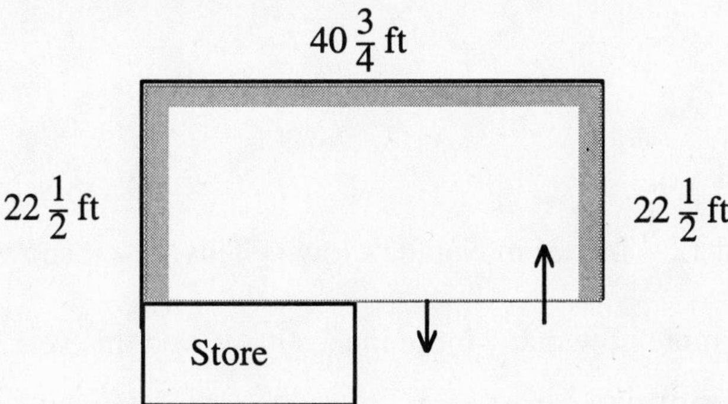

57. The table below lists the lengths of five famous tunnels. What would be the length of a tunnel made by placing these five tunnels end-to-end?

Name	Length
Moscow Metro	$23\frac{1}{2}$ miles
St. Gotthard Road Tunnel (Switzerland to Italy)	$10\frac{1}{5}$ miles
Lincoln Tunnel (NY)	$2\frac{1}{2}$ miles
Yerba Buena Island (CA)	$\frac{1}{10}$ miles
Chesapeake Bay Bridge - Tunnel (VA)	$17\frac{2}{3}$ miles

Source: The Guiness Book of Records 1993

58. You want to put a wallpaper border on two sides of your room. One wall is 10 1/2 ft and the other is 9 1/3 ft. Wallpaper border comes in rolls that are 5 ft long. How many do you need?

Lesson 6-5 Objective 1: Subtract mixed numbers mentally.

Dynamic Item

59. Subtract. $6\frac{2}{19} - 4\frac{1}{19}$

[A] $2\frac{1}{38}$ [B] $3\frac{1}{19}$ [C] $2\frac{1}{19}$ [D] $\frac{1}{19}$

Dynamic Item

60. Subtract: $8 - 4\frac{2}{5}$

61. Last year it snowed $12\frac{1}{6}$ inches in Natalie's town. This year it snowed $15\frac{7}{9}$ inches. Determine how many more inches it snowed this year. Which measurement is CLOSEST to that number?

[A] 4 [B] $2\frac{1}{2}$ [C] $3\frac{1}{2}$ [D] 3

62. Last Wednesday it snowed $5\frac{1}{2}$ in. On Sunday it snowed $4\frac{1}{4}$ in. Which day did it snow more? How much more?

63. Your puppy weighed $5\frac{1}{8}$ lb last week. This week he weighs $6\frac{1}{4}$ lb. How much weight has he gained?

64. You are helping out with the costumes for the school play. A particular costume needs $5\frac{2}{3}$ yd of material, but there are only $3\frac{1}{2}$ yd. How much more is needed?

65. The chart below shows the snowfall one winter. What month had the greatest snowfall? How much greater was it than the next closest month?

Dec.	Jan.	Feb.	Mar.
$8\frac{1}{4}$"	$15\frac{7}{8}$"	$14\frac{1}{2}$"	$6\frac{9}{10}$"

Lesson 6-5 Objective 2: Subtract mixed numbers by renaming.

Dynamic Item

66. Subtract: $5\frac{4}{5} - 3\frac{5}{8}$

[A] $2\frac{9}{40}$ [B] $2\frac{1}{3}$ [C] $2\frac{7}{40}$ [D] $2\frac{1}{40}$

Dynamic Item

67. Subtract: $5\frac{1}{2} - 3\frac{3}{4} =$

68. What is the next number in the pattern $5\frac{1}{3}, 8\frac{1}{12}, 10\frac{5}{6}$? Explain how you found your answer.

69. Rashid is $5\frac{4}{6}$ ft tall and his younger brother is $4\frac{3}{8}$ ft tall. How much taller is Rashid than his brother?

70. The weights of some award-winning fruits and vegetables are shown in the chart below. Organize the fruits and vegetables into a new chart in order of weight. Be sure to include the difference in weight between successive items. Explain how you developed your chart.

Item	Potato	Celery	Pumpkin	Turnip
Weight (lb)	$7\frac{1}{16}$	$46\frac{1}{16}$	$816\frac{1}{2}$	$48\frac{3}{4}$
Item	Pineapple	Onion	Garlic	Grapefruit
Weight (lb)	$17\frac{1}{2}$	$10\frac{7}{8}$	$2\frac{5}{8}$	$3\frac{1}{8}$

Source: The Guiness Book of Records 1993

71. Suppose that you spent $1\frac{1}{2}$ hours on homework on Monday, and 1 hour and 20 minutes on Tuesday. Which day did you work longer? How much longer? Give your answer as a fraction or a mixed number.

72. You want to make muffins that call for $2\frac{1}{4}$ cups of flour. You have only $1\frac{2}{3}$ cups. How much more flour do you need?

73. Which pair of numbers below has a difference of $3\frac{5}{6}$?

[A] $6\frac{5}{6}-3\frac{5}{6}$ [B] $6\frac{7}{12}-4\frac{1}{6}$ [C] $8\frac{2}{3}-4\frac{1}{6}$ [D] $8\frac{1}{6}-4\frac{1}{3}$

74. Write a word problem involving subtraction of mixed numbers that has an answer of $5\frac{1}{8}$.

Lesson 6-6 Objective 1: Solve a problem by drawing a diagram.

75. Sandra poured 18 gallons of water into a tank to make it $\frac{3}{5}$ full. How many gallons does the tank hold?

[A] 30 [B] 36 [C] 21 [D] 78

76. There are 20 people in Susie's class. When Susie took a poll about winter sports, she found that nine people enjoy figure skating, six people enjoy skiing, one person plays ice hockey, and four people simply do not enjoy cold weather. In addition, she found out that three of those people who enjoy figure skating also enjoy skiing. Draw a diagram to figure out how many people enjoy figure skating but not skiing.

[A] 1 [B] 3 [C] 4 [D] 6

77. Mr. Alan's family room is a rectangle that measures 7 meters by 5 meters. In the room is a fireplace that extends out from the wall 0.5 meter and measures 1 meter across. Mr. Alan wants to cover the floor with carpet that costs $12 per square meter. How much will the carpet cost?

78. The wall behind Mrs. Port's stove is covered with tiles that measure 15 cm by 15 cm. The wall measures 3 m by 4.2m. How many tiles cover the wall?

79. Emily's parents want to fence in their backyard, which measure $20\frac{1}{2}$ meters by $15\frac{3}{4}$ meters. The house, which is 18 m long, will be used as part of one of the sides. How many meters of fence will they need?

80. John and Shelly are decorating the classroom as a special art project. They are covering part of a wall with strips of posterboard. They are using strips of black posterboard that are 6 inches wide and 4 feet long and strips of red posterboard that are 9 inches wide and 4 feet long. If they alternate colors, how many of each color strip will cover a wall that is $5\frac{3}{4}$ feet wide and 4 feet tall?

81. Elizabeth has to walk 8 miles for a charity event. She walks half the distance during the first two hours and a fourth of the remaining distance during the next half hour. How far does she have to go to complete the walk?

Lesson 6-6 Objective 2: Solve a problem using any strategy.

82. Tyrone earns $20 helping a carpenter on Friday afternoon and $10 delivering newspapers on Saturday morning. On Sunday he buys a CD for $17.89, sees a movie for $7.50, eats lunch for $6.25, and gets a haircut for $11.00. He has $7.30 left over. How much money must he have had to start with on Friday morning?

83. Samuel has won an award and therefore gets to choose three items from a list of prizes. There are 8 prizes on the list. How many possible combinations of three prizes can he choose?

84. Angela is taking a tour. During the first part of the tour she takes an airplane to travel from San Diego, California, to Tucson, Arizona. This is 50% of the distance of her entire tour. She then drives 100 miles from Tucson to Phoenix, Arizona. She finishes the tour by taking a bus to travel the remaining 300 miles from Phoenix to Las Vegas, Nevada. What fraction of the trip did she travel by bus?

Lesson 6-7 Objective 1: Multiply fractions by fractions.

Dynamic Item

85. Multiply. $\frac{1}{4} \times \frac{5}{7}$

[A] $2\frac{6}{7}$ [B] $5\frac{3}{5}$ [C] $\frac{5}{28}$ [D] $\frac{7}{20}$

Dynamic Item

86. Multiply: $\frac{9}{4} \times \frac{2}{15}$

87. One half of Jack's class has pets. One third of those who have pets, have cats. Explain how to determine what fraction of students in the class have cats.

88. Explain why multiplying a proper fraction by another proper fraction results in a number that is always smaller than 1.

89. Write a multiplication sentence for the model below. Write a problem that can be solved using this sentence.

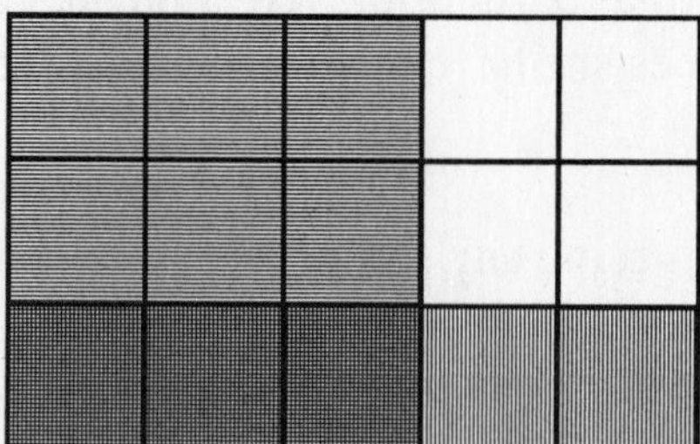

90. Choose the product that is represented by the model below.

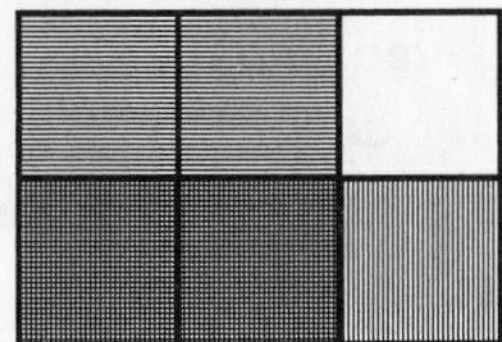

[A] $\frac{1}{3}\times\frac{5}{2}$ [B] $\frac{1}{2}\times\frac{2}{3}$ [C] $\frac{3}{4}\times\frac{1}{3}$ [D] $\frac{2}{3}\times\frac{2}{3}$

91. Lyle is $\frac{3}{4}$ as tall as Kevin. Annie is $\frac{1}{2}$ as tall as Lyle. What fraction of Kevin's height is Annie's height?

92. Mt. Whitney in California is $\frac{5}{7}$ the height of Mt. McKinley in Alaska. Cambell Hill in Ohio is $\frac{1}{10}$ the height of Mt. Whitney. What fraction of Mt. McKinley's height is Cambell Hill?

Lesson 6-7 Objective 2: Multiply whole numbers by fractions.

Dynamic Item

93. Find the product: $\frac{2}{63}$ of 21

[A] $\frac{2}{9}$ [B] $\frac{6}{7}$ [C] $\frac{2}{3}$ [D] $\frac{14}{9}$

Dynamic Item

94. Multiply: $\frac{2}{45}\times 5$

95. Use the table below. What desert is $\frac{1}{7}$ times the size of the Sahara desert?

Desert	Location	Approximate Size sq mi
Arabian	E. of Africa	70,000
Gobi	Asia	500,000
Kalharia	Africa	225,000
Sahara	Africa	3,500,000

Source: The World Almanac 1993

CHAPTER 6

96. (a) Write a fraction that describes the fraction of the days of the week that are weekend days. Use the fraction to write a multiplication sentence to find the fraction of the days of the week that are Sundays.
(b) Write a fraction that describes the fraction of the days of the week that are weekdays. Then use the fraction to write a multiplication sentence to find the fraction of the days of the week that are Mondays.

97. Suppose that you have 24 muffins. You give a friend $\frac{1}{3}$ of them. How many are left?

98. You are making scarves for presents. Each scarf needs $\frac{3}{4}$ yd of fabric. How many yards do you need for 6 scarves?

99. When you multiply a whole number by a fraction less than 1. what do you know about the product?

Lesson 6-8 Objective 1: Estimate products of mixed numbers.

Dynamic Item

100. Estimate: $4\frac{4}{7} \times 2\frac{2}{5}$

[A] 8 [B] 46 [C] 10 [D] 7

Dynamic Item

101. Estimate: $1\frac{7}{8} \times 3\frac{1}{2}$

102. Gerry bought a carpet for her room. She wants to carpet an area that is $4\frac{1}{2}$ yd^2. The carpet is $1\frac{1}{2}$ yd by $2\frac{4}{5}$ yd. Is this enough carpet?

103. Which number below is closest to the product of $3\frac{1}{2} \times 1\frac{4}{5}$?

[A] $4\frac{1}{2}$ [B] 7 [C] $5\frac{1}{2}$ [D] 6

104. Which number below is the solution to the equation $y \div 3\frac{1}{4} = 5\frac{1}{2}$?

[A] $17\frac{7}{8}$ [B] $15\frac{1}{4}$ [C] $16\frac{1}{2}$ [D] $21\frac{3}{4}$

Lesson 6-8 Objective 2: Multiply mixed numbers.

Dynamic Item

105. Multiply: $2\frac{1}{2} \times 4\frac{2}{3}$

[A] $11\frac{2}{3}$ [B] $1\frac{1}{3}$ [C] 14 [D] $4\frac{1}{8}$

Dynamic Item

106. Multiply: $3\frac{3}{5} \times 5\frac{2}{3}$

107. Jimmy placed three crates in a row to make a shelf. The base of each crate measures $1\frac{3}{5}$ ft by $2\frac{1}{6}$ ft. What is the area of his shelf?

108. Suppose that you are going to make cookies for a class party. The recipe calls for 2/3 cup of brown sugar. You want to triple the recipe. How much brown sugar do you need?

109. You had $2\frac{1}{2}$ pounds of raisins. You used up $\frac{3}{4}$ of them. How many pounds of raisins are left?

110. A gallon of water weighs $8\frac{1}{3}$ lb. How much does $1\frac{1}{5}$ gal of water weigh?

[A] $11\frac{1}{2}$ lb [B] $8\frac{1}{15}$ lb [C] 10 lb [D] 12 lb

111. Write a word problem using multiplication of mixed numbers with a product of $\frac{7}{8}$.

112. You want to cover a bookshelf with contact paper. The shelf is $6\frac{2}{3}$ in. deep and $15\frac{3}{4}$ in. long. A roll of paper contains $100\,\text{in.}^2$. Is that enough paper to cover the shelf completely? Explain your answer.

CHAPTER 6

Lesson 6-9 Objective 1: Divide fractions.

Dynamic Item

113. Divide: $\frac{4}{5} \div \frac{8}{5}$

[A] $3\frac{1}{8}$ [B] $1\frac{1}{5}$ [C] 1 [D] $\frac{1}{2}$

Dynamic Item

114. Divide: $\frac{3}{5} \div \frac{9}{5}$

115. How do you find a reciprocal of a fraction and how are reciprocals used when dividing by fractions?

116. Megan can divide whole numbers by whole numbers, but she is having difficulty dividing fractions by whole numbers. Explain to her the similarity between the two processes. Use an example in your explanation.

117. Write a word problem that can be solved by dividing 9 by $\frac{1}{3}$. Explain how to solve your problem.

118. Which quotient is greater than 2?

[A] $\frac{1}{6} \div \frac{2}{6}$ [B] $6 \div \frac{3}{4}$ [C] $\frac{2}{3} \div 2$ [D] $\frac{4}{5} \div \frac{2}{5}$

119. Maureen, Frank, Tashia, Zane, Eric, and Wesley are addressing envelopes for volunteer work at a local charity. They were given $\frac{3}{4}$ of an entire mailing to address to be evenly divided among six of them. What fraction of the entire mailing does each person address?

Lesson 6-9 Objective 2: Divide mixed numbers.

Dynamic Item

120. Divide: $1\frac{1}{9} \div 4\frac{1}{6}$

[A] $5\frac{2}{5}$ [B] $\frac{4}{15}$ [C] $1\frac{1}{5}$ [D] $\frac{11}{15}$

Dynamic Item

121. Find the quotient. $1\frac{2}{9} \div 4\frac{2}{7}$

122. Explain how you would divide $40 \div 1\frac{1}{4}$.

123. Which quotient is less than 1?

[A] $4\frac{2}{5} \div 1\frac{1}{3}$ [B] $2\frac{1}{4} \div 2\frac{1}{4}$ [C] $3\frac{2}{6} \div 4\frac{1}{2}$ [D] $6\frac{1}{8} \div 3\frac{1}{2}$

124. Lena is sewing costumes for a children's ballet recital. She has 9 yards of fabric. She needs $1\frac{3}{7}$ yards for each costume. How many complete costumes can she make? Explain.

125. Lonny is preparing a chicken dish for a dinner party. Each serving requires $\frac{2}{5}$ lb of chicken and he has $6\frac{2}{3}$ lb. How many servings can he prepare? Explain how you found your answer.

126. Mitch bought 14 lb of groceries at the store. Each bag can hold $3\frac{1}{3}$ lb. How many bags must he use to carry his groceries home?

127. A mountain climber needs to buy new rope. The rope he buys is $103\frac{3}{4}$ feet long. How many lengths of rope that are $20\frac{3}{4}$ feet long can he make out of it?

128. The table below shows the number of hours in a day on each planet. A day on Earth is 24 hours because that is how long it takes for the planet to rotate on its axis. Other planets rotate at different speeds and therefore have longer or shorter days than does the Earth. How many days pass on Saturn during one Earth day?

Planet	Number of hours in a day
Mercury	$1407\frac{3}{5}$
Venus	$5832\frac{1}{5}$
Earth	24
Mars	$24\frac{3}{5}$
Jupiter	$9\frac{4}{5}$
Saturn	$10\frac{1}{5}$
Uranus	$17\frac{1}{5}$
Neptune	$16\frac{1}{10}$
Pluto	$153\frac{3}{10}$

Lesson 6-10 Objective 1: Change units of length, weight, and capacity.

Dynamic Item

129. 27 feet = ___ yards

[A] 8 [B] 81 [C] 324 [D] 9

Dynamic Item

130. Convert 13 cups to quarts.

131. How can you determine the number of inches in $2\frac{1}{2}$ yards? Explain whether or not you should multiply or divide.

132. Why is it important to be able to change from one unit to another?

133. Write a problem involving changing from one unit to another that can be solved by multiplying $3\frac{1}{4} \times 16$. Find the answer to your problem.

134. Uyen is mixing and bagging nuts, sesame seeds, and raisins for 24 children at the summer camp to take on a hike. She used $2\frac{3}{8}$ lb of cashews, $1\frac{1}{2}$ lb of walnuts, $2\frac{1}{4}$ lb of roasted peanuts, $1\frac{1}{8}$ lb of sesame seeds, and $1\frac{3}{4}$ lb of raisins. How many ounces of mix can Uyen put in each bag so that each child has the same amount?

[A] 6 [B] $\frac{3}{8}$ [C] 5 [D] 8

135. The North building of the World Trade Center is 1,368 ft tall. Estimate how many yards tall it is.

[A] 400 [B] 40 [C] $\frac{1}{4}$ [D] 4,000

136. Gregg is running in a race. He has just passed the 1056-foot marker. How many miles has he run so far?

137. Timmy has 3 gallons of orange juice. He wants to give 2 cups of orange juice to each of the 21 players on the football team. Will he have enough juice?

<u>**Lesson 6-10**</u> Objective 2: Compare amounts by expressing them in the same units.

Dynamic Item

138. The pattern you are following calls for 5 yards of fabric. You have 10 feet of fabric.
a) Do you have enough fabric?
b) How much more fabric do you need? **or** How much extra fabric do you have?

139. Tina has a package of pet food that contains 252 oz. Her pet eats $4\frac{1}{5}$ pounds of food each week. How many weeks will the package last?

140. Mrs. Sharf was unable to find a large container of apple juice, so she bought 6 pint containers instead. How many quarts did she buy? Explain.

141. The Kentucky Derby is $1\frac{1}{4}$ miles long. How many feet long is it?

CHAPTER 6

142. A truck weighs 4,600 pounds. Can it cross a bridge that does not hold over $2\frac{1}{4}$ tons?

143. Tracey needs $2\frac{3}{5}$ c of milk for a recipe. She has 12 ounces of milk in a container and she has borrowed 10 ounces from her neighbor. Does she have enough milk? Explain.

Chapter 7: Ratios, Proportions, and Percents

Lesson 7-1 Objective: Explore the meaning of ratio.

Dynamic Item

1. Reuben sold 55 tickets to the school play and Millicent sold 65 tickets. What is the ratio of the number of tickets Reuben sold to the number of tickets Millicent sold?

Dynamic Item

2. The Harford Bears had a record of 45 wins and 25 losses. What was the ratio of wins to losses?

   [A] 5 to 3 [B] 3 to 5 [C] 5 to 9 [D] 9 to 5

3. Describe what a ratio is and give an example.

4. There are 3 apple pies and 7 apples. Explain how there can be four different ratios to describe the apples and pies.

5. Which two figures below have areas with a ratio of 1:4?

   [A] 

   [B] 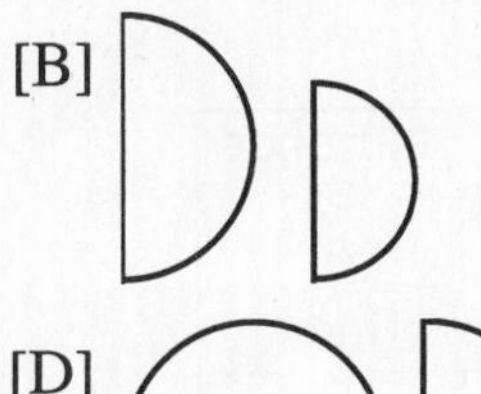

   [C]

   [D] 

6. There are three computers and six computer diskettes. Find the ratio of computers to computer disks.

   [A] 6:3 [B] 6:9 [C] 3:9 [D] 3:6

7. Use the table below to write the ratio of black mollys to red platys. Write your answer as a fraction.

Fish in an Aquarium

Fish	Number
red platy	5
catfish	9
black molly	3

8. Sanjeev says that the ratio of inches to feet is 12:1 and the ratio of feet to yards is 3:1. Is he correct? Explain. What is the ratio of inches to yards?

9. There are 4 baseballs and 2 baseball bats. Write a ratio of baseballs to baseball bats.

10. Draw a picture to represent the ratio of 5 socks to 2 shoes.

11. A study found that for every left-handed girl there are three left-handed boys. What is the ratio of left-handed boys to left-handed girls?

12. A picture contains 3 bicycles, 2 cars, and 5 skateboards. Write the ratio for each of the following:
    a. skateboards to cars
    b. cars to bicycles
    c. bicycles to skateboards

13. Use the table below. Which two figures are described in each of the following ratios?

Figure	Number of Sides
Triangle	3
Square	4
Pentagon	5
Hexagon	6
Octogon	8
Decagon	10

    a. 4:3
    b. 8:10
    c. 5:6

14. Use the table below. Write ratios that describe the number of endangered fishes to amphibians, plants to insects, and mammals to birds.

SPECIES LISTED AS ENDANGERED

Species	Number Endangered
Birds	225
Reptiles	74
Amphibians	14
Fishes	64
Snails	5
Clams	39
Crustaceans	8
Insects	11
Plants	187
Mammals	303

Lesson 7-2 Objective 1: Write equal ratios.

Dynamic Item

15. Which group contains ratios that are all equivalent to $\frac{1}{3}$?

[A] $\frac{2}{6}, \frac{3}{9}, \frac{4}{12}$ [B] $\frac{2}{3}, \frac{4}{6}, \frac{6}{9}$ [C] $\frac{1}{4}, \frac{1}{5}, \frac{1}{6}$ [D] $\frac{2}{3}, \frac{3}{3}, \frac{4}{3}$

Dynamic Item

16. Write three equal ratios for the ratio 4 : 32.

17. Explain what it means to say that two ratios are equal ratios.

18. Which of the following are equal ratios?

[A] 4:5 and 8:10 [B] 1:3 and 6:2 [C] 2:3 and 3:2 [D] 5:3 and 10:9

CHAPTER 7

19. Find the values that make the ratios equal.

$\frac{4}{8}, \frac{\quad}{24}, \frac{36}{\quad}$

[A] 12, 72 [B] 12, 40 [C] 16, 72 [D] 3, 4

20. Use multiplication and division to write two ratios that are equal to each of those given:

a. 9:12
b. $\frac{3}{15}$
c. 14 to 10

21. Express the ratios $\frac{10}{40}$ and $\frac{25}{50}$ in simplest form.

22. Count the number of ones, twos, and threes in the pattern below. Then write each ratio as a fraction in simplest form.

1
1 2 2 1
3 1 3
1 2 3 2 1
1 2 1
3 2

a. ones : threes
b. twos : ones
c. threes : twos

23. Use the table below.

HEART RATES

	beats / min
Newborn human baby	120
Average human adult	72
Hummingbird	1,000
Elephant	25

Find the following.
a. The number of times a hummingbird's heart beats in 3 min.
b. The number of times an elephant's heart beats in $\frac{1}{2}$ min.
c. The number of times a baby's heart beats in 5 min.

24. Three students were each asked to find a ratio whose simplest form is 2:5. Ricky's answer was 6 to 15. Jessica's answer was 10:25. And Filomina's answer was $\frac{14}{35}$. Explain how all three students can be correct.

Lesson 7-2 Objective 2: Find unit rates.

Dynamic Item

25. A manufacturer can produce 1,230 parts in 5 h. What is the unit rate in parts per hour?

[A] 6,150 parts/h [B] $\frac{1}{5}$ parts/h [C] 246 parts/h [D] $\frac{1}{246}$ parts/h

Dynamic Item

26. Write the rate 128 pens in 8 boxes as a unit rate.

27. What is a rate? Give an example. What is a unit rate?

28. Grace and Jim each bought notebooks for school. Grace got 4 notebooks for $4.80. Jim got 3 notebooks for $3.90. Jim says he got a better deal. Explain whether or not he is correct and how you know.

29. Find the unit rate for

a. 360 miles in 13 hours
b. 3 peaches for $0.99
c. 15 steps in 5 seconds

30. Grete Waitz won the New York Marathon nine times. The rate at which she ran during her last victory in 1988 was 26 mi in 148 min. Find the unit rate for her race.

Lesson 7-3 Objective 1: Recognize proportions.

Dynamic Item
31. Which of the following pairs of ratios **DO NOT** form a proportion?

[A] $\frac{3}{7}, \frac{12}{28}$ [B] $\frac{3}{7}, \frac{9}{21}$ [C] $\frac{27}{63}, \frac{3}{7}$ [D] $\frac{3}{7}, \frac{9}{28}$

Dynamic Item
32. Do the ratios $\frac{5}{7}$ and $\frac{10}{21}$ form a proportion?

33. Define proportion in your own words.

34. Janelle does not understand why the statement $\frac{3}{5} = \frac{9}{15}$ is true. How would you explain this to her?

35. Which pair or pairs of ratios form(s) a proportion?
a. $\frac{6}{9}, \frac{12}{27}$ b. $\frac{3}{4}, \frac{12}{16}$ c. $\frac{1}{5}, \frac{5}{25}$

36. Do the ratios $\frac{4}{5}$ and $\frac{8}{20}$ form a proportion?

Lesson 7-3 Objective 2: Solve proportions.

Dynamic Item
37. Solve: $\frac{c}{3} = \frac{6}{54}$

[A] 18 [B] $\frac{1}{3}$ [C] 3 [D] $\frac{1}{18}$

Dynamic Item

38. Solve: $\frac{q}{2} = \frac{6}{24}$

39. Thomas is filling his fish tank with water. He needs to know if the stand can hold the weight of the water when it is full. Thomas finds that 5 gal of water weigh 40 lb. The tank weighs 20 lb empty and can hold 30 gal of water. The stand can hold a total of 300 lb. Can the stand hold the fish tank when it is full of water? Explain how you found your answer.

40. You can buy 3 peaches for $1.20. Which proportion is set up to find the cost of 5 peaches?

[A] $\frac{5}{1.20} = \frac{3}{x}$ [B] $\frac{3}{1.20} = \frac{x}{5}$ [C] $\frac{3}{1.20} = \frac{5}{x}$ [D] $\frac{1.20}{5} = \frac{3}{x}$

41. If $\frac{14}{3} = \frac{56}{n} = \frac{p}{6}$, what are n and p?

[A] 45, 28 [B] 12, 28 [C] 14, 26 [D] 12, 24

42. Find the missing number. Show how you found your answer.

$\frac{12}{26} = \frac{}{78}$

43. During the summer, Mary read 8 books in 12 weeks. The rate at which Kevin read books was proportional to the rate at which Mary read books, but Kevin read fewer books. Suggest the rate at which Kevin read. Explain how you got your answer.

44. During his career, Michael Jordan scored an average of 33.5 points per game. Given this average, how many games do you think it took him to score 134 points?

45. The price of licorice is proportional to its length. It costs $0.50 to buy 5 in. How much licorice can you get for $1.80?

46. Use the table below. In what form of exercise will a 150-pound man burn 325 calories in $\frac{1}{2}$ h?

Activity	Calories burned / hour *
Cross-country skiing	1,100
Running	900
Bicycling	850
Swimming	650
Tennis	600
Aerobics	530

* by a 150-pound male

Lesson 7-4 Objective 1: Solve problems by solving a simpler problem.

Dynamic Item

47. If 15 points are arranged in a circle, how many lines are needed to join every point to every other point once?

[A] 113 [B] 105 [C] 98 [D] 120

Dynamic Item

48. If 16 points are arranged in a circle, how many lines are needed to join every point to every other point once?

49. The football team is having a fundraiser to buy new uniforms. Football bumper stickers cost the football team $2.00 each. The football team sells them for $4.75. Which expression shows the number of bumper stickers (S) that must be sold for the football team to make a profit of $137.50?

[A] S = $137.50 ÷ $4.75 - $2.00 [B] S = $137.50 ÷ $2.00

[C] S = $4.75 – $2.00 [D] S = $137.50 ÷ $2.75

50. Which is worth more, 260 dimes or 500 nickels?

51. The houses on 5th Street are numbered 15 - 93. How many house numbers contain at least one 5 in their address?

52. A thirsty camel can drink more than 28 gallons of water in 10 minutes. Estimate how many gallons of water the camel can drink in 1 hour.

53. A queen termite can lay eggs at a rate of one per second. Estimate how many eggs a queen termite can lay in one year.

54. Refer to the data in the graph below. How many more spelling words did Susan know during the fifth week than the third week of school?

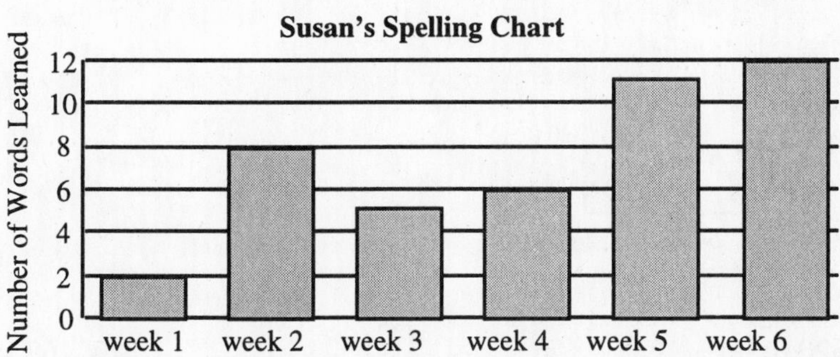

Lesson 7-4 Objective 2: Solve problems using any strategy.

55. Explain how you would find the sum of the first 50 even numbers. What is the sum?

56. There are 7 players in a chess tournament. Each player must play each of the other players once. How many chess games will be played?

[A] 14 [B] 21 [C] 49 [D] 35

57. There are 10 girls and 10 boys at a school dance. Each boy dances with each girl one time. How many dances are there in all?

[A] 10 [B] 100 [C] 1000 [D] 20

58. Refer to the data in the table below. How long will it take each printer to print a fifty page document?

Printer	No. of Pages Printed Per Minute
1	2
2	5
3	8
4	10

Lesson 7-5 Objective 1: Enlarge or reduce designs to make a scale drawing.

Dynamic Item

59. A scale drawing is to be made of the floor of a rectangular room whose dimensions are 54 feet by 30 feet. The scale to be used is 6 feet = 1 inch. What will the perimeter of the scale drawing be?

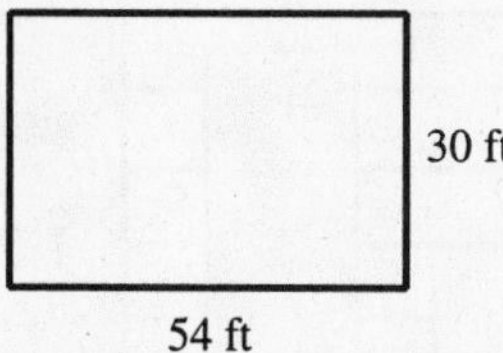

[A] 1620 in. [B] 28 in. [C] 23 in. [D] 168 in.

Dynamic Item

60. A rectangle has a width of 36 cm. A drawing of the rectangle is made using a scale of 1:4. What is the width of the rectangle in the drawing?

61. The length of a gymnasium floor is shown in a drawing as 2 cm long. The actual length of the floor is 30 m. What is the scale of the drawing?

62. A designer has been given a scale drawing, but it is much too small to follow. How can the designer enlarge the figure without altering the actual sizes being described?

63. Reggie is going to make a scale model of a Tyrannosaurus Rex dinosaur. Tyrannosaurus Rex was 46 ft long, 20 ft high, and had teeth that were 6 in. long. The model should be no more than 8 inches tall. What scale should he use? Explain.

64. A designer creates two scale drawings. The scale for the first is 1 cm = 3 m. The scale for the second is $\frac{1}{2}$ cm = 5 m.. Write the scale for each drawing as a ratio.

Lesson 7-5 Objective 2: Find the actual size of an object.

Dynamic Item

65. A map has a scale of 1 cm = 16 km. If two cities are 4 centimeters apart on the map, what is the actual distance between the two cities to the nearest tenth of a kilometer?

[A] 64 km [B] 4 km [C] 2.5 km [D] 0.3 km

Dynamic Item

66. On a blueprint, the scale indicates that 9 centimeters represent 15 feet. What is the length of a room that is 14.4 centimeters long and 9 centimeters wide on the blueprint?

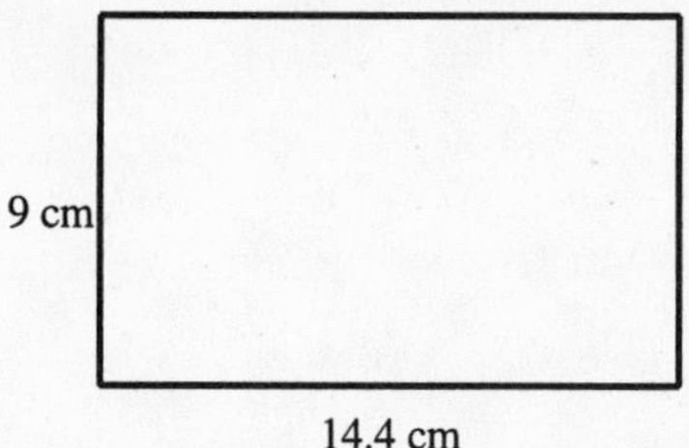

67. Explain how you can use the scale on a drawing to find the actual size of an object.

68. The height of an elephant in a scale drawing is 4 cm. The scale in the drawing is $\frac{1}{2}$ cm to 50 cm. What is the actual height of the elephant?

[A] 200 cm [B] 400 cm [C] 25 cm [D] 53.5 cm

69. A map shows the distance between the corner of Cactus Road and 1st Street and the corner of 1st Street and Merle Road as 3 in. The scale is 1 in. to 3.7 mi. What is the actual distance?

[A] 1.3 mi [B] 11.1 mi [C] 22.2 mi [D] 111 mi

70. The scale for a drawing of a gorilla is 1 mm = 4 cm. The gorilla is 184 cm tall. What is the height of the gorilla in the drawing?

[A] 46 cm [B] 46 mm [C] 181 mm [D] 4.6 mm

71. A truck in a scale drawing is 4.5 cm long. If the scale is $\frac{1}{2}$ cm = 1 m, what is the actual size of the truck?

72. A rectangular room is 8 m long and 5 m wide. Make a scale drawing using the scale 1 mm = 20 cm.

73. The Empire State Building in New York City is 381 m tall. It is the fourth tallest building in the world. Determine its height in a drawing with a scale that is $\frac{1}{2}$ cm = 20 m.

Lesson 7-6 Objective: Model percents.

Dynamic Item

74. Write a percent for the shaded part of this box.

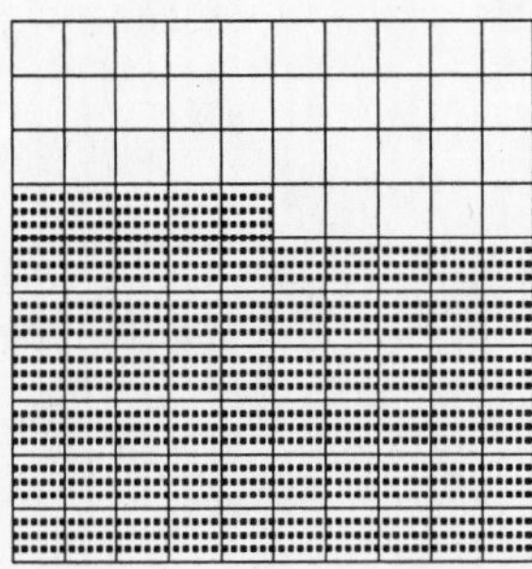

[A] 65% [B] 25% [C] 35% [D] 75%

Dynamic Item

75. What percent of the square is shaded?

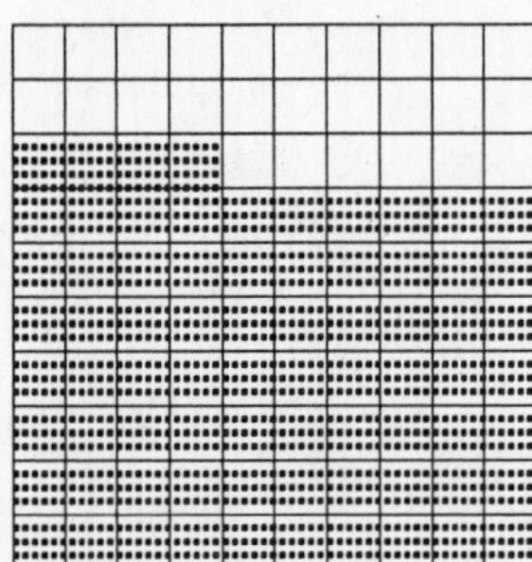

76. Explain what it means to find a percent.

77. When you are told that a certain percent of a group of people answered no to a survey question, you always know what percent of the group did not say no to that question. Explain why.

78. Which measurement is the greatest percent of one meter?

[A] 89 mm [B] $\frac{1}{4}$ [C] 100 mm [D] 32 cm

79. What percent of the numbers from 1 to 100 have at least one digit that is an 8?

[A] 19% [B] 81% [C] 10% [D] 12%

80. Danielle has 30% of \$100. Explain to her how much more money she needs to have 60% of \$100.

81. Mario had \$100. He spent \$42 on clothes, \$24 on school supplies, and \$6 on lunch. Explain to him how he can determine what percent of his money he has left.

82. What percent of the grid below is shaded?

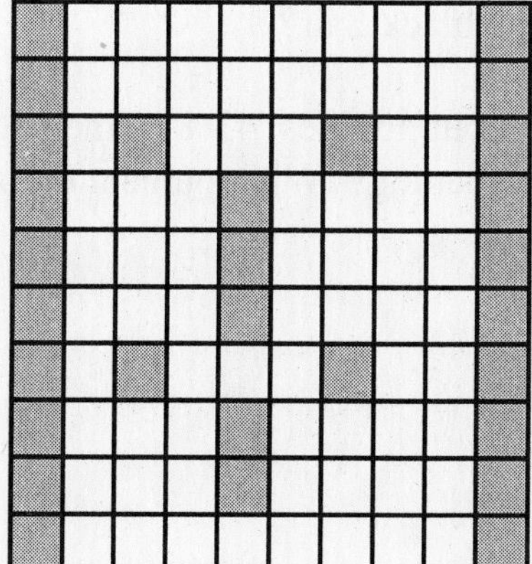

83. There are two quarters, three dimes, one nickel, and three pennies. Compare the value of the coins to \$1. What percent of \$1 are the coins?

84. Use a 10×10 square of graph paper to model 28%.

85. The graph below shows the number of students that have each hair color described.

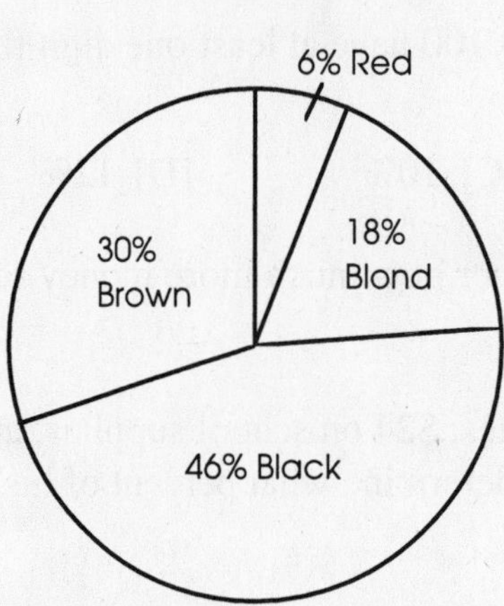

What percent of the students have brown hair?
What percent of the students do not have black hair?

86. The list below shows that when asked about hobbies, 43% of the people listed reading. What percent did not list reading? What percent did not list swimming?

MOST - PREFERRED
HOBBIES

Activity	Percent (%)
Reading	43
Cooking	34
Music	32
Gardening	26
Pets	25
Fishing	24
Swimming	20
Travel	20

Lesson 7-7 Objective 1: Write percents as fractions and decimals.

Dynamic Item

87. Write 54% as a fraction in simplest form.

[A] $\frac{27}{50}$ [B] 540 [C] $\frac{27}{5}$ [D] 5400

Dynamic Item

88. Write 24% as a decimal.

89. Explain how a percent can be written as a fraction in simplest form.

90. Explain how 18%, 0.18 and $\frac{18}{100}$ are related. Do you see a pattern?

91. Describe the shaded area in the figure below as a fraction in simplest form, a decimal, and a percent.

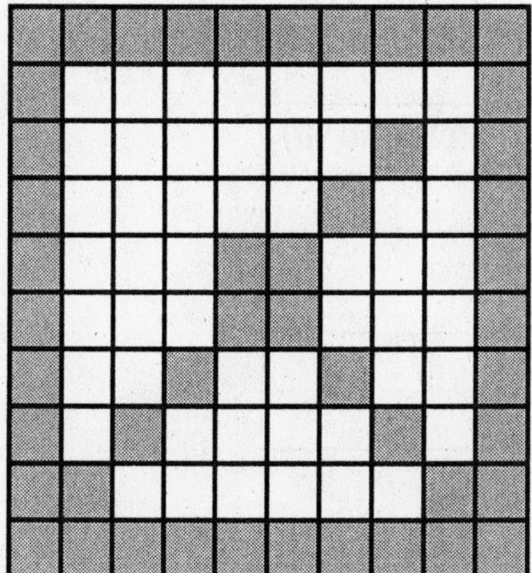

92. The outermost layer of the Earth is made up of several elements. It is 45.6% oxygen, 8.4% aluminum, and 4.7% calcium. Express each percent as a fraction and a decimal.

93. Kyle was filling a certain percent of the squares in the figure below when he was distracted. He had already filled half of the squares he needed. What percent of the squares did he need to fill? Write the percent as a decimal and a fraction.

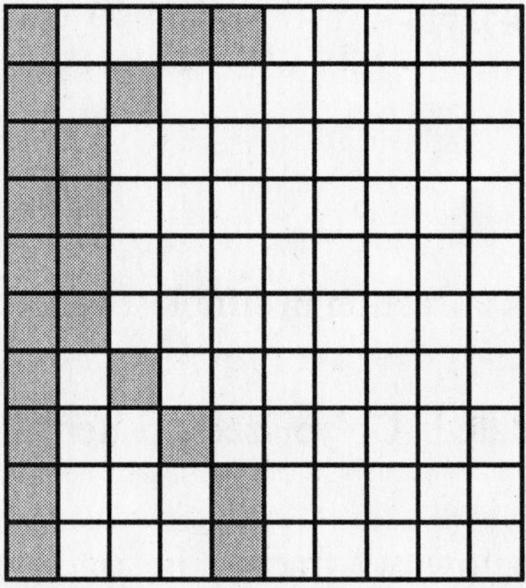

94. A baseball player's batting average shows the percent of times at bat the player got a hit. Fill in the missing terms for the players shown below.

Player	Fraction	Decimal	Percent(%)
Willie McGee		.34	
Eddie Murray	$\frac{33}{100}$		
Andre Dawson			31%
Rafael Palmeiro		0.32	
Wade Boggs	$\frac{3}{10}$		

Source: National and American Leagues of Professional Baseball Clubs

Lesson 7-7 Objective 2: Write decimals as fractions and percents.

Dynamic Item

95. What is 0.28 as a percent?

[A] 280% [B] 2.8% [C] $\frac{28}{100}$% [D] 28%

Dynamic Item

96. Write $\frac{9}{10}$ as a percent.

[A] 0.9% [B] 900% [C] 9% [D] 90%

97. Which of the following can also be written as 84%?

[A] $\frac{21}{25}$ [B] 0.16 [C] $\frac{84}{25}$ [D] 8.4

98. One quarter $\left(\frac{1}{4}\right)$ of the months of the year begin with the letter J. The months beginning with J can be described by which of the following?

[A] 0.4 [B] 0.75 [C] 40% [D] 0.25

99. Amanda says that 67% of the students in the class have a pet. Ramon says that $\frac{67}{100}$ students have a pet. How can both be correct?

100. Emma has already read 7 of the 20 books on her summer reading list. Express the number of books she has read as a decimal and a percent.

101. Of the 100 students who went on the picnic, 62 had fruit in their lunch boxes. Express the percent of students with fruit as a decimal and as a fraction in simplest form.

102. In a survey at a supermarket, $\frac{3}{4}$ of the people surveyed said that they shopped more than once a week. What percent of the people is that? What percent shop only once a week or less?

Lesson 7-8 Objective 1: Estimate percent using models.

103. Determine the amount represented by the model below.

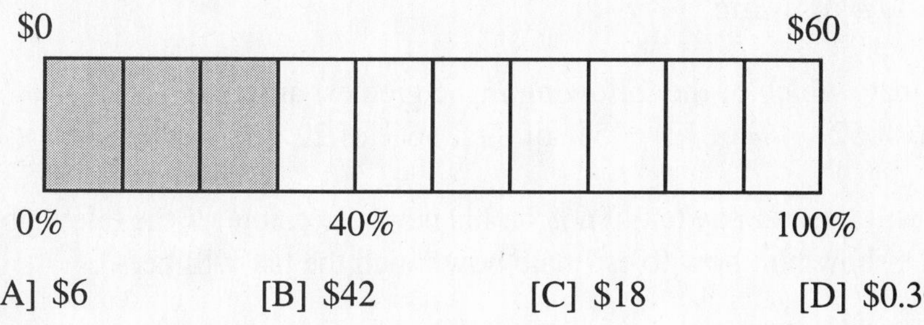

[A] $6 [B] $42 [C] $18 [D] $0.30

104. The movie matinee at the local theater costs 20% less than the regular movie price of $6.95. Draw a model to estimate the price of the matinee.

105. Draw a model that helps you estimate 11% of 58.

106. Draw a model to estimate 21% of 25.

Lesson 7-8 Objective 2: Estimate percent using mental math.

Dynamic Item

107. Estimate 81% of 54.

[A] 40 [B] 28 [C] 45 [D] 35

Dynamic Item

108. Estimate 29% of 20.

109. One store's ad says that jewelry is on sale for 80% of its normal price. Another store's ad says that jewelry has been marked down 25%. Explain which ad shows the better sale and why.

110. There were 952 fans at a basketball game. If 72% of the fans were rooting for the home team, estimate the number of fans who supported the home team. Explain how you estimated.

111. Estimate which of the following would be a 15% tip for a bill of $38.49.

[A] $7.70 [B] $5.80 [C] $3.85 [D] $1.90

112. Azeeb wants a new winter coat that retails for $56.99. It is on sale for 80% of the regular price. She has $49. Explain how to estimate the sale price of the coat. Does she have enough money to buy the coat?

113. Determine the best estimate for 68% of 50.

114. Mayflies live for a total of about 2 h. How long does it take for a mayfly to live 40% of its life?

115. Estimate which of the following is the greatest amount.
12% of 52 4% of 73 15% of 89 36% of 22 21% of 36

116. Joe will have to pay tax of 6% on his new television. If the television costs $199, show him how to estimate how much the tax will be.

Lesson 7-9 Objective 1: Find a percent of a number using modeling or a calculator.

Dynamic Item

117. What is 40% of 350?

[A] 140 [B] 234 [C] 187 [D] 93

Dynamic Item

118. What is 13% of 233?

119. Explain why it is easier to use a fraction to find 50% of 320 and a decimal to find 13% of 320.

120. Which of the following is the smallest value?

[A] 5% of 220 [B] 11% of 72 [C] 8% of 120 [D] 92% of 4

121. Kathleen earned $820 working a summer job. If she saved 55% of her money, how much did she save?

Lesson 7-9 Objective 2: Find percent of a number using proportions.

Dynamic Item

122. 60% of 90 is what number?

[A] $\frac{2}{3}$ [B] 15 [C] $\frac{3}{2}$ [D] 54

Dynamic Item

123. Find 24% of 650.

124. Which expression represents 32% of 520?

[A] $\frac{32}{100}$ [B] 0.32×520 [C] 0.68×520 [D] $\frac{32}{520}$

125. Which expression represents 68% of 190?

[A] $\frac{68}{100} \times 190$ [B] $\frac{0.68}{100}$ [C] $\frac{68}{190}$ [D] $\frac{32}{100} \times 190$

126. Enrico sent out a survey to all of the customers on his paper route. He received responses from 20% of the 50 customers. He wants to receive responses from at least 35% of the people. Explain to Enrico how to figure out how many more responses he needs.

127. A jellyfish is about 95% water. If a jellyfish weighs 45 g, how much is water weight?

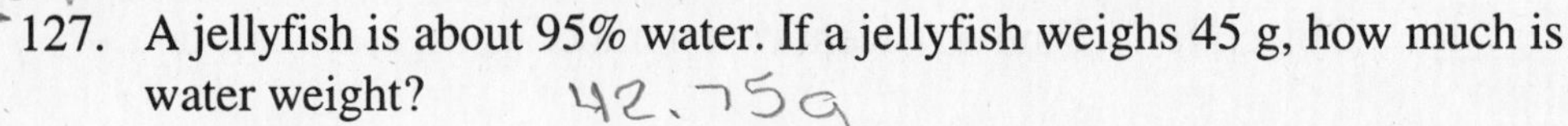

128. Jill's team won 68% of their 19 games. How many games did they win?

129. Everyone in Sandy's class has to do a science project. Out of 34 students, 82% have completed their projects. How many students still need to do their projects?

130. There are 70 flowers in Mrs. Mill's garden. 30% of the flowers are red, 28% are yellow, 19% are white, 7% are orange, and 16% are a combination of colors. Find the number of each kind of flower.

131. Use the table below to find the approximate number of people whose names begin with the letter B in a group of 200 people, the letter C in a group of 320 people, and the letter E in a group of 150 people.

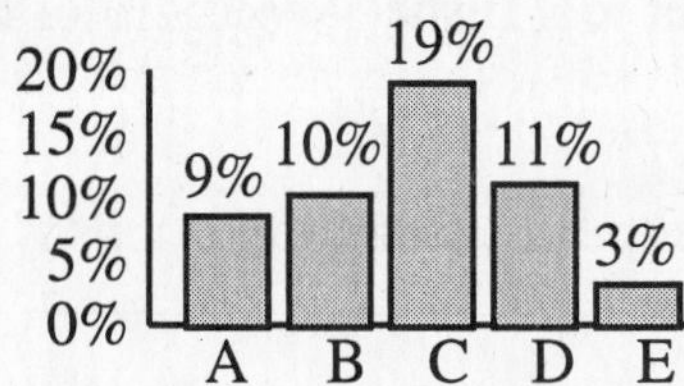

Lesson 7-10 Objective: Sketch circle graphs.

Dynamic Item

132. What percent of the circle is shaded?

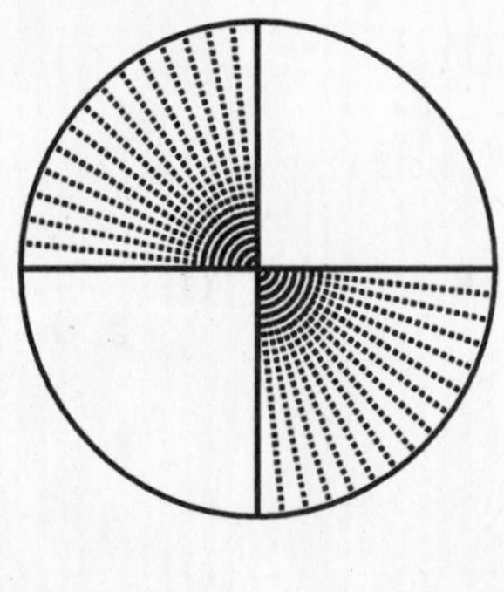

[A] 0.40% [B] 40% [C] 50% [D] 0.50%

Dynamic Item

133. Draw a circle graph with $\frac{2}{4}$ shaded.

134. How can you construct a circle graph by finding the number of degrees related to each group of data in a table?

135. Gerry and Richard are each given the same table of data and told to present the information as a circle graph. Gerry's circle has a diameter of 10 cm. Richard's circle has a diameter of 6 cm. Do the angles in their circle differ as well? Explain.

136. Melissa took a survey to find out what percentage of people watch certain sports. She found that 38% chose football, 27% chose baseball, 22% chose basketball, 8% chose soccer, and 5% chose other sports. When Melissa made a circle graph to show her findings, which sport was represented by a section with an angle measure of 79.2°?

[A] soccer [B] basketball [C] baseball [D] football

137. According to the data, what would be the angle measurement of the section representing those who answered "Yes" if the data were converted to a circle graph?

No	Yes	Unsure
39%	46%	15%

[A] 54° [B] 165.6° [C] 194.4° [D] 140.4°

138. Susie surveyed students in her class about the type of movies they like. When she added up her results, she found that 13% enjoy scary movies, 43% prefer funny movies, 8% like sad movies, 34% like mysteries, and 2% do not have a preference. Explain to Susie how she can make a circle graph to represent her findings.

139. Scott took a survey about how many students do chores at home. He found that 34% set or clear the table, 28% throw out the garbage, and 19% take care of the pets. Unfortunately, Scott lost the last page of his research that listed the percent of students who vacuum and the percent of students who put away the groceries. Suggest what the missing data might be if each student does only one chore. Explain how you arrived at your answer.

140. The circle graph below shows how the students in one city get to school. The labels are in the wrong section. Tell which section should have each percent label.

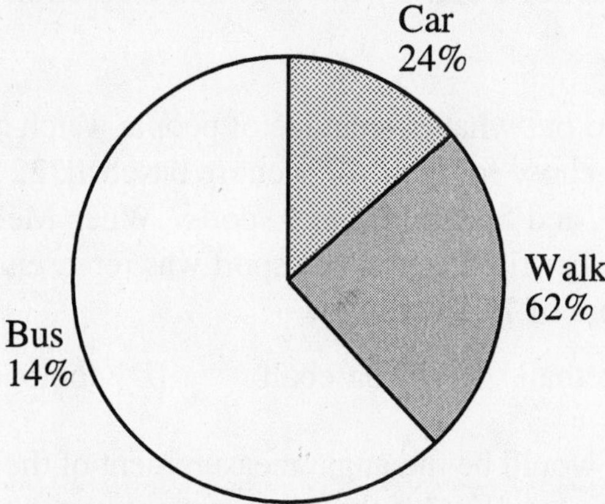

141. Convert the information in the table below to a circle graph.

Types of Energy Consumed in the U.S.	
Natural Gas	24%
Coal	23%
Petroleum Products (Oil)	42%
Nuclear Power	7%
Water Power	4%

142. The main countries responsible for the production of cocoa beans are:

Country	Percent
Malaysia	10%
Ivory Coast	30%
Ghana	13%
Brazil	16%
Other	31%

Convert the information to a circle graph.

143. Construct a circle graph to display the information in the table below.

What Americans throw away	
Paper and cardboard	36%
Yard Wastes	20%
Food Wastes	9%
Metals	9%
Glass	8%
Plastics	7%
Rubber and Leather	3%
Other	8%

Chapter 8: Tools of Geometry

Lesson 8-1 Objective 1: Identify and work with points, lines, segments, and rays.

Dynamic Item

1. Which figure shows a ray?

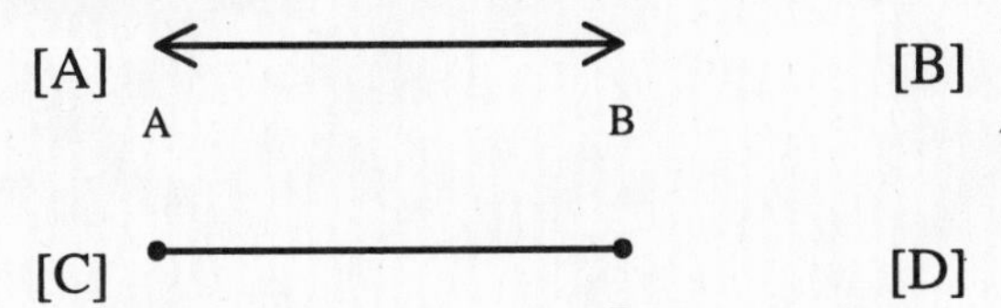

[B] A B

[D] A

Dynamic Item

2. Draw a labeled diagram for a point.

3. A point can be described as belonging to a plane, line, ray, or line segment. Explain why this statement is true.

4. A large wall at the local park casts a shadow. Are the wall and its shadow in the same plane or different planes? Explain.

5. Lines MN and OP are intersecting lines, yet you do not see them cross. Explain how this can be true.

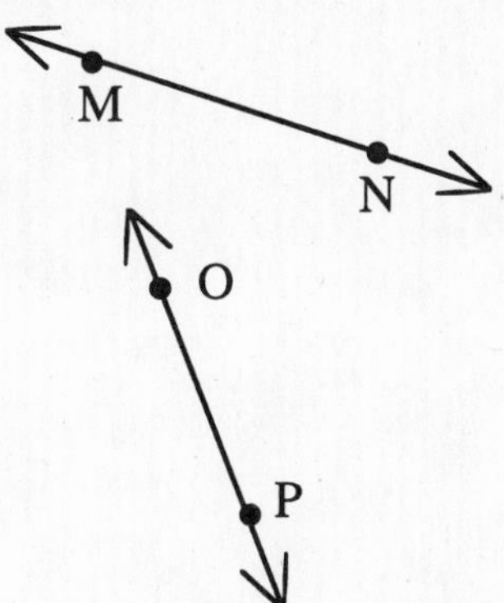

6. Which of the following names describes the line?

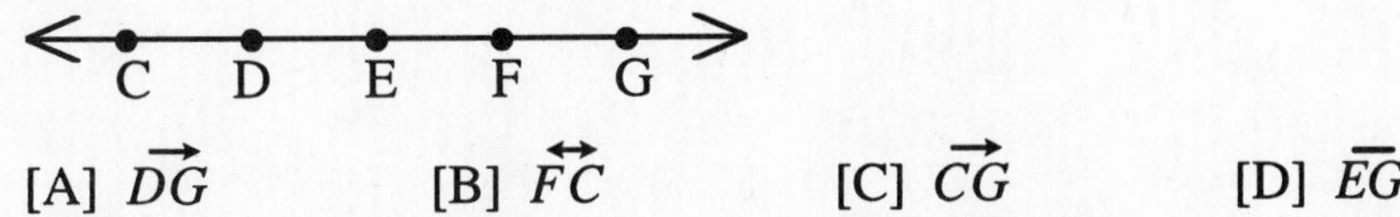

[A] $\overrightarrow{DG}$ [B] $\overleftrightarrow{FC}$ [C] $\overrightarrow{CG}$ [D] $\overline{EG}$

7. The floors in an apartment building belong to different

[A] segments. [B] points. [C] rays. [D] planes.

CHAPTER 8

8. Name 3 noncollinear points, 3 collinear points, and 2 rays on the diagram below.

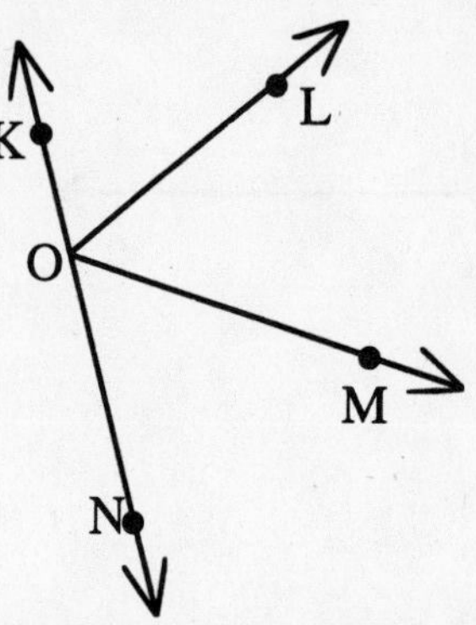

9. Use the following information to draw a diagram: Points A, C, and D are collinear, points B, C, and F are collinear, and points E, F, and G are collinear. DG is parallel to AE which is parallel to CF. AD is parallel to EG. BD and AB intersect at point B.

10. Think of a map of the United States. Describe how you would indicate the location of a city or town. Describe the connection between 2 cities. Are locations within the United States on the same plane? Could more than two cities have collinear locations?

Lesson 8-1 Objective 2: Investigate relationships between special pairs of lines.

Dynamic Item

11.

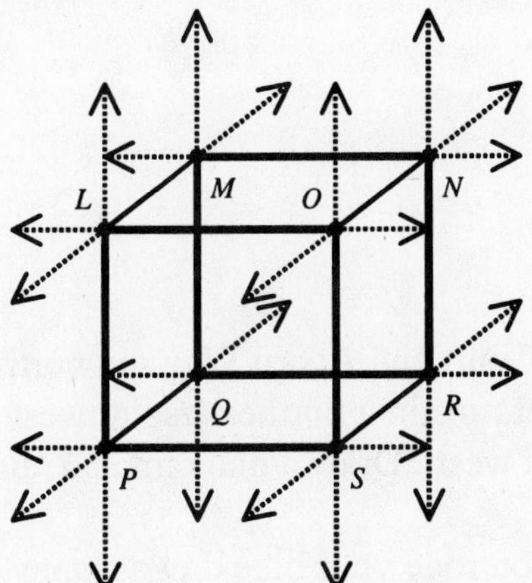

Which of the following lines from the figure above is skew to line $\overleftrightarrow{MN}$?

$\overleftrightarrow{QM}$, $\overleftrightarrow{SP}$, $\overleftrightarrow{PL}$

12. $\overrightarrow{BA}$ and $\overleftrightarrow{DE}$

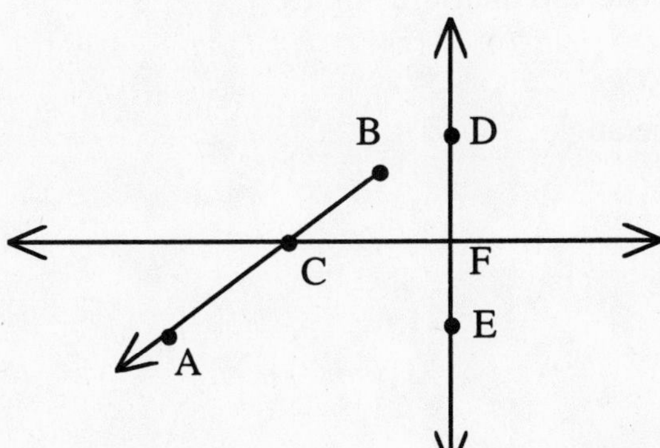

[A] will never meet.

[B] are collinear.

[C] are parallel.

[D] will intersect.

13. The figure shown below is a regular octagon. Name the parallel segments of the figure.

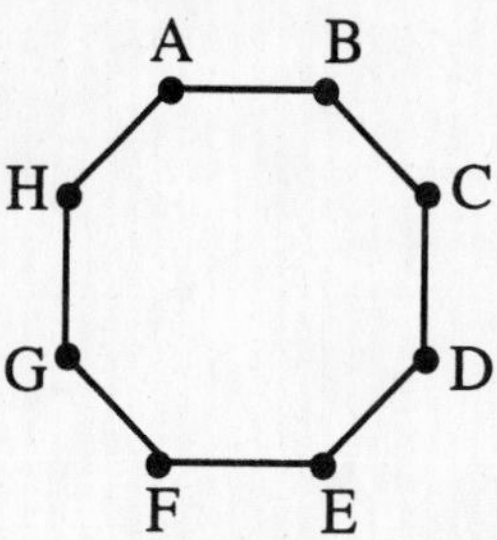

14. On a street map of Anytown, Sunny Court and Acorn Way run north and south across town. Criss-Cross Street runs in a northeast/southwest direction. Park Avenue runs east and west. Draw a diagram and answer the following questions.
a. Which streets would you cross if you rode your bike down Sunny Court?
b. Name two streets that are parallel.
c. What streets does Criss-Cross Street intersect?
d. What streets does Park Avenue intersect?

15. Draw $\overleftrightarrow{AB}$ parallel to $\overleftrightarrow{CD}$ intersecting $\overleftrightarrow{XY}$.

Lesson 8-2 Objective 1: Estimate and measure angles.

Dynamic Item

16. Estimate the measure of the angle:

[A] 120° [B] 240° [C] 90° [D] 180°

Dynamic Item

17. Draw a 67° angle.

18. You are given a set of angles to be measured. All you have is a protractor, a pencil, and a sheet of paper. Explain how you will measure the angles.

19. Which name does NOT describe either of the angles shown?

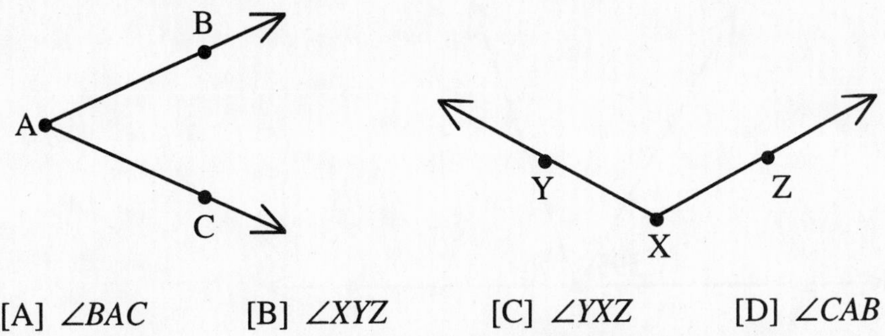

[A] ∠*BAC* [B] ∠*XYZ* [C] ∠*YXZ* [D] ∠*CAB*

20. Use a protractor to determine which measurement describes one of the angles shown.

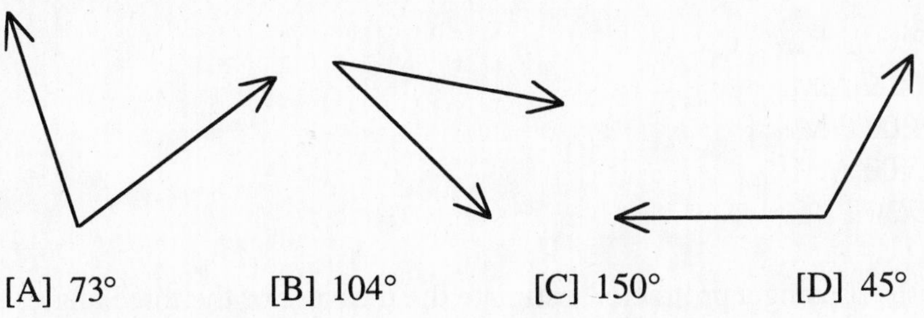

[A] 73° [B] 104° [C] 150° [D] 45°

21. Maria is confused about angles. She read that because the sides of squares are perpendicular, all squares have the same angles. Angles in triangles, however, can differ. How can you clear up Maria's confusion? You may use diagrams in your answer.

22. You and a friend go for a walk. Initially you walk on a flat path. As your walk continues, you climb an incline that gradually becomes steeper. As the incline increases, your walking becomes more and more difficult. Draw illustrations to show the path of your walk. Explain how angles are involved in your walk.

23. Describe how to draw an angle using a protractor. Then use a protractor to draw angles with each measure listed:

a. 90°
b. 7°
c. 145°

24. Draw an obtuse angle called ∠*ABC* and an acute angle called ∠*DEF*.

25. What is the measure of $\angle CBD$? Explain how you determined its measure.

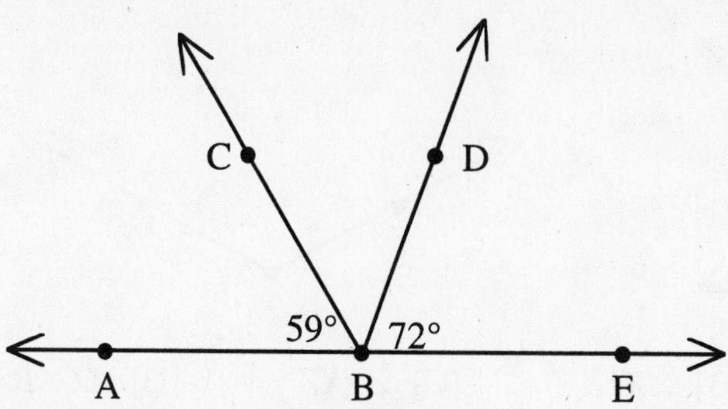

26. What angle is formed by the hands of a clock at each of the following times?

a. 3:00 P.M.
b. 6:00 A.M.
c. 9:00 P.M.
d. 2:00 A.M.
e. 5:30 P.M.

27. Without using a protractor, estimate the measure of the three angles shown below. Explain why you arrived at each estimate. When you have finished, determine the actual measurements with your protractor. Were your estimates close to the actual measurements? Explain.

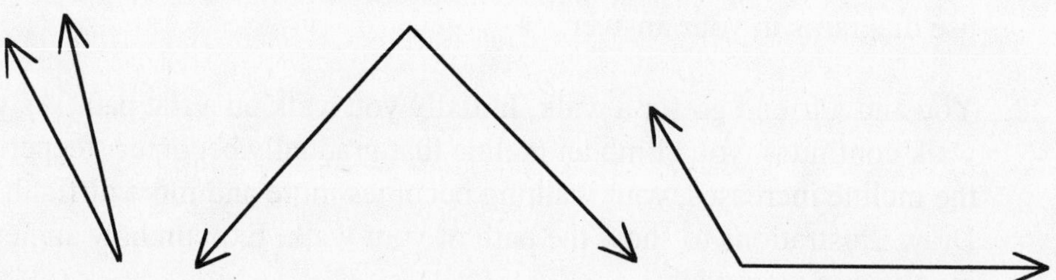

Lesson 8-2 Objective 2: Classify angles as acute, right, obtuse, or straight.

Dynamic Item

28. Classify the angle below.

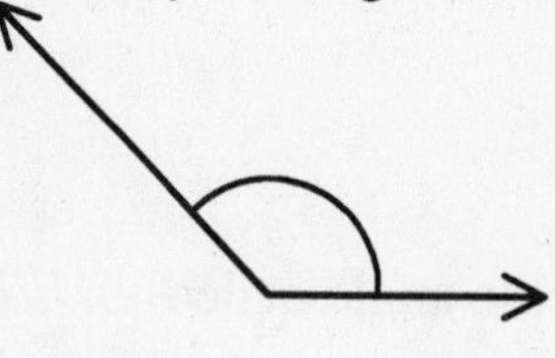

[A] right [B] acute [C] obtuse [D] straight

Dynamic Item

29. The measure of angle A is 172°. Classify angle A .

[A] straight [B] obtuse [C] acute [D] right

30. The infield of a professional baseball diamond is a square with sides of 90 ft. Draw a diagram of the infield. How many angles are there? Are the angles obtuse, acute, or right? The pitcher's mound is located at the center of the square, 60 ft 6 in. from home plate, and is 10 in. higher than the surrounding ground. Suppose a ball that is pitched from the mound hits home plate. Draw the angle the ball would make with the ground. Estimate whether the angle would be obtuse, acute, or right.

31. Which angles below are acute?

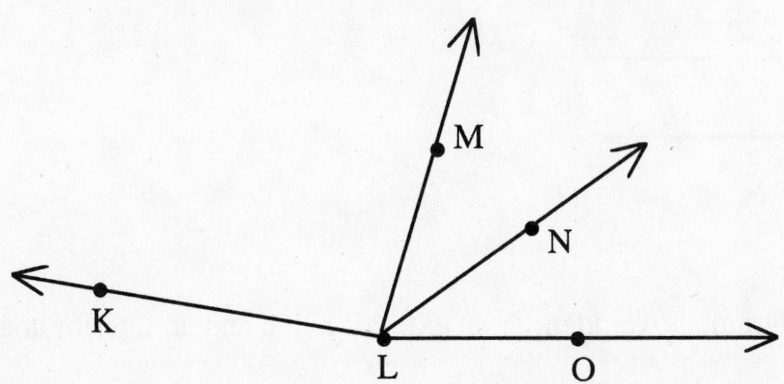

Lesson 8-3 Objective: Identify congruent, complementary, supplementary, interior, and exterior angles.

Dynamic Item

32. Name an angle supplementary to $\angle AOC$.

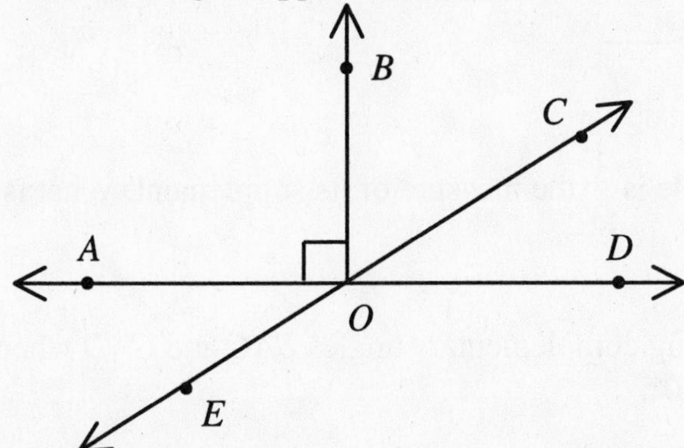

[A] $\angle AOE$ or $\angle COD$ [B] $\angle AOD$

[C] $\angle EOC$ or $\angle BOD$ [D] $\angle DOE$

Dynamic Item

33. Identify a pair of supplementary angles.

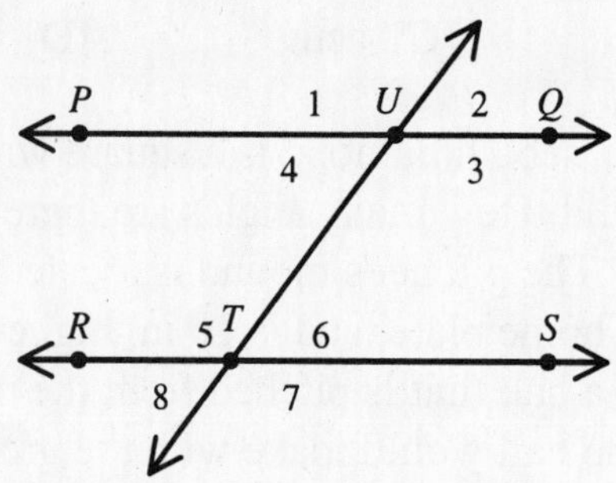

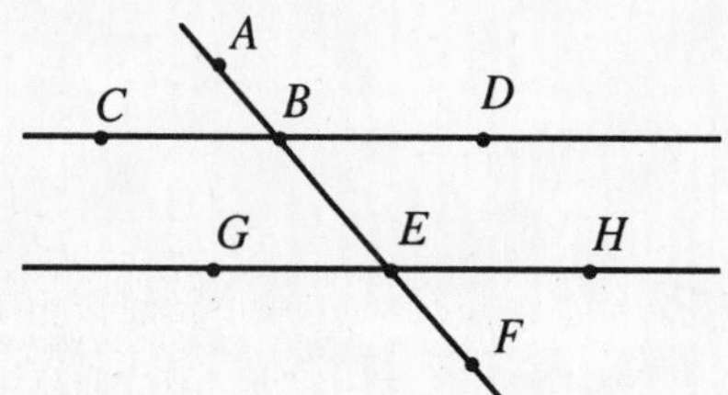

34. Use the diagram above. Identify an exterior angle and an interior angle.

35. In the diagram above, name two angles adjacent to ∠GEF.

36. Use the diagram below. What is the measure of ∠DBC?

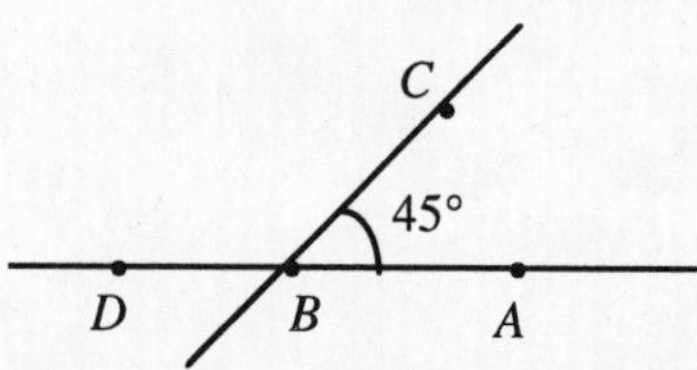

37. The measure of an angle is $\frac{1}{3}$ the measure of its supplement. What is the measure of the angle?

38. Draw a diagram showing complementary angles *BAC* and *CAD* where the measure of ∠*BAC* is 50°.

39. Use the diagram below. Identify a pair of congruent angles.

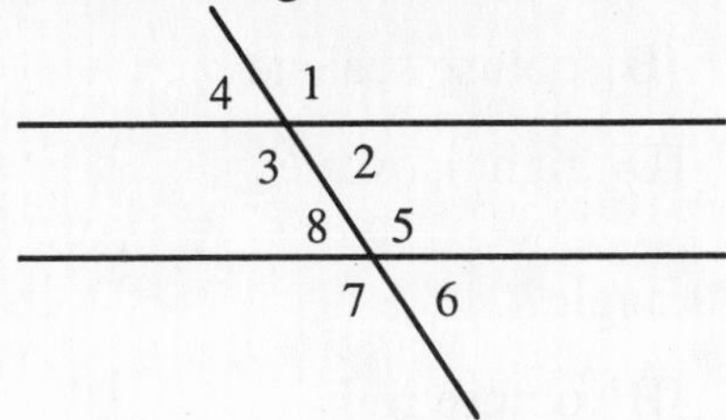

40. The measure of one angle of a pair of complementary angles is twice the measure of the other. What are their measures? Explain how you know.

41. In your own words, define congruent angles. How can you tell if angles are congruent?

42. True or false? Both angles of a pair of complementary angles are always acute. Explain your answer.

Lesson 8-4 Objective: Identify triangles by their angles or by their sides.

Dynamic Item

43. Classify the triangle with sides of length 12, 12, and 16.

[A] scalene [B] equilateral [C] straight [D] isosceles

Dynamic Item

44. Classify the triangle with angles measuring 52°, 38°, and 90°.

45. Upon looking at a triangle, you decide that it is equilateral but your friend says that it is isosceles. How can you both be correct? In what instance might only one of you be correct?

46. Two of the angles of a triangle measure 33° and 46°. Is the triangle acute, obtuse, or right? How do you know?

47. Draw at least three equilateral triangles with varying measurements. What do you notice about the angles in equilateral triangles?

48. Given the following angle measures, which triangle is acute?

[A] 125°, 32°, 23° [B] 48°, 60°, 52°

[C] 91°, 48°, 41° [D] 103°, 29°, 48°

49. Which triangle does not exist?

[A] right equilateral

[B] obtuse scalene

[C] acute scalene

[D] right isosceles

50. Which is a realistic description of a triangle?

[A] scalene equilateral

[B] obtuse right

[C] acute equilateral

[D] obtuse equilateral

51. If a triangle has sides of lengths 12, 5, and 9, what type of triangle is it?

52. Draw a right scalene triangle.

53. Draw an acute isosceles triangle.

54. Draw an equilateral triangle.

55. Classify each triangle as equilateral, isosceles, or scalene.

a. ΔXYZ with $XY = 12$, $YZ = 12$, and $XZ = 10$
b. ΔUVW with $UV = 15$, $VW = 15$, and $UW = 15$

56. Judging by appearance, name the triangles below that fit each description.

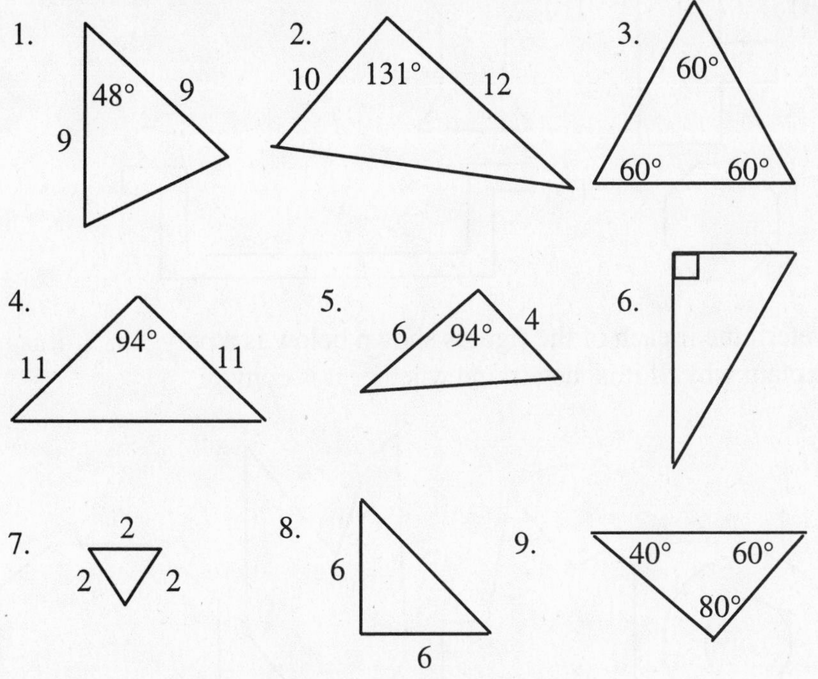

a. right b. scalene c. obtuse
d. isosceles e. equilateral f. acute

Lesson 8-5 Objective: Identify types of convex polygons.

Dynamic Item

57. Which one of the statements below is FALSE?

[A] An octagon has 8 sides. [B] A pentagon has 5 angles.

[C] A circle is a polygon. [D] A quadrilateral has 4 angles.

Dynamic Item

58. Name a polygon with 6 sides.

59. Draw a convex polygon. Count the number of angles formed. Then draw a polygon that is not convex and try to count the number of angles formed. What do you discover about these angles?

60. Which polygon below is a convex polygon?

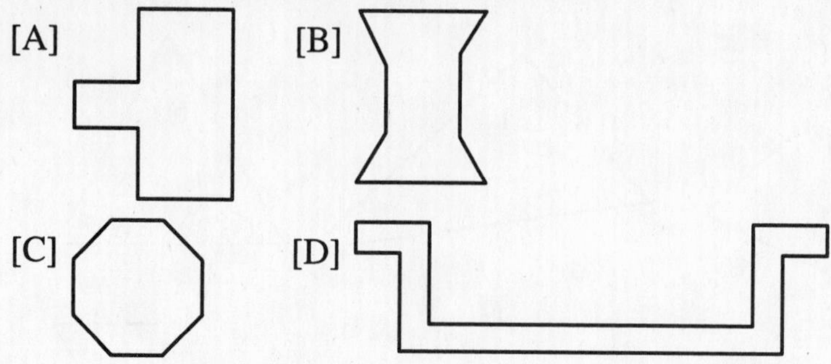

61. Determine if each of the figures shown below is a polygon. If it is not, explain why. If it is, determine whether it is convex.

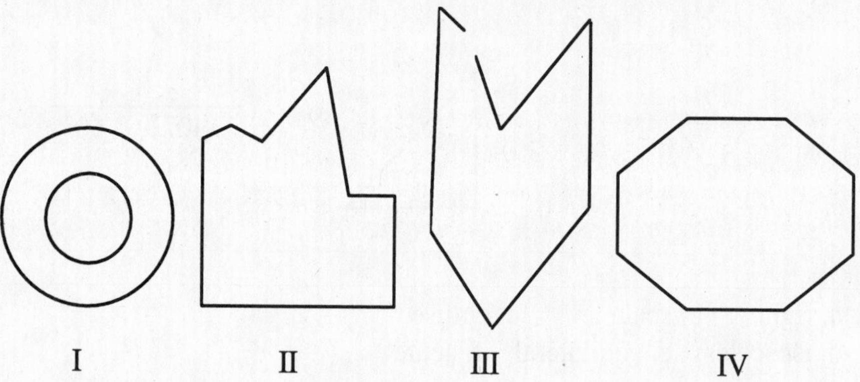

62. Is it possible to draw a 3-sided polygon that is not convex? Explain.

63. Which polygon is among those shown below?

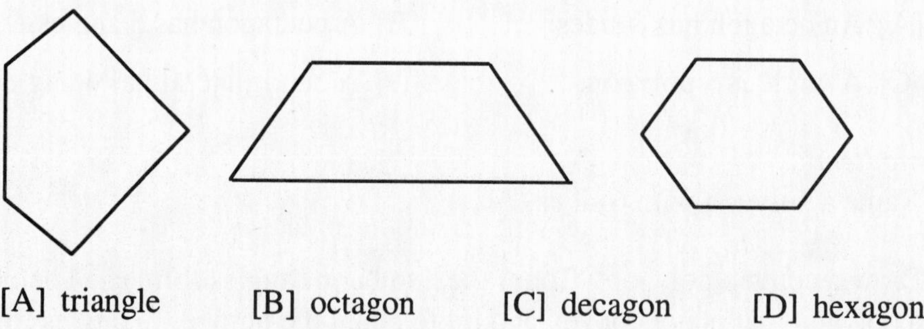

[A] triangle [B] octagon [C] decagon [D] hexagon

64. A prefix is a group of letters joined to the beginning of a word to create a new word. The following prefixes are related to numbers.

1	uni –	2	bi –	3	tri –	4	quad –
5	pent –	6	hex –	8	oct –	10	dec –

Think of words using each of these prefixes. Then write a sentence or sentences explaining what the word means and showing how it is used in a sentence.

65. Your friend Samantha was carrying a box of tracing patterns when she accidentally dropped them. The patterns used to construct polygons got mixed up with each other and with other shapes in the box. Explain to Samantha how she can pick out the polygons and how to separate the polygons into groups.

66. Draw a triangle, a quadrilateral, and a pentagon. Describe similarities and differences among the three polygons.

67. Draw a hexagon, octagon, and decagon. Explain how the figures are alike and how they are different.

68. Draw a figure that is a convex hexagon.

69. Draw a convex octagon.

70. If A and B are any two points inside a convex polygon, can segment AB intersect the polygon? If A and B are any two points in the interior of a polygon that is not convex, can segment AB intersect the polygon?

Lesson 8-6 Objective 1: Identify quadrilaterals.

Dynamic Item

71. Describe the figure using as many of these words as possible: rectangle, trapezoid, square, quadrilateral, parallelogram, rhombus

Dynamic Item

72. Identify the quadrilateral which has all sides and angles congruent.

73. The figure below is all of the following except a

[A] polygon. [B] parallelogram. [C] quadrilateral. [D] rectangle.

74. You are supposed to trace shapes for class. Unfortunately, you have only triangles of different sizes. Explain how you can draw a parallelogram, square, rhombus, rectangle, and a trapezoid using only those triangles. Use diagrams in your answer.

75. Sketch a parallelogram that is not a rectangle or a rhombus.

76. Sketch a quadrilateral that is not a parallelogram.

Lesson 8-6 Objective 2: Classify quadrilaterals.

Dynamic Item

77. Select the geometric figure that possesses all of the following characteristics:
i. opposite sides are parallel
ii. diagonals are not equal
iii. four sides

[A] isosceles triangle [B] trapezoid

[C] parallelogram [D] rectangle

78. Describe the similarities and differences among the five special quadrilaterals.

79. Explain why a square is a rhombus, but a rhombus is not always a square.

80. Complete the following sentence. All ____________.

[A] rectangles are rhombuses [B] parallelograms are squares

[C] rhombuses are parallelograms [D] trapezoids are parallelograms

81. Your friend Timothy is having trouble understanding the relationships among the various types of quadrilaterals. For example, all squares are rectangles, but not all rectangles are squares. He has asked you to construct a visual chart or diagram to help him. Construct such a diagram to show the relationship among the following terms: quadrilateral, trapezoid, parallelogram, rectangle, square, and rhombus.

82. a. How many quadrilaterals are shown below?
    b. How many squares are shown below?

83. Based on appearance, give three correct names for the figure shown below. Then select the best name and explain your reasoning.

84. Based on appearance, give five names for the figure shown below. Then select the best name and explain your reasoning.

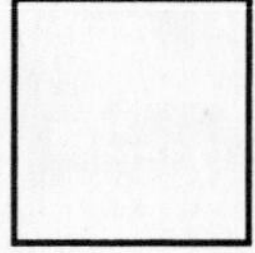

85. How many parallelograms are in the diagram below?

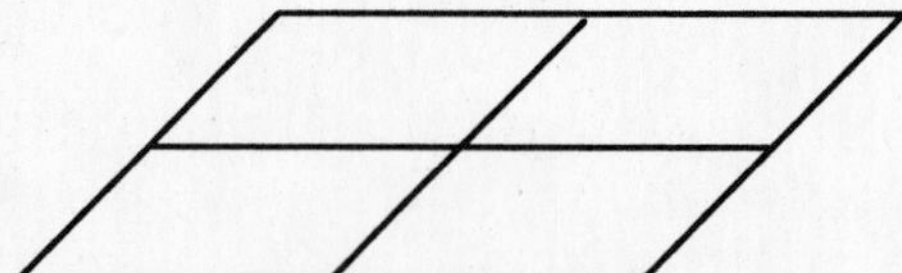

Lesson 8-7 Objective: Solve problems using logical reasoning.

86. Out of 28 students, 12 have at least one brother and 13 have at least one sister. Eight students have both brothers and sisters. How many students do not have either a brother or a sister?

[A] 8 [B] 4 [C] 5 [D] 11

87. Out of 18 people in the Glee club, 11 have dogs and 7 have cats. Four people have both cats and dogs. How many club members have only cats?

[A] 3 [B] 5 [C] 7 [D] 4

88. The Venn diagram below describes the flowers in Randy's garden. How many nonpink roses are in the garden?

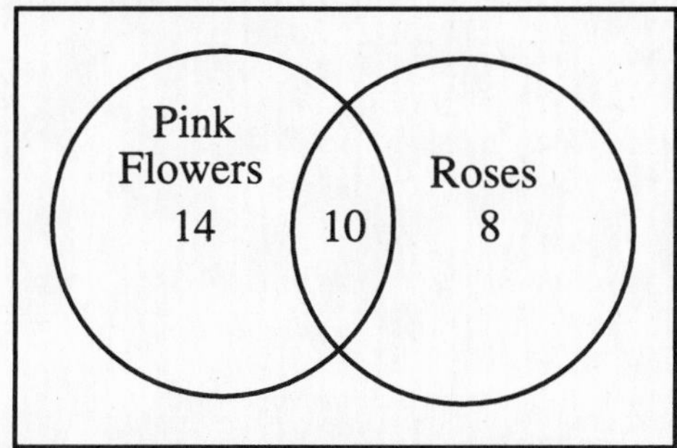

89. Mrs. Lane's class ordered sandwiches for the class outing. There are 33 students in the class.
* Nine students ordered peanut butter and jelly, 16 ordered ham and cheese, and 8 ordered roast beef.
* Nine of the ham and cheese sandwiches and 6 of the roast beef sandwiches were on rolls.
* All together, 17 sandwiches were on rolls.

Draw a Venn Diagram to show the relationship among the different types of sandwiches.

90. Keisha has 13 hair ribbons. Seven ribbons have bows. Six ribbons are blue. Two ribbons are blue and have bows. How many ribbons are blue without bows?

91. There are 43 students in the 6th grade. Twenty-one students play basketball after school, 13 are in the math club, and 14 take karate class. Three students play basketball and are in the math club. Four students are in the math club and take karate class. Five students play basketball and take karate class. One student plays basketball, takes karate class, and is in the math club. How many students take karate class but are not involved in other activities? Draw a diagram to support your answer.

92. Nina is putting photographs in her album and she is trying to decide how many to put on each page. When she divides the photographs into groups of 2, she has one left over. When she divides them into groups of 3, there are 2 left over. Groups of 4 leave 3 photographs. How many photographs does she have?

93. Without using coins or six $1 bills, how many combinations of money can total $26? List the combinations.

94. One of the charts below lists the 10 movie videos that sold the most copies in a particular year. The other chart lists the 10 movie videos that sold the most copies of all time. How many movies that are on the list for a single year are also on the all-time list?

BEST-SELLING MOVIE VIDEOS IN 1990

1. The Little Mermaid
2. Teenage Mutant Ninja Turtle
3. Peter Pan (animated)
4. Pretty Woman
5. Honey, I Shrunk the Kids
6. Indiana Jones and the Last Crusade
7. All Dogs Go to Heaven
8. Total Recall
9. Peter Pan (live-action)
10. Lethal Weapon II

BEST-SELLING MOVIE VIDEOS OF ALL TIME

1. E.T.--The Extraterrestrial
2. Batman
3. Bambi
4. The Little Mermaid
5. Teenage Mutant Ninja Turtle
6. Who Framed Roger Rabbit
7. Cinderella
8. Peter Pan (animated)
9. Pretty Woman
10. Honey, I Shrunk the Kids

Source: Video Store (1991)

95. Use the baseball statistics below to draw a Venn diagram that shows how many baseball players hit over 400 home runs AND were Most Valuable Players in consecutive seasons.

Major League Players, 400 or More Home Runs			
Player	HRs	Player	HRs
Hank Aaron	755	Eddie Mathew	512
Babe Ruth	714	Mel Ott	511
Willie Mays	660	Lou Gehrig	493
Frank Robinson	586	Stan Musial	475
Hamon Killebrew	573	Willie Stargell	475
Reggie Jackson	563	Carl Yastremski	452
Mike Schmidt	548	Dave Kingman	442
Mickey Mantle	536	Billy Williams	426
Jimmie Foxx	534	Darrell Evans	414
Willie McCovey	521	Duke Snider	407
Ted Williams	521	Dave Winfield	406
Ernie Banks	512		

A MOST VALUABLE TEAM
Only nine players have won the Most Valuable Player Award in consecutive seasons; oddly enough there is only one from each fielding position.

Position	Player	Team	Years
First Base	Jimmie Foxx	Philadelphia A's	1932-33
Second Base	Joe Morgan	Cincinnati Reds	1975-76
Third Base	Mike Schmidt	Philadelphia Phillies	1980-81
Shortstop	Ernie Banks	Chicago Cubs	1958-59
Outfield	Mickey Mantle	N.Y. Yankees	1956-57
Outfield	Roger Maris	N.Y. Yankees	1960-61
Outfield	Dale Murphy	Atlanta Braves	1982-83
Catcher	Yogi Berra	N.Y. Yankees	1954-55
Pitcher	Hal Newhouser	Detroit Tigers	1944-45

Lesson 8-8 Objective: Determine whether figures are congruent or similar.

Dynamic Item

96. Which statement is FALSE?

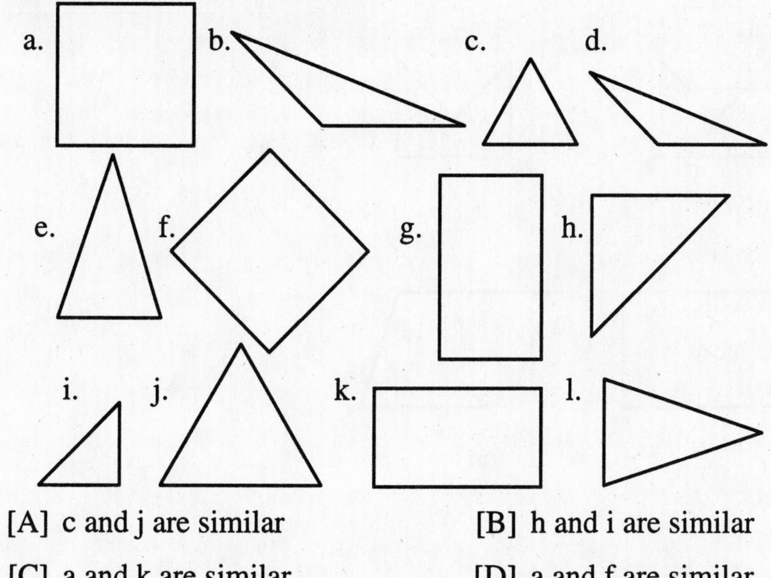

[A] c and j are similar

[B] h and i are similar

[C] a and k are similar

[D] a and f are similar

Dynamic Item

97. Which is a pair of congruent figures?

[A]

[B]

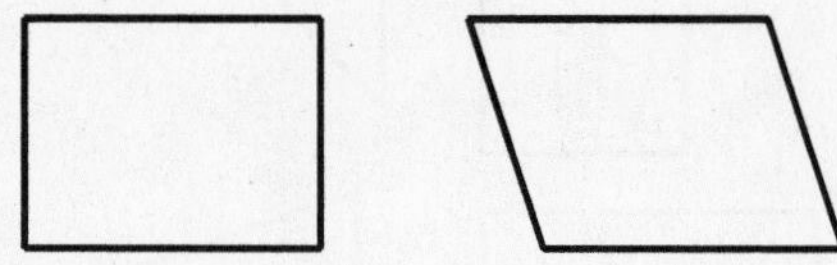

[C]

[D]

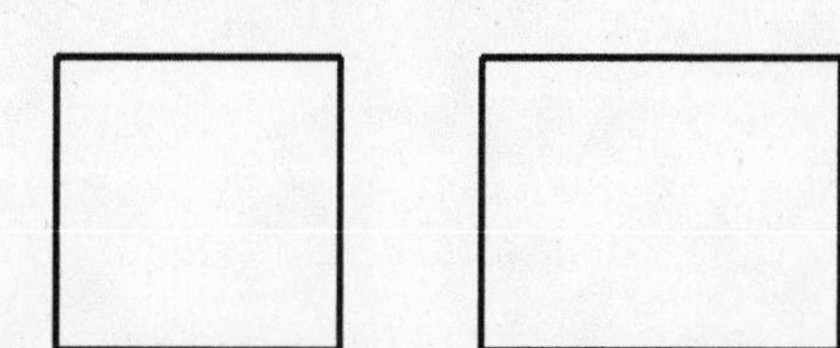

Dynamic Item

98. Determine if the figures are similar.

Dynamic Item

99. Tell whether the polygons are congruent, similar, or neither.

100. Explain what it means for two figures to be congruent. How do congruent figures differ from similar figures?

101. Sketch several equilateral triangles. Are all equilateral triangles congruent? Are all equilateral triangles similar? Explain.

102. Draw several rectangles of different size. Are all rectangles congruent? Are all rectangles similar? Explain.

103. Your neighbor shows you a plan that includes measurements for the dimensions of a new building. You draw the same building plans, but on a smaller scale. How are the figures in your drawing related to those in your neighbor's plans?

104. Which square is congruent to the square shown?

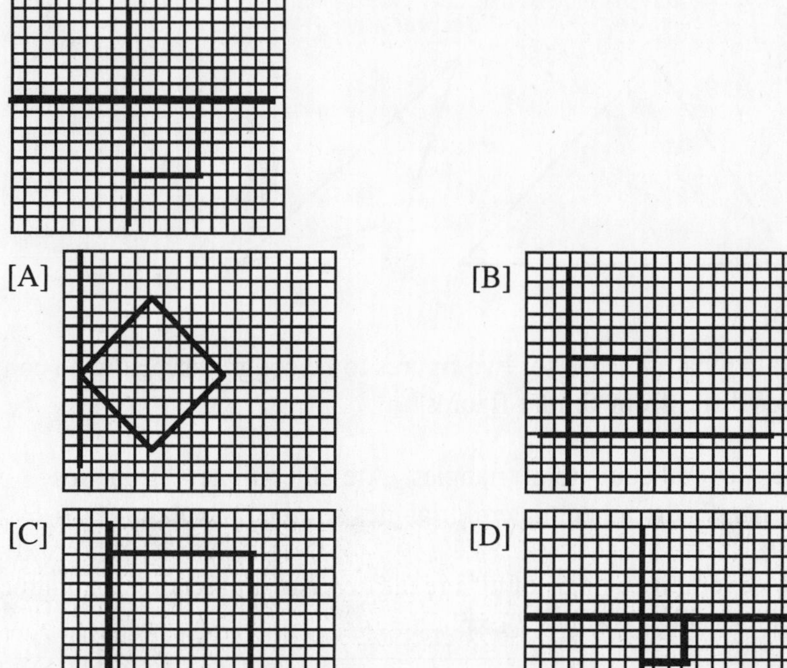

105. Which rectangle is similar to the rectangle shown?

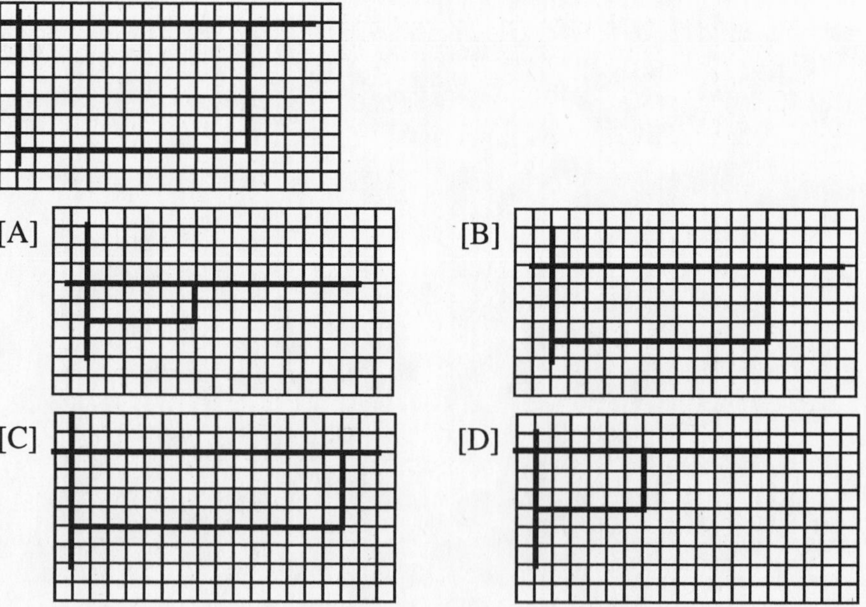

106. You have borrowed your classmate's notebook to catch up on the class notes. She has written the following sentence: "Congruent figures are always similar, but similar figures are not always congruent. " How can you explain this in your own notebook? Use illustrations in your explanation.

107. Do each of the pairs of figures below appear to be congruent? Explain why or why not.

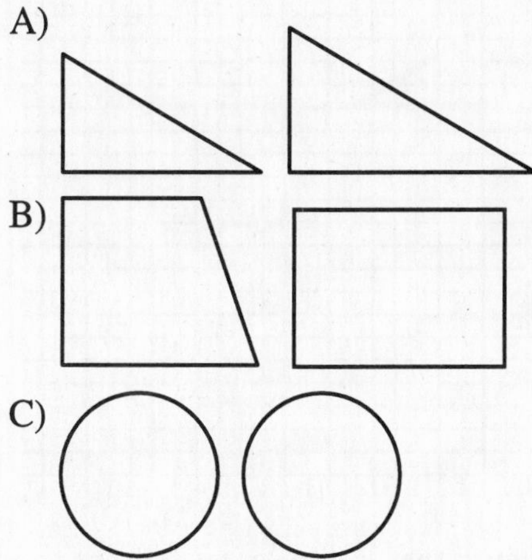

108. List the pairs of shapes below that appear to be congruent.

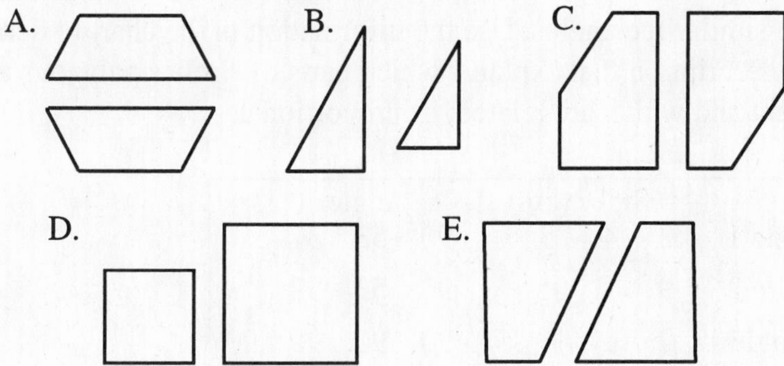

109. List the pairs of figures below that appear to be similar.

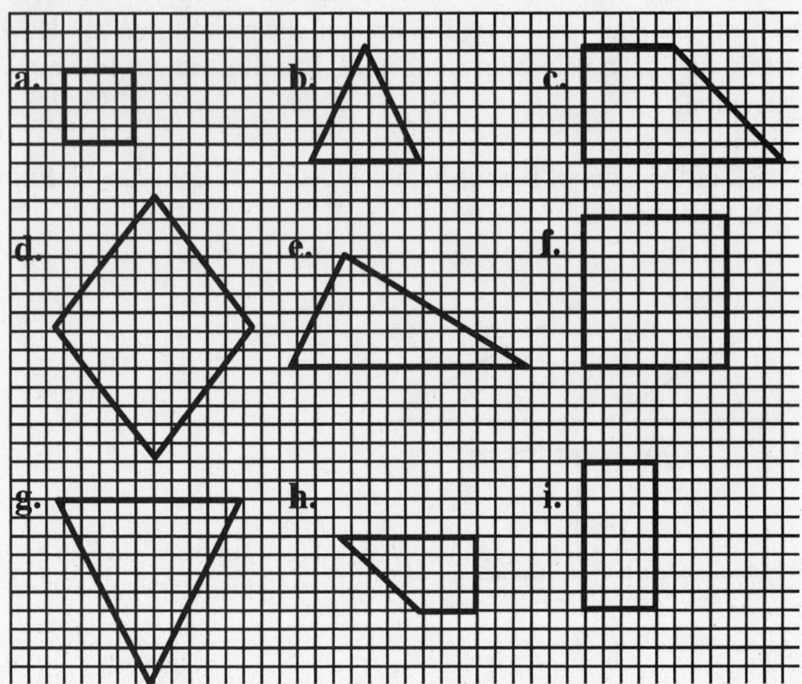

110. Draw a polygon. Then draw a figure that is similar to, but not congruent to, the polygon.

111. The chart gives the angle and side measurements for two similar triangles and two similar rectangles. Use the information in the chart to derive a general description that explains which parts of similar polygons are congruent and which are related, or proportional.

	Sides (cm)				Angles (°)			
Triangle 1	3	4	5		90	53	37	
Triangle 2	9	12	15		90	53	37	
Rectangle 1	2	2	4	4	90	90	90	90
Rectangle 2	4	4	8	8	90	90	90	90

Lesson 8-9 Objective: Determine whether a figure has a line of symmetry.

Dynamic Item

112. For the figure below, draw all the lines of symmetry.

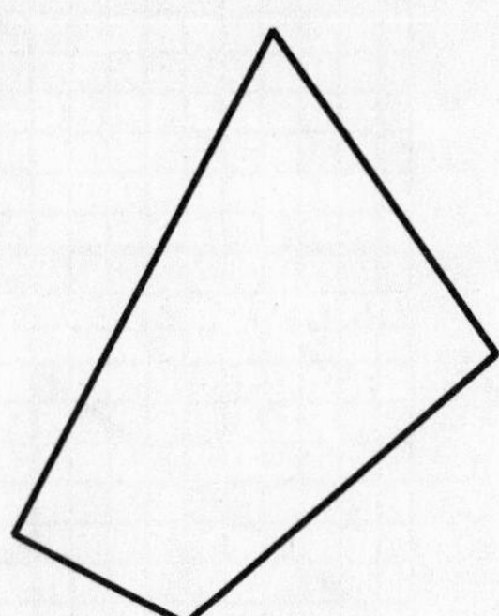

How many lines of symmetry are there?

[A] 4 [B] 1 [C] none [D] 2

Dynamic Item

113. Is the statement true or false? The line is a line of symmetry for the shape.

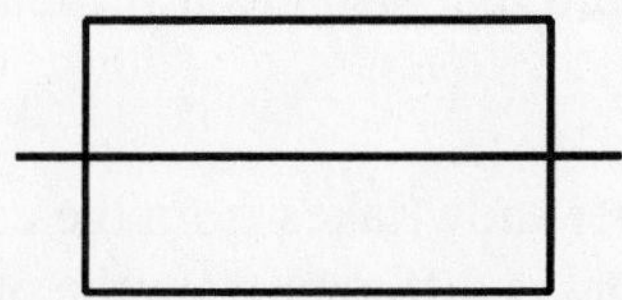

114. Explain what it means when someone says that a figure has a line of symmetry.

115. Which word has a horizontal line of symmetry?

[A] HIP [B] BED [C] HAD [D] LIT

116. Which figure below has three or more lines of symmetry?

[A] 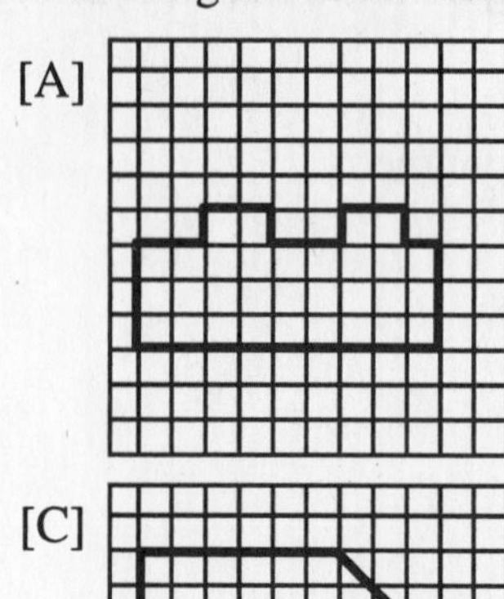

[B] 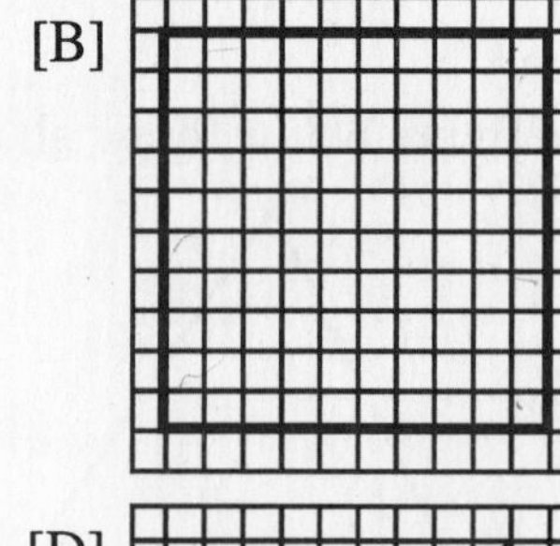

[C] 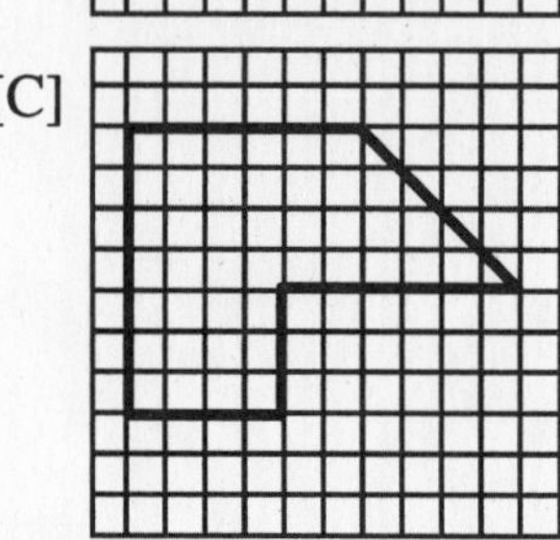

[D] 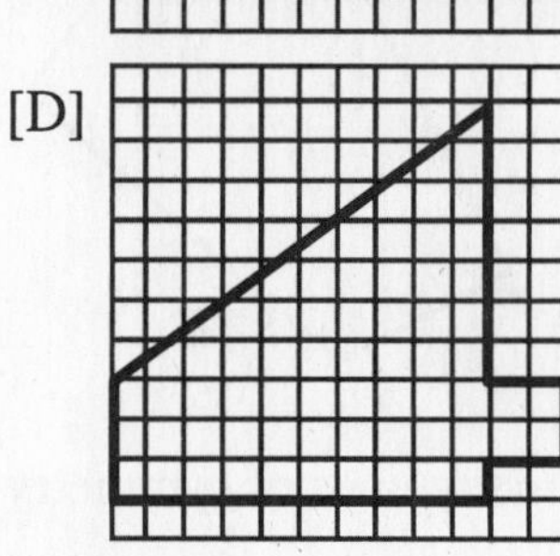

117. Which number has a vertical line of symmetry?

[A] 2 [B] 3 [C] 6 [D] 8

118. The word WAIT has a vertical line of symmetry when the letters are written in a column. Find another word that also has a vertical line of symmetry.

119. Your teacher has hung beautiful paper snowflakes from the ceiling. Each snowflake has many small cutouts and is different from the others. Suggest how your teacher may have made them and how you could go about making one on your own.

120. How many lines of symmetry are there in a hexagon with equal sides? Draw a hexagon and sketch the lines of symmetry.

121. How many lines of symmetry does the figure below have? Describe each line of symmetry as horizontal, vertical, or neither.

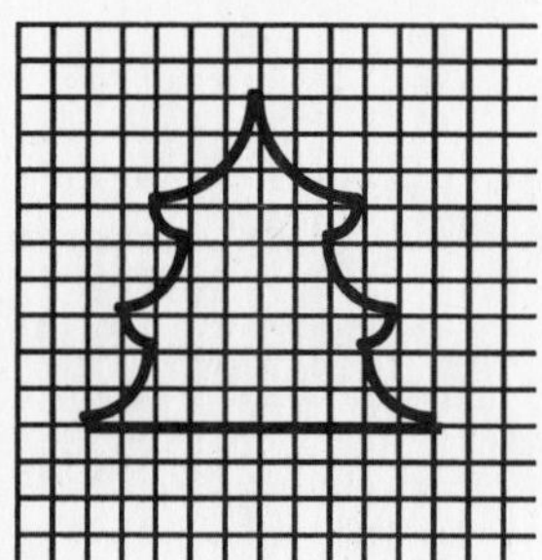

122. Complete the figure below so that the line shown is a line of symmetry.

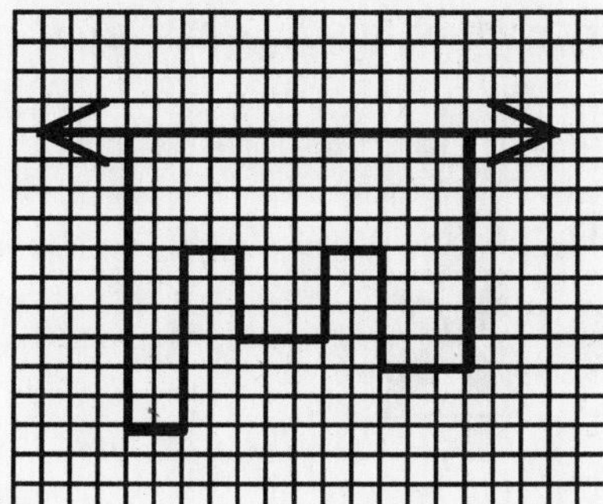

123. Draw an octagon with equal sides and show all the lines of symmetry. How many lines of symmetry do you show?

124. The diagram below shows the top faces of number cubes. Do the dots change the lines of symmetry from those on a blank square? Explain which numbers change and which do not.

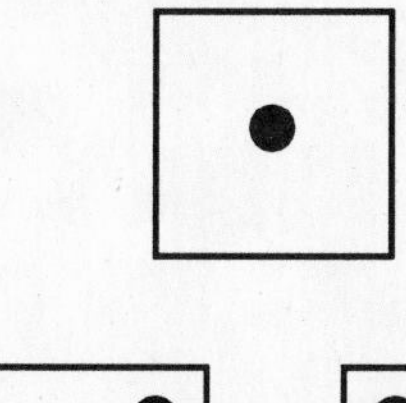

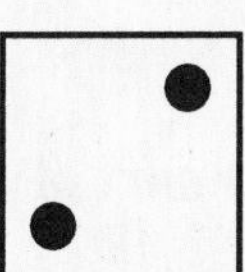

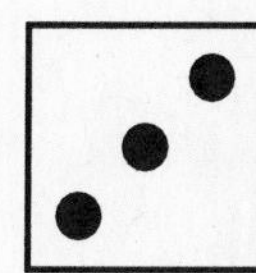

125. Ships at sea can send messages to one another using a code of flags. The flags that the United States Navy uses to show numbers are shown below. Determine how many lines of symmetry each of the flags has. How many of the flags have only one line of symmetry?

U.S. Navy numeral pennants

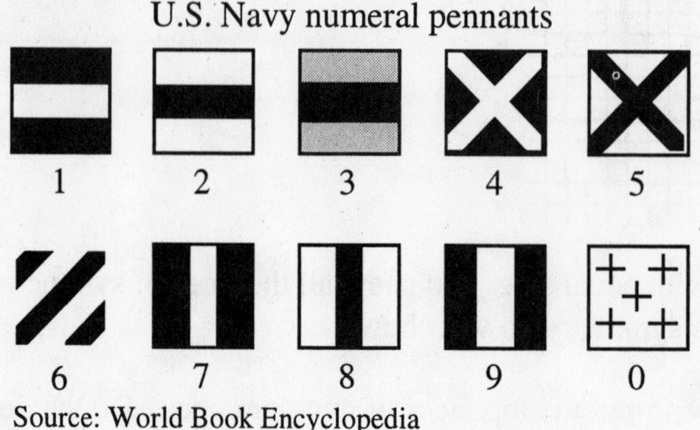

Source: World Book Encyclopedia

Lesson 8-10 Objective: Identify parts of a circle and identify central angles.

Dynamic Item

126. Identify the **dotted part of** the circle.

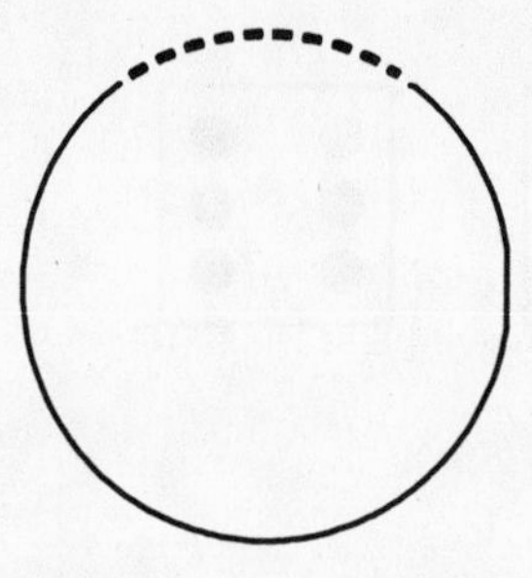

[A] chord [B] arc [C] circumference [D] radius

Dynamic Item

127. In circle O below, $\overline{BO}$ is ______________.

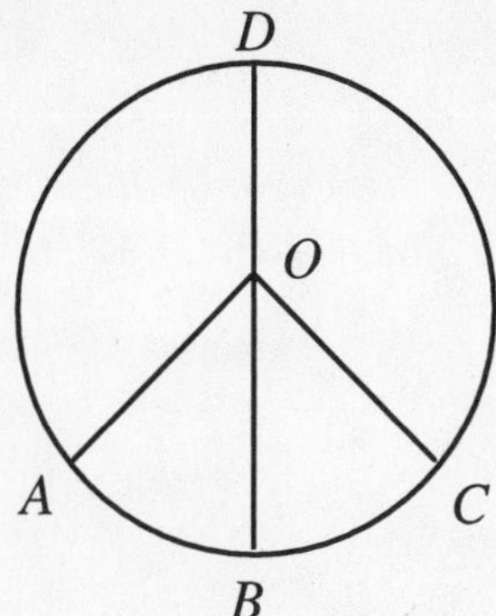

[A] a diameter [B] a central angle [C] an arc [D] a radius

Dynamic Item

128. Name the **dotted line**.

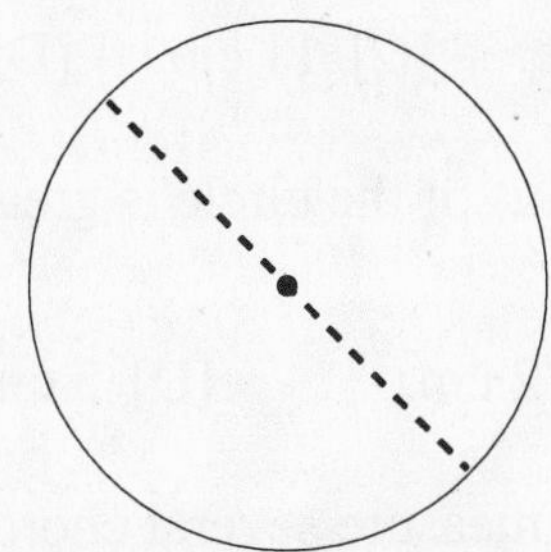

129. Explain how the terms center, radius, diameter, chord, and central angle can be used to describe a circle.

130. Which name describes the circle below?

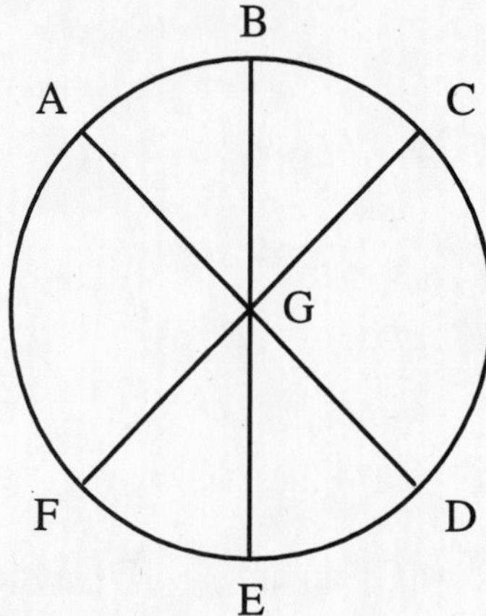

[A] circle A [B] circle BGD [C] circle G [D] circle FC

131. If the radius of a circle is 11 cm, the diameter is

[A] 5.5 cm. [B] impossible to determine. [C] 11 cm. [D] 22 cm.

132. If the diameter of a circle is 18 cm, the radius of the circle is greater than that of a circle with a radius of

[A] 10 cm. [B] 17 cm. [C] 12 cm. [D] 3 cm.

133. Use a compass to draw a circle. Draw and measure several chords in the circle. What is the length of the shortest chord? The longest chord?

134. Draw a circle and label it. Label and identify 3 radii, 2 diameters, 2 chords, and 2 central angles.

135. Nathan has a bank that sorts coins by size. Use the terms circle, diameter, and radius to explain how the bank might work.

136. Name two radii, one diameter, two central angles, and a chord for the circle shown below.

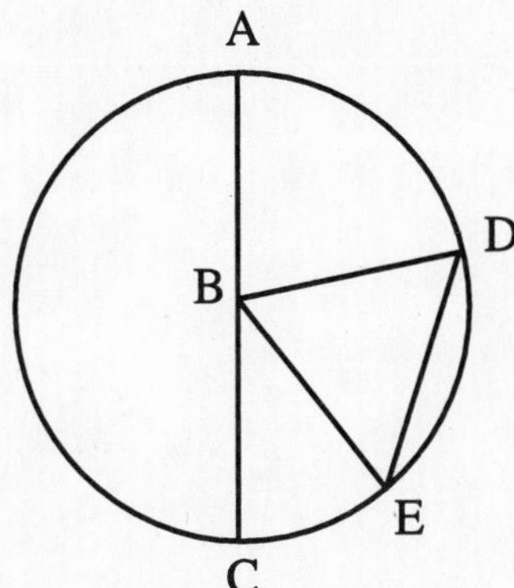

137. Add up all of the angle measures in each circle below. What can you conclude about the sum of the central angles in a circle?

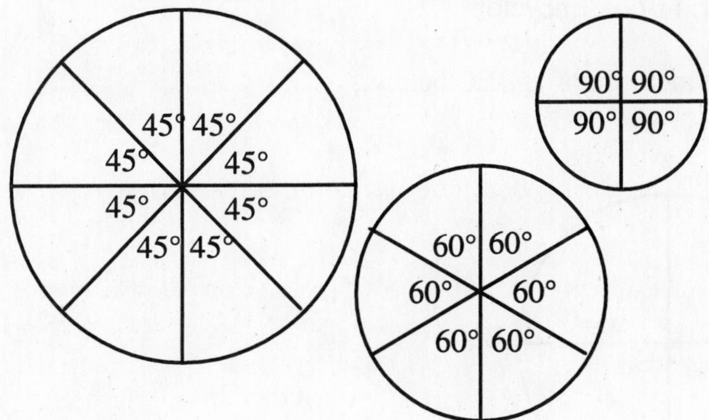

138. Name 3 chords, 2 radii, and 1 central angle for the circle below.

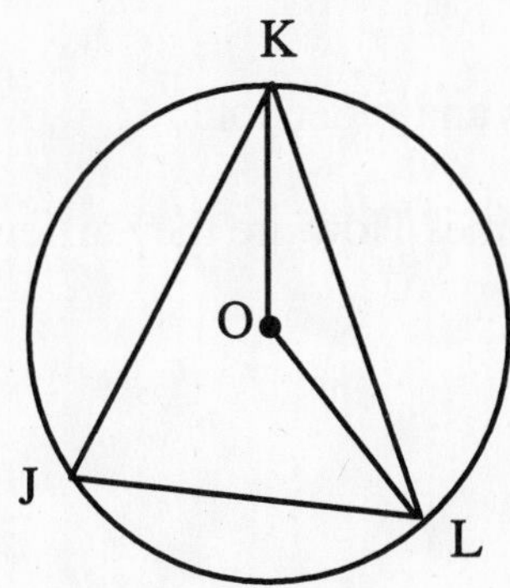

139. If a line is drawn around the center of a planet, such as the Earth, the line forms a circle. The chart gives the diameter of those circles for each of the nine planets. Find the planets that have the longest and shortest radii.

Planet	Diameter (miles)
Mercury	3000
Venus	7500
Earth	8000
Mars	4200
Jupiter	88,000
Saturn	75,000
Uranus	32,000
Neptune	31,000
Pluto	1400

Source: World Book Encyclopedia

140. Estimate the measure of $\angle BEC$ below.

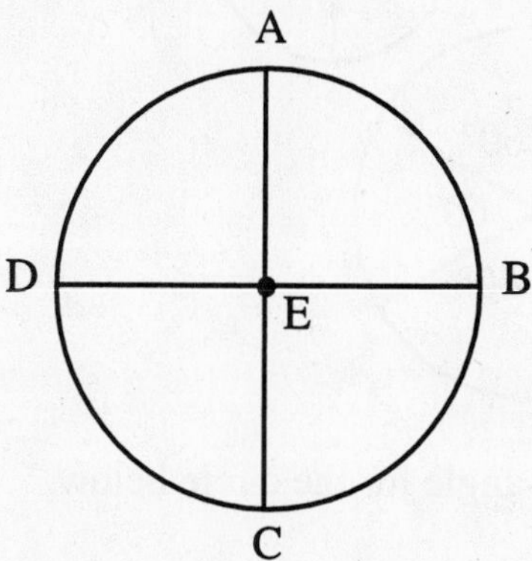

Lesson 8-11 Objective 1: Explore translations and reflections.

141. How are translations and reflections the same? How are they different?

142. Which of the figures below could be a translation of

[A] [B] [C] [D]

143. What does the term "line of reflection" mean?

144. Which of the figures below is not a reflection of the given figure?

[A]

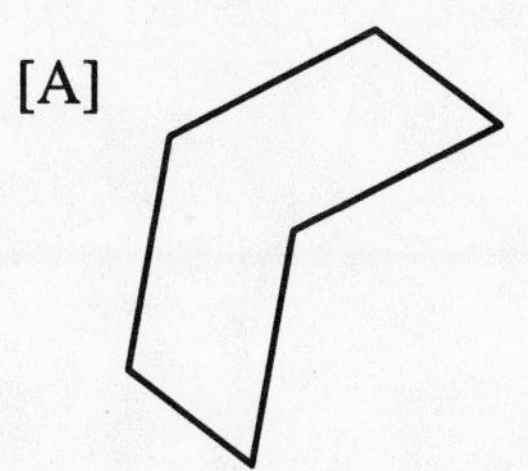

[B]

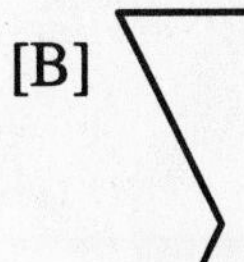

[C]

[D]

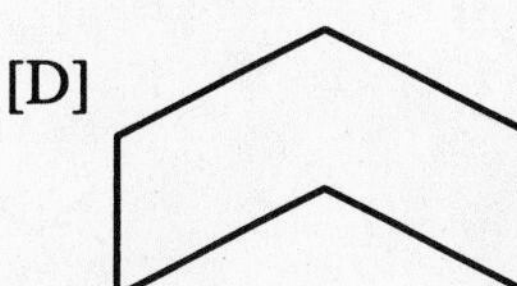

145. Draw the translation of the figure below if it is moved 2 spaces left and 3 spaces down.

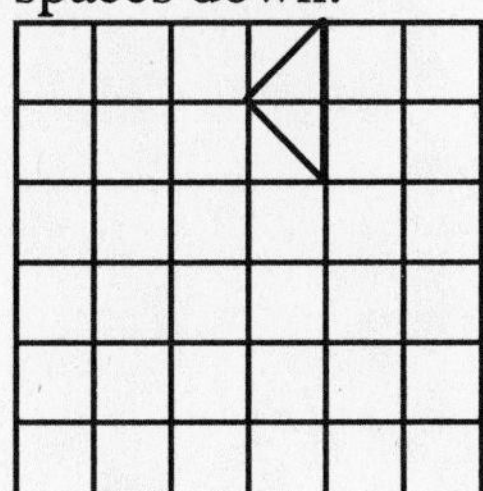

146. Suppose the figure below is reflected over the line shown. Describe what the reflection image will look like.

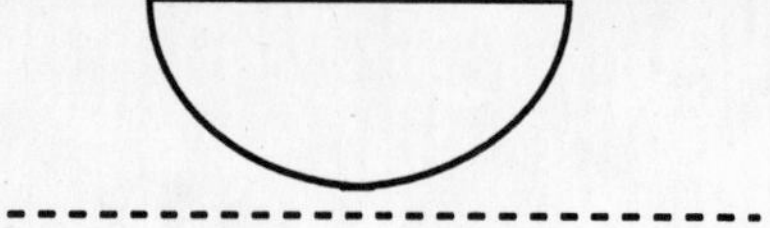

Lesson 8-11 Objective 2: Explore rotations.

147. Draw the next figure in the pattern below.

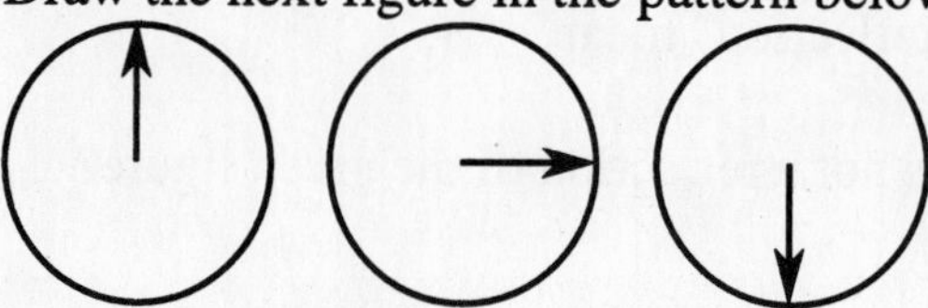

Lesson 9-1 Objective: Estimate area.

Dynamic Item

1. Which is the area of the figure drawn on the grid?

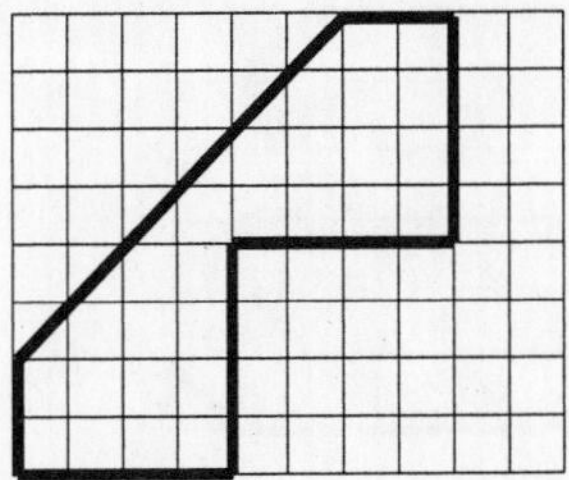

[A] 30 square units [B] 40 square units
[C] 22 square units [D] 23 square units

Dynamic Item

2. Find the area of the figure. The area of each square is 16 cm^2.

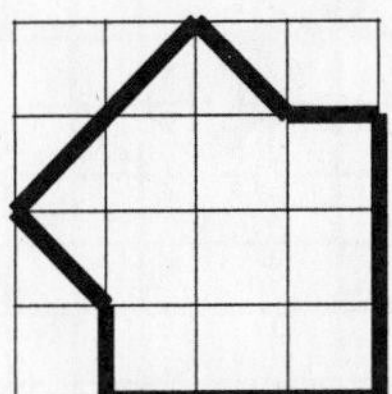

[A] 256 cm^2 [B] 176 cm^2 [C] 181.5 cm^2 [D] 184 cm^2

3. Explain the meaning of the statement below:
The area of Tennessee is 42,146 square miles.

4. Hanna drew a picture of her cat on grid paper for her art class. Will her picture fit the shaded part of the picture frame below? Explain.

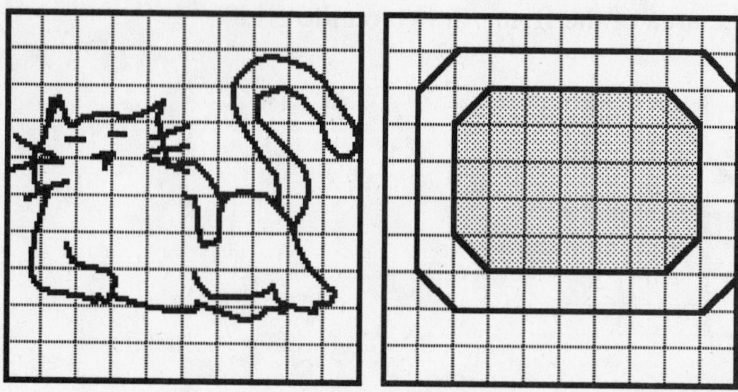

5. Each square below represents 3 m^2. Which figure has the greatest area?

[A]

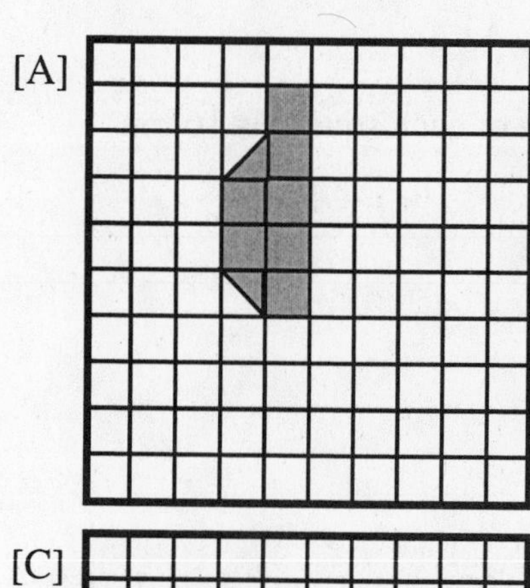

[B]

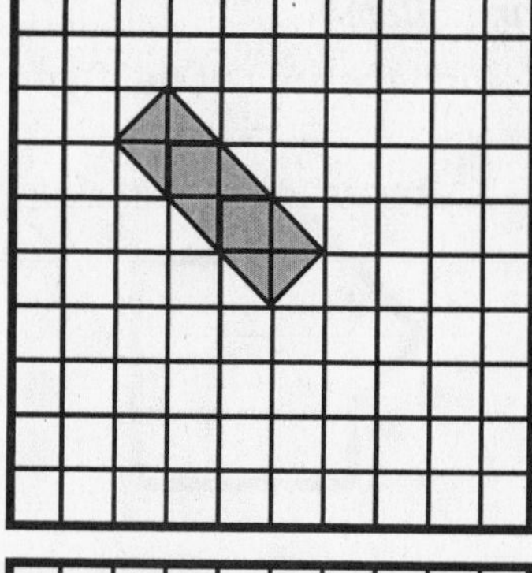

[C]

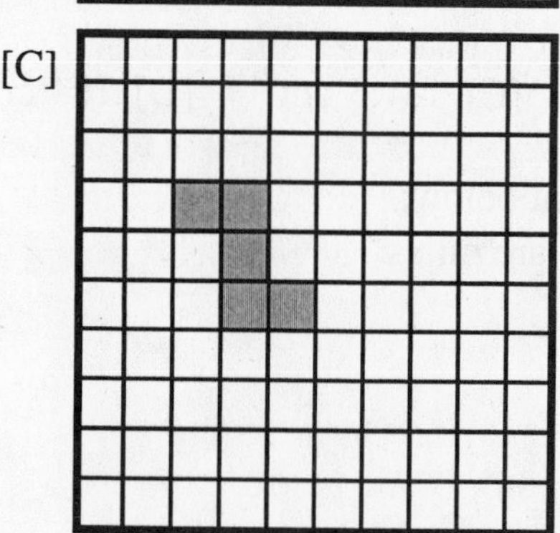

[D]

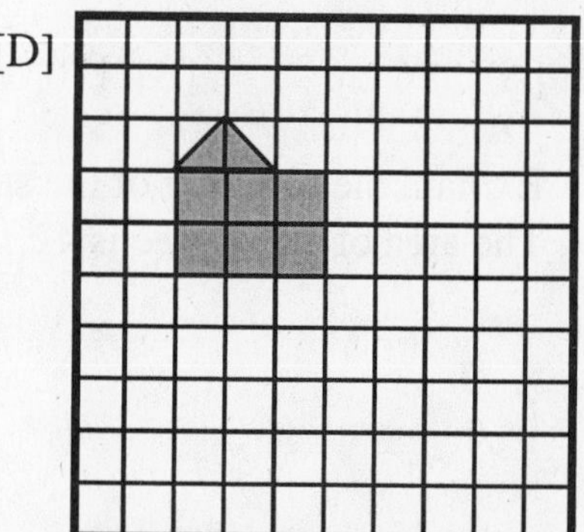

6. Nina and Bert entered a drawing contest. For the contest they had to draw a picture of a sail boat. Suppose each unit is 2 cm. What is the difference between the areas of the sails of the boats?

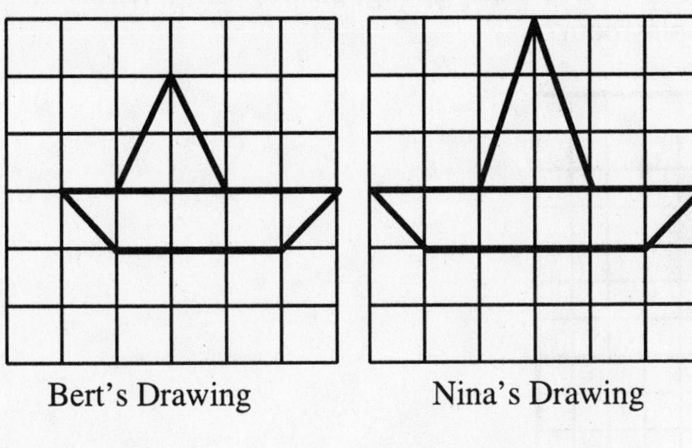

Bert's Drawing   Nina's Drawing

[A] 12 cm^2 [B] 16 cm^2 [C] 4 cm^2 [D] 2 cm^2

7. Draw a figure on centimeter graph paper that has an area of 16 ft^2. Assume that each square represents 2 ft^2.

8. Draw three shapes with five boundary dots and four interior dots. Find the area of each figure. Explain how the dots are related to the area.

9. The area of a rectangle is 18 $in.^2$. How many rectangles whose sides are measured in whole numbers can be drawn using this area?

10. If a rectangular figure measures 6 squares across and 8 squares down, how many squares will it take to cover the figure?

11. Joanne is sponge painting a border around her sister's playroom. She drew the shape of the sponge on the grid paper below before cutting the actual shape out of the sponge. If the space that she is sponge painting is 25 units long and 2 units wide, how many sponge shapes will fit horizontally on one wall of the playroom?

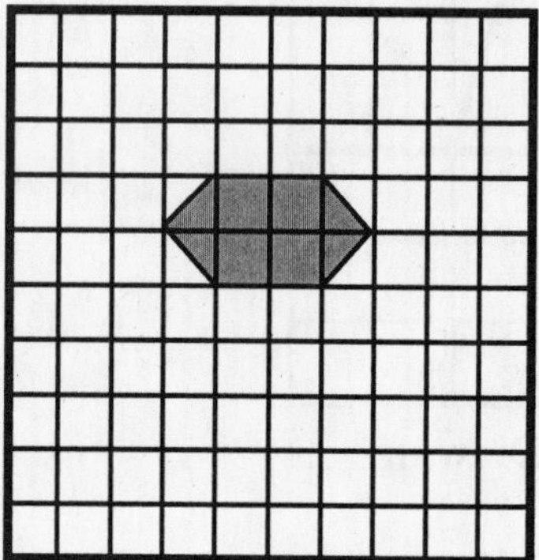

12. Using the spreadsheet below, predict the area of a shape with 36 boundary dots and one interior dot. Draw a shape to support your prediction.

	A	B	C	D
1	Shape	Boundary Dots	Interior Dots	Area
2	I	8	1	4
3	II	6	1	3
4	III	4	1	2

13. One acre is equal to 4,840 square yards. How many acres are in one square mile? Use a drawing to show how you found the answer. (Hint: 1 mile = 1,760 yards).

14. Study the spreadsheet below. Describe the relationship between the number of boundary dots, the number of interior dots, and the area.

	A	B	C	D
1	Shape	Boundary Dots	Interior Dots	Area
2	I	8	1	4
3	II	6	1	3
4	III	4	1	2

Lesson 9-2 Objective 1: Find perimeters and areas of rectangles.

Dynamic Item

15. Find the perimeter of the rectangle.

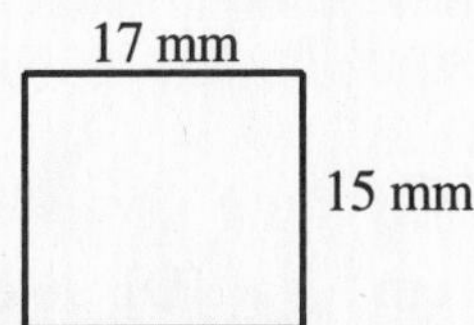

Dynamic Item

16. Find the area of the rectangle.

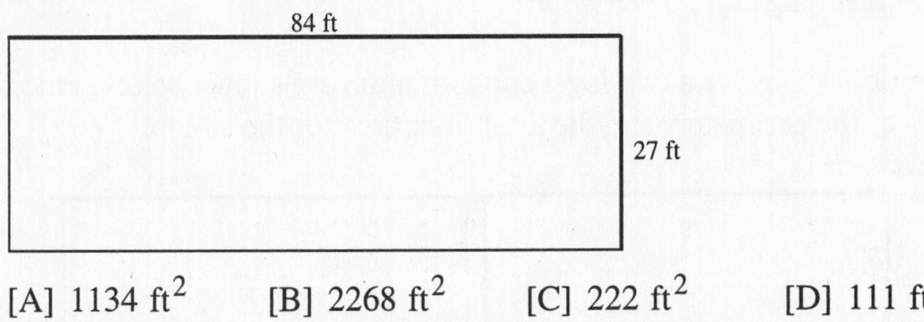

[A] 1134 ft^2 [B] 2268 ft^2 [C] 222 ft^2 [D] 111 ft^2

17. Explain what will happen to the area of the rectangle below if side a is doubled. Give an example to support your reasoning.

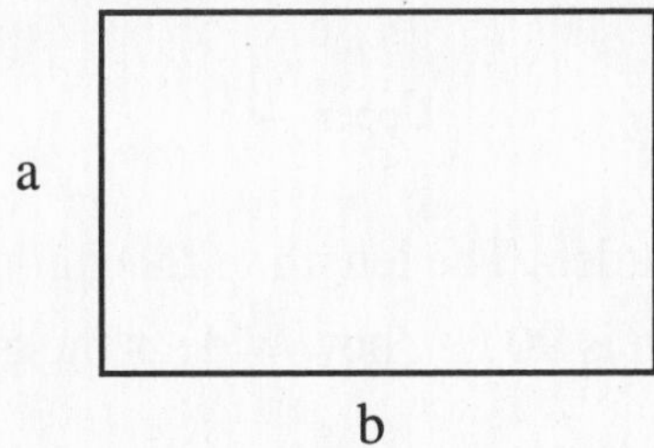

18. The base of the Great Pyramid in Egypt is a square whose sides measure about 752 ft. Estimate the area in acres of the base of the Great Pyramid to the nearest hundredth. (Hint: 1 acre = 43,560 ft^2.)

[A] 12.90 acres [B] 12.8 acres [C] 13.00 acres [D] 12.98 acres

CHAPTER 9

19. Use the figure below. What is the area of the shaded region?

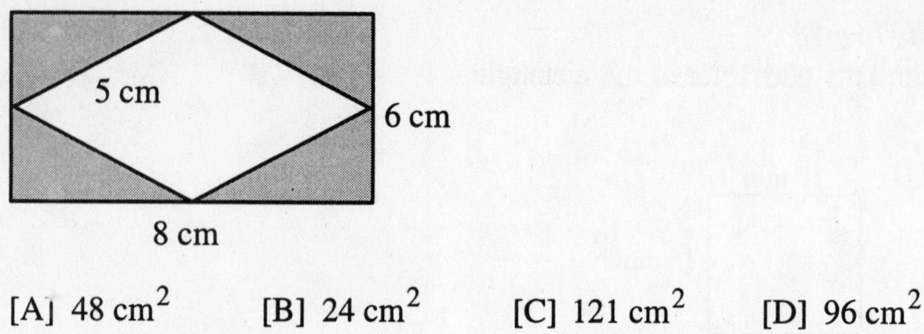

[A] 48 cm^2 [B] 24 cm^2 [C] 121 cm^2 [D] 96 cm^2

20. Draw a figure that has an area of 36^2 yd .

21. Rosina is having her driveway paved. It costs $1.30 per square foot to pave a driveway. How much will it cost Rosina to pave her driveway that is 54 feet long and 10 feet wide?

22. The floor plans for a two level condominium are shown below. Find the sum of the perimeters and the total floor area for the condo.

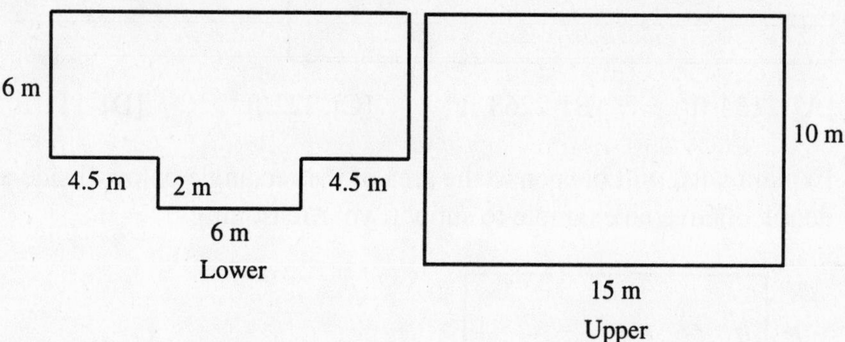

23. Mrs. Walsh has a rectangular-shaped garden. The length of the garden is 15 ft. If the area of Mrs. Walsh's garden is 90 ft^2, how wide is the garden?

Lesson 9-2 Objective 2: Find perimeters and areas of squares.

Dynamic Item

24. What is the perimeter of the square below?

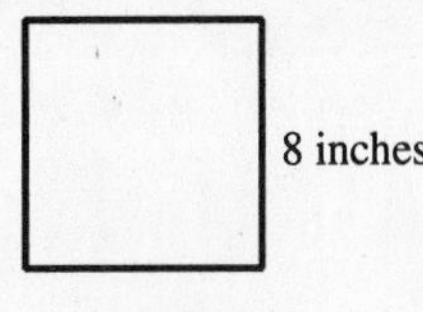

[A] 16 inches [B] 17 inches [C] 32 inches [D] 31 inches

Dynamic Item

25. What is the area of a square that has sides 15 centimeters in length?

26. Use centimeter grid paper to draw a square whose perimeter in units is equal to its area in square units. Can you draw more than one such square? What is the length of each side of the square?

27. A square that measures 8 centimeters on one side is enclosed in a larger square that measures 15 centimeters on one side. What is the difference between the perimeters of the two squares? The area?

28. Bob has 28 ft of fencing. He plans to fence in a play yard for his children. What is the greatest area Bob can fence in? What is the length and width of the play yard?

29. Derreck plays second base for the Blue Devils. The measurement from base to base on the baseball field is 90 ft. If Derrick hit two home runs during the championship game, what is the total distance Derrick ran?

30. Mr. Close is remodeling his square kitchen. He plans to put down ceramic tile. The perimeter of the kitchen is 52 ft. Explain how you would find the area of Mr. Close's kitchen so he can calculate the amount of tile he needs. What is the area?

Lesson 9-3 Objective 1: Find areas of parallelograms and triangles.

Dynamic Item

31. Find the area of the triangle.

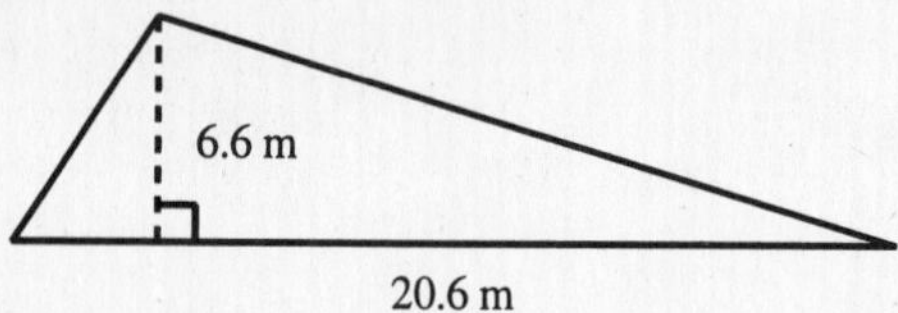

[A] 65.85 m^2 [B] 135.96 m^2 [C] 67.98 m^2 [D] 33.99 m^2

Dynamic Item

32. Find the area:

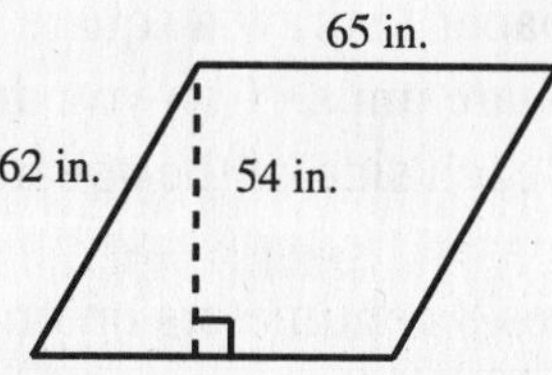

[A] 3429 $in.^2$ [B] 4030 $in.^2$ [C] 3770 $in.^2$ [D] 3510 $in.^2$

Dynamic Item

33. Find the area of the triangle.

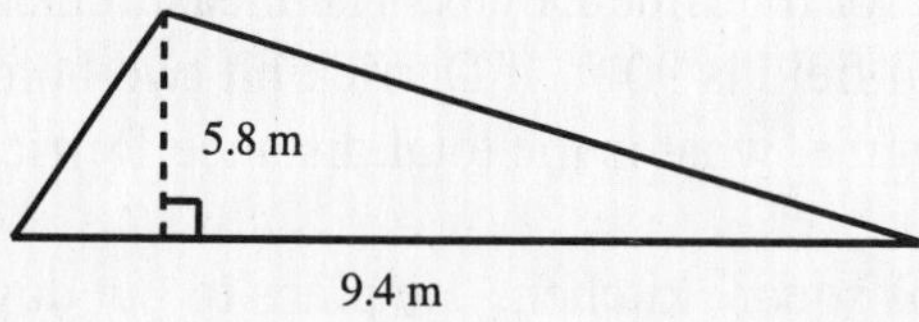

Dynamic Item

34. Find the area:

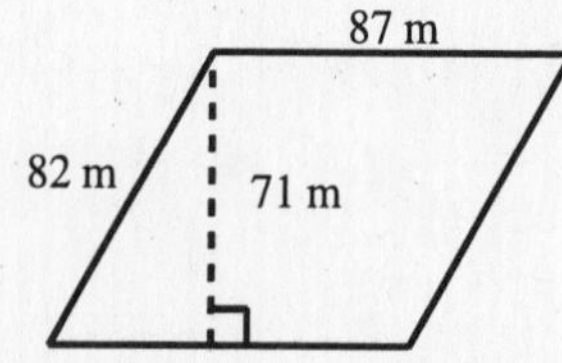

35. Write three statements about the parallelogram and the rectangle below:

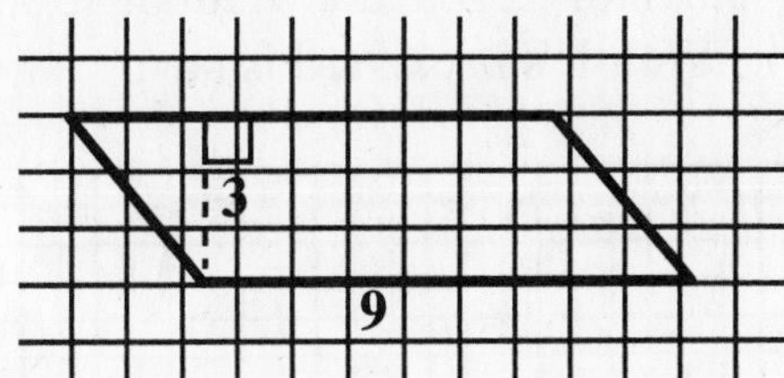

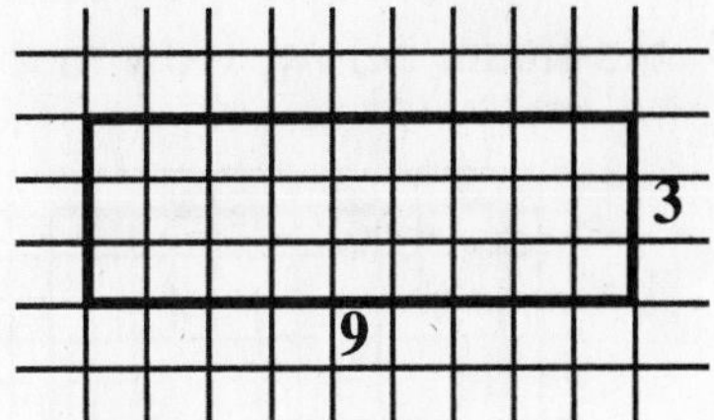

36. Complete: The height of a parallelogram is equal to the length of each of its sides when ____________.

37. The Football Rally Club is cutting out triangular pennants from a rectangular piece of felt. The piece of felt is 36 in. long and 26 in. wide. The Rally Club cuts five triangular pennants, each with a base of 25 in. and a height of 14 in. How much felt does the Rally Club have left over?

[A] 875 in.^{2} [B] 175 in.^{2} [C] 61 in.^{2} [D] 936 in.^{2}

38. Use the figure below. What is the area of the shaded square?

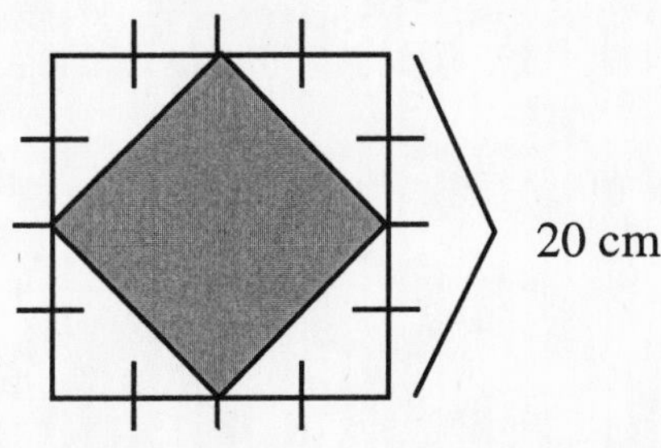

[A] 100 cm^2 [B] 400 cm^2 [C] 50 cm^2 [D] 200 cm^2

39. Draw a triangle and a parallelogram that each have an area of 36 in.^{2}.

40. Maggie and Heather play tennis every Saturday morning. The length of the tennis court is three feet less than three times the width of the tennis court. The width of the tennis court is 27 ft. What is the area of the tennis court?

41. The area of a parallelogram is 240 cm^2. The length of the base is 15 centimeters. What is the height of the parallelogram?

42. The Wehrle's have an irregular-shaped back yard. They installed a rectangular inground pool with a length of 32 ft and a width of 15 ft. Use the figure below. How much of the Wehrle's back yard is lawn?

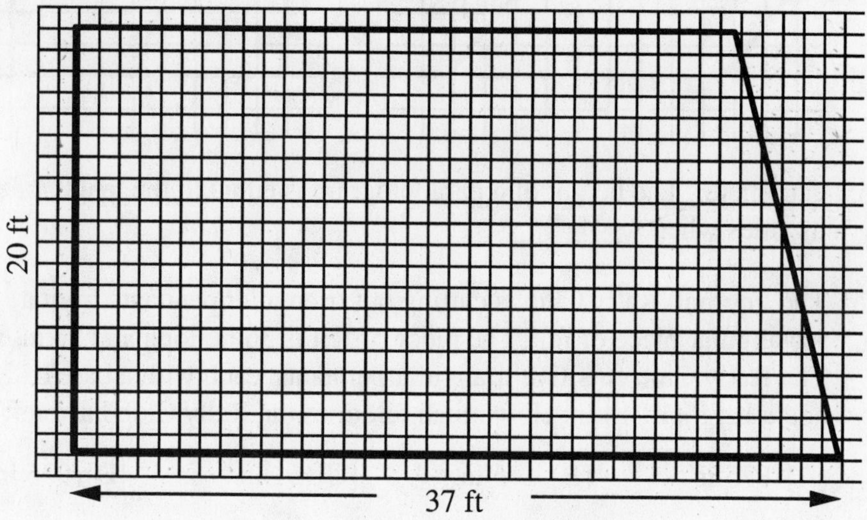

Lesson 9-3 Objective 2: Find areas of complex figures.

Dynamic Item

43. Find the area of the polygon.

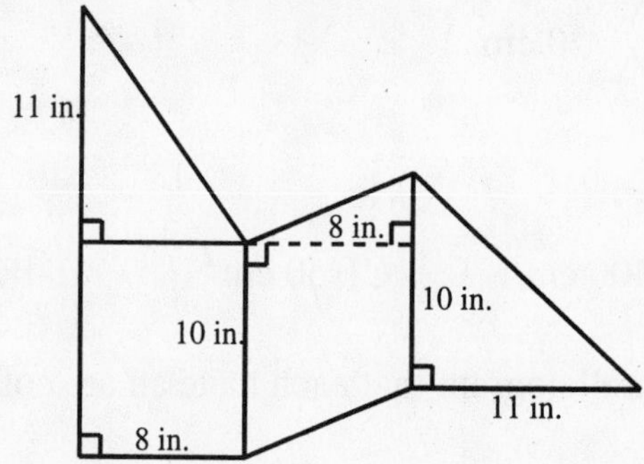

44. How much carpet do you need to cover the floor shown below?

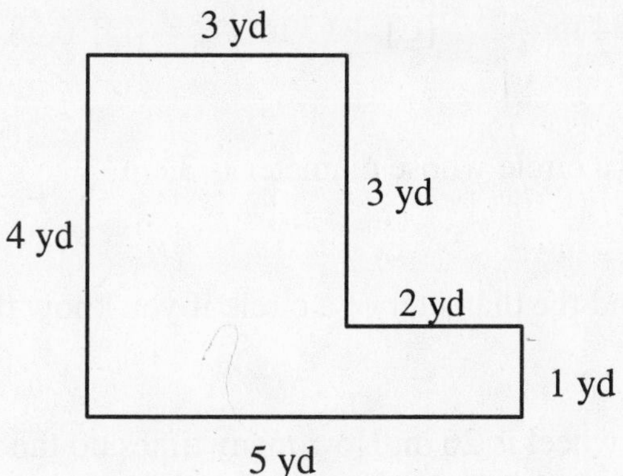

45. Coby and Jean made mobiles for donation to the hospital's nursery. Coby's mobile included a triangle with a base of 6 in. and a height of 22 in. Jean's mobile also included a triangle. Her triangle has a base of 12 in. and a height of 44 in. Compare the triangles made by Coby and Jean. What conclusion can you draw?

46. Explain how to find the area of the figure below. What is the area of the figure?

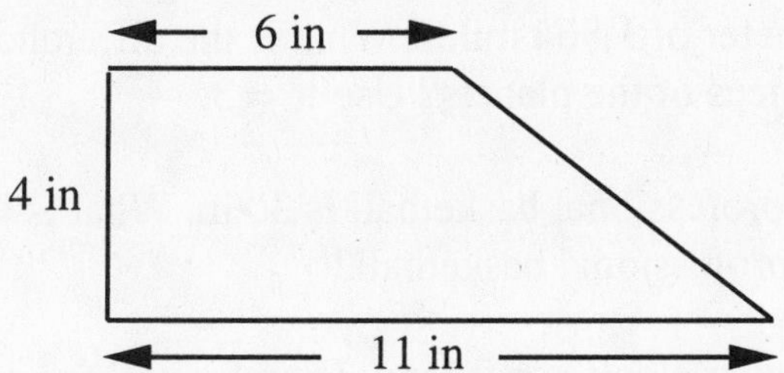

Lesson 9-4 Objective 1: Estimate pi and the circumference of a circle.

No items in this objective.

Lesson 9-4 Objective 2: Use pi to find the circumference of a circle.

Dynamic Item

47. If a circle has a radius of 9 inches, what is the circumference rounded to the nearest whole number? (Use $\pi = 3.14$)

[A] 254 in. [B] 29 in. [C] 57 in. [D] 114 in.

Dynamic Item

48. A circle has a circumference of 21 meters. Find its diameter.

[A] 5.25 m [B] 3.34 m [C] 10.5 m [D] 6.68 m

Dynamic Item

49. Find the circumference of a circle whose diameter is 3 cm. (Use $\pi = 3.14$)

50. Explain how you could find the diameter of a circle if you know the circumference.

51. The diameter of a bicycle wheel is 26 in. How many times do the wheels revolve in a distance of one mile? Express your answer to the nearest unit. (Hint: 1 mile = 5,280 ft).

[A] 82 [B] 65 [C] 776 [D] 1552

52. The diameter of Earth is about 8,000 mi. Suppose a jet is traveling around Earth at an altitude of 30,000 ft. How many miles will the jet travel in a complete circle around Earth? (1 mi = 5,280 ft)

[A] 38,000 mi [B] 94,247.8 mi [C] 25,156.7 mi [D] 8,005.7 mi

53. The diameter of the Earth is 7,926 miles. Pluto, the furthest planet in our solar system, has a diameter of 1,864 miles. What is the difference between the circumferences of the planets? Use $\pi = 3$.

54. The circumference of a professional basketball is 30 in. What is the radius, to the nearest unit, of a professional basketball?

55. The minute hand on a tower clock is 6 ft long. How far will the arrow on the minute hand travel in 2 hours? Round to the nearest unit.

56. Every spring Andrew plants flowers in his circular garden. The radius of his garden is 2 ft. Andrew wishes to plant petunias around the outer edge of the garden. If the petunias are to be spaced every six inches, how many petunias can Andrew plant in his garden?

57. The drive wheels on a locomotive are 66 inches in diameter. What is the circumference of a drive wheel on a locomotive?

58. A paper crown is made from seven triangles. The diameter of the crown is 14 in. If each triangle has the same dimensions, what is the measure of the base of each triangle? Round your answer to the nearest unit.

59. Use the spreadsheet below.

	A	B	C
1	Circle	Radius (cm)	Circumference (cm)
2	Green	5	
3	Blue	10	
4	Red	15	
5	Orange	20	
6	Purple	25	

a. Write a formula for cell C2 to determine the circumference of the green circle.
b. Copy and complete the spreadsheet. What is the circumference of each circle?

60. Study the completed spreadsheet below. What pattern do you observe? Suppose a yellow circle with a radius of 30 cm was added. Using the pattern you observed, find the circumference of the yellow circle.

	A	B	C
1	Circle	Radius (cm)	Circumference (cm)
2	Red	15	94.2
3	Orange	20	125.6
4	Purple	25	157.0

61. Without solving, determine if the circumference of a circle with a diameter of 31 cm is more or less than 100 cm. Explain your reasoning.

Lesson 9-5 Objective 1: Find the area of a circle.

Dynamic Item

62. What is the area of a circular region whose diameter is 6 centimeters? (Use $\pi = 3.14$)

[A] 113.04 cm^2 [B] 37.68 cm^2 [C] 18.84 cm^2 [D] 28.26 cm^2

Dynamic Item

63. Find the area of a circle whose radius is 8 cm. (Use $\pi \approx 3.14$.)

64. Explain what will happen to the area of a circle if the radius is doubled. Give an example to support your reasoning.

65. Mr. Bruno's pizza parlor advertises a special on 12 in. pizza on Tuesday and a special on 14 in. pizza on Thursday. On Tuesday, Jim and five schoolmates go to Mr. Bruno's for pizza. Mr. Bruno divides the 12 in. pizza equally among Jim and his schoolmates. On Thursday, Jim and eight schoolmates go to Mr. Bruno's for pizza. Mr. Bruno divides the 14 in. pizza equally among Jim and his schoolmates. Would Jim's slice of pizza be larger on Tuesday or Thursday? Explain your reasoning.

66. The circumference of a circle is 31.4 inches. Explain how you can find the area of the circle. What is the area of the circle?

67. Mr. Leopold's science class is making a display model of the solar system for the Science Fair. Suzette and Jennifer have been assigned to create a model of the earth. Mr. Leopold's directions state that the circumference of the model must be 30 in. Use $\pi = 3$ to estimate the area of the display model of the earth.

[A] 30 in.^{2} [B] 75 in.^{2} [C] 25 in.^{2} [D] 10 in.^{2}

68. List two real world situations where the area of the circle is important.

69. The first circular school building to be built in the United States was St. Patrick Central High School in Kankakee, Illinois. The building has a radius of 100 ft. Find the circumference and the area of the circular school building. Use $\pi = 3.14$.

70. Sammy and Toby enrolled in Mr. Welfel's Industrial Arts class for the spring semester. Their first project was to make a regulation size hockey stick. Mr. Welfel was so impressed with their work, he wanted to display the hockey sticks on Open House Night. Mr. Welfel thought it would be great if Sammy and Toby made a regulation size hockey puck to match the stick for the Open House Display. The diameter of a National League Hockey puck is 3 in. Sammy and Toby asked you to help find the circumference and area of the top of a National League hockey puck. Use $\pi = 3.14$. Round your answer to the nearest hundredth.

71. Which is larger, the area of a circle 8 in. in diameter or the area of a square whose side is 8 in. long? What is the difference in areas?

72. Find a circle whose area is equal to its circumference. What is the radius of the circle?

Lesson 9-5 Objective 2: Find combined areas of circles and polygons.

Dynamic Item

73. Find the area of the region shown.

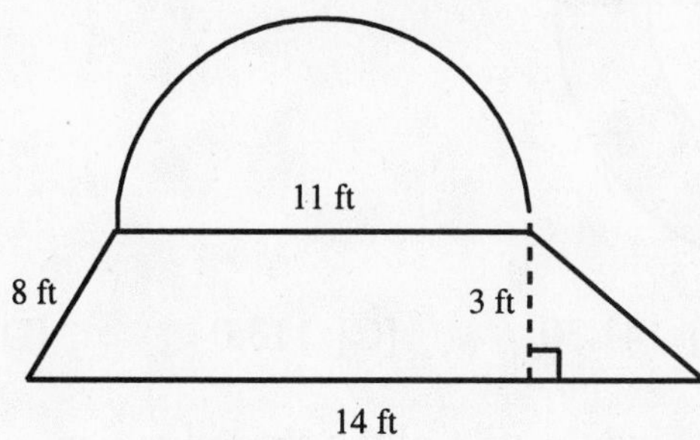

[A] $(30.25\pi + 100)$ ft^2 [B] $(60.5\pi + 37.5)$ ft^2

[C] $(15.125\pi + 42)$ ft^2 [D] $(15.125\pi + 37.5)$ ft^2

Dynamic Item

74. Find the area of the composite shape.

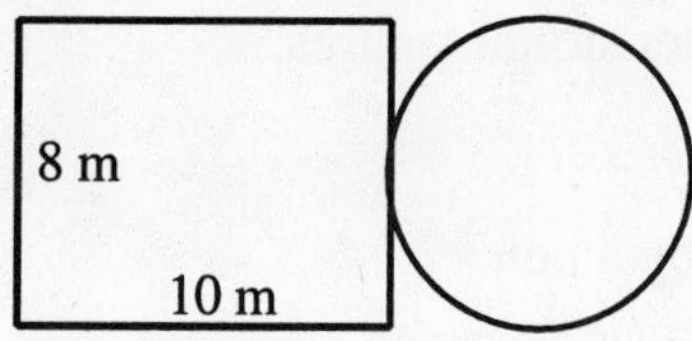

[A] 381.593 m^2 [B] 281.062 m^2

[C] 237.062 m^2 [D] 130.265 m^2

75. Find the area of the outer ring of the figure below.

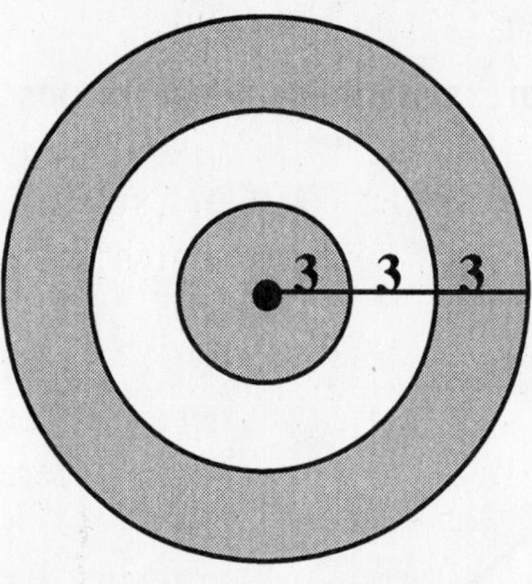

[A] 28.26 [B] 141.30 [C] 113.04 [D] 254.34

76. Use the figure below. Find the area of the shaded region.

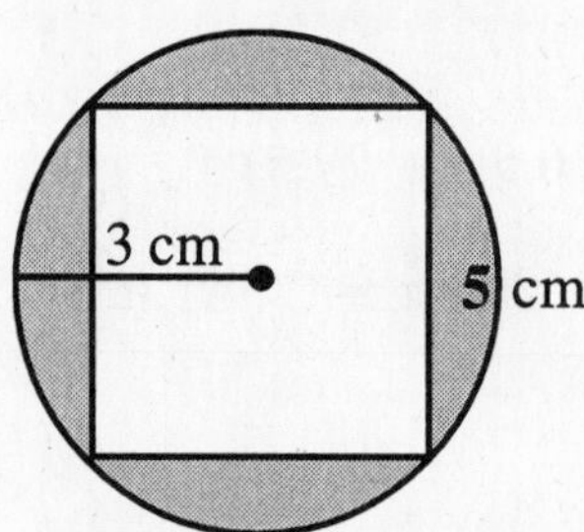

Lesson 9-6 Objective: Identify three-dimensional figures.

Dynamic Item

77. Name the geometric solid suggested by a pen.

[A] cylinder [B] sphere [C] rectangular prism [D] cube

Dynamic Item

78. Draw the net of a domino.

79. Describe a three-dimensional figure and give several examples.

80. Explain how the terms face, base, edge, and vertex can be used to describe a three-dimensional figure.

81. What figure is MOST LIKE a cone?

[A] sphere [B] pyramid [C] prism [D] cylinder

82. Which figure has exactly four vertices?

[A] triangular pyramid
[B] square pyramid
[C] cylinder
[D] triangular prism

83. Jamie and Tomasina each drew different nets for a cube. Explain how both of them can be correct. Draw examples of the nets they might have drawn. Are there more than two possibilities?

84. Explain how prisms and cylinders are alike and how they are different. Explain how pyramids and cones are alike and how they are different.

85. Draw a net for a square pyramid. Can the net be folded in more than one way? Explain.

86. Draw the prism described in the table below.

Figure	Vertices	Edges	Faces	Bases
Prism	8	12	6	2
Pyramid	5	8	5	1

a. What kind of prism did you draw?
b. Describe the shapes of the faces of the figure.
c. Describe the relationships among the edges.

87. Draw the pyramid described in the table below.

Figure	Vertices	Edges	Faces	Bases
Prism	8	12	6	2
Pyramid	5	8	5	1

a. What type of pyramid did you draw?
b. Describe the shape(s) of the faces of the figure.
c. Describe the relationships among the edges.

88. Sue Ellen drew a prism that has 6 vertices. Bjorn drew a prism that has twice as many vertices and edges and 3 more faces than the prism Sue Ellen drew. Geno drew a prism that has 2 more vertices, 1 more face, and 3 more edges than the prism Sue Ellen drew. If Bjorn's prism has 8 faces and Geno's prism has 12 edges, what type of prism did each person draw?

89. There is a relationship among the number of faces, vertices, and edges of three-dimensional figures. Find the relationship, or pattern, from the chart below.

Figure	Faces	Vertices	Edges
Triangular pyramid	4	4	6
Square pyramid	5	5	8
Triangular prism	5	6	9
Rectangular prism	6	8	12

90. The chart below lists several familiar items. Complete the chart to show the various three-dimensional figures that describe each item. The first one has been done for you. When the chart is complete, draw and label a diagram to represent each item.

Item	3-D Figure
can of cat food	cylinder
cereal box	
piece of pie	
book	
teepee	
basketball	
drum	
beach ball	

Lesson 9-7 Objective: Find the surface area of a rectangular prism.

Dynamic Item

91. Find the surface area of the rectangular prism.

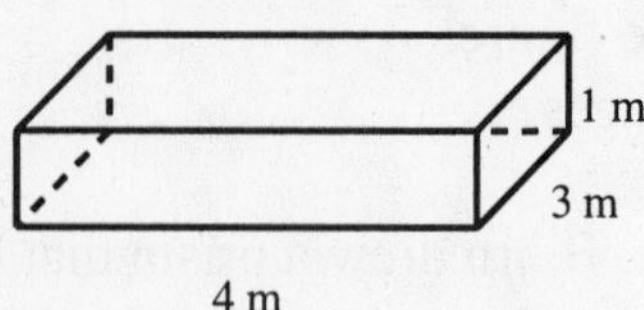

[A] 12 m^2 [B] 38 m^2 [C] 8 m^2 [D] 19 m^2

Dynamic Item

92. Find the surface area of a rectangular solid that is 17 inches long, 13 inches wide, and 9 inches high.

93. Explain how to find the surface area of a rectangular prism.

94. Sofia is designing the outside of a new package that takes the shape of a cube. Sofia calculated the surface area of the cube before being told that the length of the cube was doubled. What does the change in the size of the cube do to the surface area Sofia calculated? Give an example to support your answer.

95. The surface area of a cube is 96 cm^2. What is the length of each side?

    [A] 3 cm [B] 2 cm [C] 4 cm [D] 5 cm

96. A rectangular storage container has a surface area of 96 $in.^2$. Which of the following is being described?

    [A] A box that is 1 ft long, 2 ft wide, and 8 in. tall.

    [B] A box that is 12 in. long, 6 in. wide, and 4 in. tall.

    [C] A plastic container that is 2 in. tall, 8 in. long, and 8 in. wide.

    [D] A crate that is 28 in. long, 20 in. wide, and 80 in. tall.

97. Bryan has three sheets of mailing paper and three boxes to wrap. In which sheet should he wrap each box in order to wrap all three boxes most efficiently? Use the tables below. Explain how you found your answer.

Wrapping	Length	Width
A	2 ft	3 ft
B	10 in.	15 in.
C	20 in.	15 in.

Box	Length	Width	Height
1	7 in.	6 in.	2 in.
2	13 in.	4 in.	3 in.
3	20 in.	12 in.	6 in.

CHAPTER 9

98. Salina works in the gift-wrapping department of a local store. She has three boxes to wrap for the same customer. The measurements of the boxes are as follows:

	Length (ft)	Width (ft)	Height (ft)
Box 1	1	0.5	0.25
Box 2	2	1	0.3
Box 3	3	1	0.5

If the wrapping paper the customer selected costs \$0.40/ft^2, how much will the customer pay for all three boxes?

99. A room is 20 ft long, 15 ft wide, and 8 ft high. Samuel is painting the walls blue and the ceiling white. Paint costs \$8 per gallon. One gallon covers 280 ft^2 and two coats are needed to cover the old paint. If Samuel also wishes to cover the floor with carpeting that costs \$5/ft^2, how much will the entire job cost?

100. Draw and label a net for a toy chest with a base that is 20 cm × 15 cm and a height of 30 cm. Use the net to find the surface area of the chest.

101. Joann's lunch box is 25 cm long, 15 cm wide, and 10 cm high. She wants to cover the surface of the lunch box with stickers. If each sticker is 50 cm^2, how many stickers does she need?

102. Lee's classroom has a box in it that is used to store supplies. The box is 24 in. long, 16 in. wide, and 12 in. high. Lee's teacher is going to cover the box with colored paper. Each sheet of paper is 80 $in.^2$. How many sheets does the teacher need? How does your answer change if you are told that the box has no top?

103. Juan is insulating his tool shed. There are several different qualities of insulation. The price of each quality is listed in the table. Juan's shed is 10 ft long, 6 ft wide, and 8 ft tall. If Juan has $625, what is the best quality insulation he can afford to insulate the walls and ceiling of his shed? Use the table below. Explain how you found your answer.

Quality	Price ($ / ft^2)
Low	0.50
Medium	1.15
High	1.65
Super	2.30

104. Isabelle is planning to wallpaper a room in her apartment. The room is 20 ft × 10 ft × 8 ft. The room has a window that is 2 ft × 3 ft and a door that is 2 ft × 7 ft. The chart below lists her choices of wallpaper in order of preference. Which wallpaper can she buy if she only has $885 to spend?

Choice	Price ($ / ft^2)
1	2.25
2	1.90
3	1.50

Lesson 9-8 Objective 1: Find the volume of a rectangular prism.

Dynamic Item

105. Find the volume of the rectangular prism.

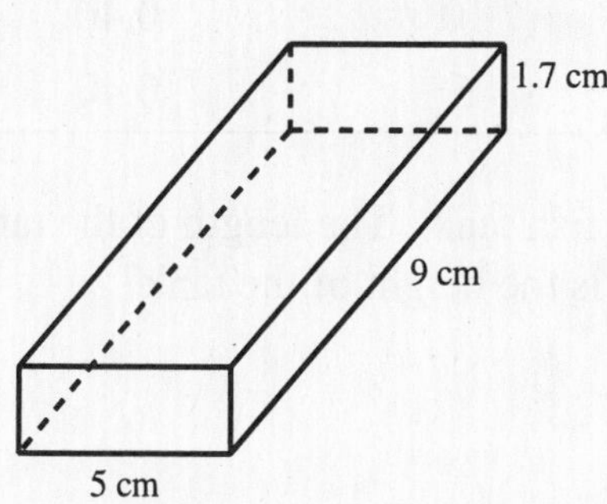

[A] 76.5 cm^3 [B] 60.3 cm^3 [C] 68.8 cm^3 [D] 62.8 cm^3

CHAPTER 9

Dynamic Item

106. Find the volume of a box 8 centimeters long, 4 centimeters wide, and 3 centimeters high.

107. Explain how you can find the volume of a rectangular prism.

108. In what units is volume measured? Why?

109. Conner knows the volume, but not the dimensions, of a rectangular package that he is expecting. The volume is 135cm^3. Draw a prism that fits the description of Conner's package.

110. Charlotte has three presents to mail to her grandmother. The dimensions of each present are listed below.

Present	Length (in.)	Width (in.)	Height (in.)
1	12	10	3
2	5	4	6
3	10	8	1

Although the cost of mailing a package depends on weight, the shipping facility that Charlotte uses charges an additional fee according to the volume of the box being shipped. There are four boxes from which Charlotte can choose. Use the table below. In which box can she send the presents for the lowest cost?

Box	Length (in.)	Width (in.)	Height (in.)	Addtional Cost ($)
1	16	15	9	0.50
2	10	10	10	0.30
3	14	12	10	0.40
4	15	12	5	0.40

111. Exactly 50.4 L of water fit Nina's fish tank. The length of the tank is 60 cm and the width is 35 cm. What is the height of the tank? ($1 \text{ L} = 1000 \text{ cm}^3$)

112.

Trunk	Length (ft)	Width (ft)	Height (ft)	Price ($)
A	3	1	1	50
B	2	2	1	60
C	3.5	2	1	80
D	4	1	0.5	40
E	3	2	0.5	60
F	3	1	2	90

Use the information in the chart above. The prices of the trunks vary according to size and style. Which is the trunk with the largest volume that Austin can afford if he has $63 to spend?

Lesson 9-8 Objective 2: Find the missing dimension of a rectangular prism.

Dynamic Item

113. An aquarium is 15 inches long, 14 inches wide and 24 inches high. The volume of water in the aquarium is 3,150 cubic inches. How deep is the water?

[A] 19 inches [B] 210 inches [C] 5 inches [D] 15 inches

Dynamic Item

114. A box that is 19 inches long and 18 inches wide has a volume of 2394 cubic inches. How deep is the box?

115. The volume of a box that is 12 in. × 4 in. × 6 in. is the SAME as the volume of a box that is

[A] 2 in. × 18 in. × 8 in. [B] 6 in. × 2 in. × 3 in.

[C] 16 in. × 2 in. × 4 in. [D] 24 in. × 8 in. × 12 in.

116. Three ft^3 of soil will exactly fill

[A] 2 flower boxes that each measure 1 ft × 0.5 ft × 0.3 ft.

[B] 1 flower box that measures 1 ft × 1 ft × 2 ft AND 1 flower box that measures 1 ft × 1 ft × 1 ft.

[C] 2 flower boxes that each measure 0.75 ft × 2 ft × 2 ft.

[D] 3 flower boxes that each measure 1 ft × 0.5 ft × 1 ft.

117. A crate of books measures 2 ft long × 1.5 ft wide × 1 ft high. What is the volume of a stack of 8 such crates?

118. Jacques is an ice sculptor who purchases ice in large blocks. The volume of each block is 1 ft^3. His freezer measures 6 ft × 2 ft ×3 ft. If each block costs $1.20, how much does it cost to fill his freezer?

119.

Trunk	Length (ft)	Width (ft)	Height (ft)	Price ($)
A	3	1	1	50
B	2	2	1	60
C	3.5	2	1	80
D	4	1	0.5	40
E	3	2	0.5	60
F	3	1	2	90

Use the information in the chart above. Austin is buying a storage trunk to take away to school. The store sells several different trunks as shown in the chart. Which trunk should Austin buy if he wants the trunk with the greatest volume?

Lesson 9-9 Objective: Solve problems by making a model.

Dynamic Item

120. A grocery clerk sets up a display of oranges in the form of a triangle using 8 oranges at the base and 1 at the top. (Only part of the display is shown below.)

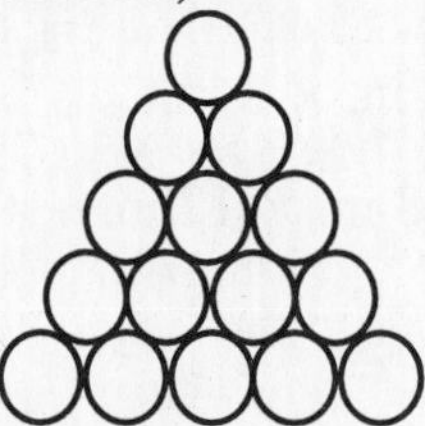

How many oranges were used by the clerk to make the arrangement?

[A] 28 [B] 52 [C] 36 [D] 44

Dynamic Item

121. A store clerk set up a display of soup cans in the form of a triangle, using 10 soup cans at the base and 1 at the top. (Only part of the display is shown below.)

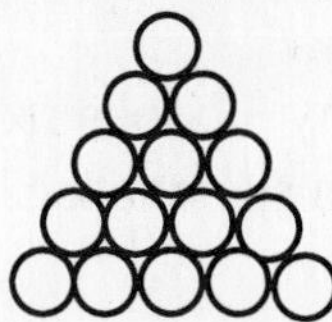

How many soup cans did the clerk use to make the arrangement?

122. Mrs. Lamb's computer class uses 42 computer disks each month. If one disk in 25 is defective, how many disks should Mrs. Lamb order for a four-month period?

[A] 168 [B] 175 [C] 193 [D] 1050

123. There are 10 students in Mr. Alvarez's art class. Throughout the year, every student must pair up with every other student to complete a project. How many projects will be finished?

[A] 45 [B] 20 [C] 100 [D] 25

124. There are 9 teams in a field hockey league. Each team plays every other team twice. How many games are played?

125. Will has $5.20 in his bank in quarters, dimes, and nickels. How many of each coin is in the bank?

126. There are several people at Renee's party. They are playing a game that requires each person to exchange a piece of information with every other person. If there are 36 exchanges of information, how many people are at the party?

127. Consuela rented a car for three days. The rate was $21 per day and $0.25 per mile after the first 100 miles. Consuela paid $117.75. How many miles did she travel?

128. The sum of three numbers is 28. The product of the numbers is 756. What are the three numbers?

129. An airplane leaves New York for Chicago every 50 minutes beginning at 6:20 A.M. What is the departure time closest to 2:30 P.M.?

130. The average age of six students is 13. Two of the students are 9 years old. Three of the students are not 9 years old, but are the same age as one another. The age of the sixth student is different from the ages of the other five. What are the ages of the 6 students?

131. There are 8 books on a reading list. Mia has to read any 3 books from the list. How many different combinations of 3 books can she choose?

Chapter 10: Algebra: Integers and Graphing

Lesson 10-1 Objective 1: Graph integers on a number line.

Dynamic Item

1. Which of the following number lines shows the graph of 4, –1, and 0?

[A] –7 –6 –5 –4 –3 –2 –1 0 1 2 3 4 5 6 7

[B] –7 –6 –5 –4 –3 –2 –1 0 1 2 3 4 5 6 7

[C] –7 –6 –5 –4 –3 –2 –1 0 1 2 3 4 5 6 7

[D] –7 –6 –5 –4 –3 –2 –1 0 1 2 3 4 5 6 7

Dynamic Item

2. Graph –1, +5, –6, and –8 on a number line.

3. How is a thermometer similar to a number line?

4. Describe the relationship between –56, –55, and 0 on a number line.

5. Graph on a number line all integers greater than –5 and less than 5.

6. Graph –3, 5, 0, –6, 8, and –1 on a number line.

Lesson 10-1 Objective 2: Compare and order integers.

Dynamic Item

7. Write the integers –3, 1, –14, 16, 14, in order from greatest to least.

[A] –14, –3, 1, 14, 16 [B] 16, 14, 1, –14, –3

[C] 16, 14, 1, –3, –14 [D] 1, 14, –3, –14, 16

Dynamic Item

8. Complete the statement using < or >. 3 _?_ –9

9. Describe at least four situations in which you might use negative integers.

10. Janice listed the integers below on the chalkboard. Which of these integer has the greatest opposite? –7, –5, 10, 3, 2, 8, –6

[A] –7 [B] –6 [C] 8 [D] 10

11. Complete the pattern: –8, –6, ____, –2, 0, ____, 4, 6, 8.

[A] 4, –2 [B] –4, –2 [C] –4, 2 [D] 4, 2

CHAPTER 10

12. The highest temperature for New York was one hundred eight degrees on July 22, 1926 at Troy. The lowest temperature was negative fifty-two degrees on February 18, 1979 at Old Forge. Write an integer to represent each temperature.

13. The lowest recorded temperature in Africa was –11°F on Feb. 11, 1935. The lowest recorded temperature in Australia was 8°F on July 22, 1947. Which of these continents had the lowest temperature?

14. On Monday the temperature was –5°F. On Tuesday the temperature was –1°F. On which day was the temperature lower?

Freezing / Boiling Points of Common Substances

Substance	Freezing Point (°C)	Boiling Point (°C)
water	0	100
mercury	–39	357
oxygen	–218	–183
nitrogen	–209	–196
iron	1535	2750

Source: Chemistry: The Study of Matter, Prentice Hall, 1989

15.

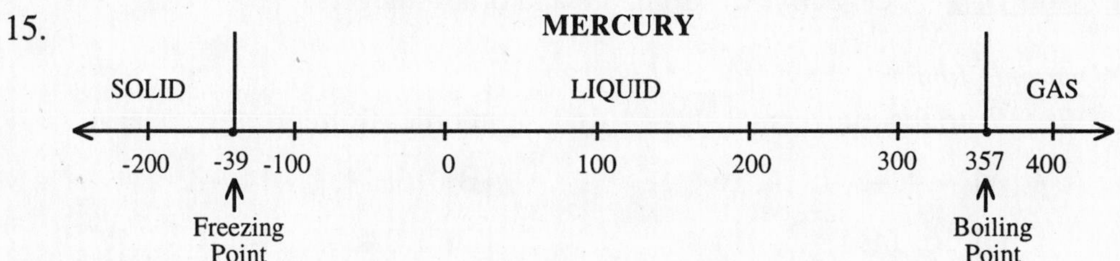

The number line above shows the changes in form of mercury, as it is affected by temperature. At –39°C, the freezing point, mercury changes from a liquid to a solid. At 357°C, the boiling point, mercury changes from a liquid to a gas. Using the data in the table above, draw and label number lines for each of the other substances. Which of the substances of the table is liquid at 90°C? At –200°C?

16.

Freezing / Boiling Points of Common Substances		
Substance	Freezing Point (°C)	Boiling Point (°C)
water	0	100
mercury	–39	357
oxygen	–218	–183
nitrogen	–209	–196
iron	1535	2750

Source: Chemistry: The Study of Matter, Prentice Hall, 1989

The table above shows the freezing and boiling temperatures for some substances. The freezing point is the temperature at which a substance changes from a liquid to a solid. The boiling point is the temperature at which a substance changes from a liquid to a gas. Which of the substances in the table are solid at 90° C?

Lesson 10-2 Objective: Use models to represent positive integers, negative integers, and zero.

Dynamic Item

17. Name the integer represented by the set of algebra tiles. Let one white tile equal +1 and one black tile equal –1.

□ □ ■ ■ ■

□ □ ■ ■ ■ ■

[A] 11 [B] –28 [C] –3 [D] 28

Dynamic Item

18. Use algebra tiles to represent the number 10 in two different ways. Draw a diagram.

19. If a zero pair is added to a model of an integer, would this change the value of the integer modeled? Explain.

20. Explain how you can use integers to describe points above and below sea level.

21. Use your algebra tiles to make two different models to represent the integer -4. Use positive and negative tiles in each model.

22. Write the integer that is represented by the model below.

[A] -4 [B] 8 [C] 0 [D] 4

23. The starting point for measuring latitude is the equator. Its latitude is 0°. Between the equator and the North Pole, there are 90° of latitude. There are also 90° of latitude between the South Pole and the equator. When giving the location of a place, geographers always state whether its latitude is north or south of the equator. A plane flew from 25° North Latitude to a city at 25° South Latitude. Through how many degrees latitude did the plane travel?

[A] -25° [B] 25° [C] 0° [D] 50°

24. A negative integer is four times as far from zero as a positive integer. The two integers are 25 units away from each other. Name the two integers.

25. Use algebra tiles to make models for the integers shown on the number line below. Draw a sketch of each model.

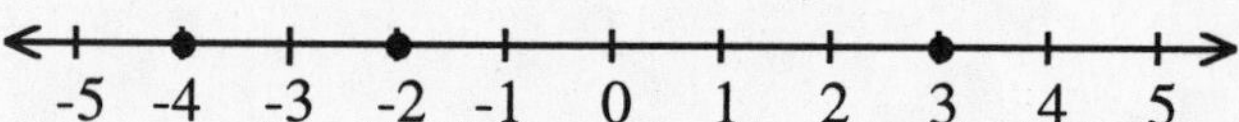

26. The lowest point in the Western Hemisphere is 282 feet below sea level in Death Valley. Write this number as an integer and write the opposite of this integer.

27. An increase of $25 in Larry's checkbook is shown by the integer 25. Which integer would show a decrease of $25?

28. On February 15, 1936 at Parshall, North Dakota, the coldest temperature ever recorded was 60 below zero. Write this temperature as an integer.

Wind Speed (mi/h)	Temperature °F												
	50	41	32	23	14	5	-4	-13	-22	-31	-40	-49	-58
	Wind-chill Temperature °F												
5	48	39	28	19	10	1	-9	-18	-27	-36	-51	-56	-65
10	41	30	18	7	-4	-15	-26	-36	-49	-60	-71	-81	-92
20	32	19	7	-6	-18	-31	-44	-58	-71	-83	-96	-108	-121
30	28	14	1	-13	-27	-40	-54	-69	-81	-96	-108	-123	-137
40	27	12	-2	-17	-31	-45	-60	-74	-89	-103	-116	-130	-144
50	25	10	-4	-18	-33	-47	-62	-76	-90	-105	-119	-134	-148

Source: *The Old Farmer's Almanac 1994*

29. The table above gives the corresponding wind-chill temperatures for temperatures ranging from 50° F to -58° F with wind speeds ranging from 5 mi/h to 50 mi/h. The wind-chill temperature on a 32° F day with a 40 mi/h wind is -2° F. Find the wind-chill temperature when the temperature is 5° F and the wind speed is 20mi/h.

30. The table above gives the corresponding wind-chill temperatures for temperatures ranging from 50° F to -58° F with wind speeds ranging from 5 mi/h to 50 mi/h. The wind-chill temperature on a 32° F day with a 40 mi/h wind is -2° F. Does it feel colder on a 5° F day with a wind of 10 mi/h or on a -4° F day with a wind of 5 mi/h?

Lesson 10-3 Objective 1: Use models to add integers with like signs.

Dynamic Item

31. Write the numerical expression for the model. Find the sum. Let one white tile equal +1 and one black tile equal –1.

    □ □ + □

    □ □ □ □ □

    [A] 5 + (–2); 3 [B] 5 + 2; 7 [C] –5 + (–2); –7 [D] –5 + 2; –3

Dynamic Item

32. Write the numerical expression for the model. Find the sum. Let one white tile equal +1 and one black tile equal –1.

    □ + □

    □ □ □

33. Summarize what you know about the sum of a positive and a negative integer.

34. Use the integers -6, -8, 2, and 4 to write two addition sentences that have the same sum.

Deepest Depressions

Description	Location	Depth (below sea level)
lowest - lying area in the U.S.A.	Death Valley, California	-282 ft
in the bedrock of of the Bentely subglacial trench	Antartica	-8,326 ft
submarine in ocean floor	the northwest Pacific	-15,000 ft
exposed depression on land	shore around the Dead Sea	-1,310 ft
deepest part of the bed in a lake	Lake Baikal, Russia	-2,388 ft

Source: Guiness Book of Records 1993

35. The table above shows the depth below sea level of some of the deepest depressions in the world. These depths are written as negative integers because they are below sea level. Find the depths of three depressions listed in the table whose sum is almost -10,000 ft. Write an equation to show the sum of the depths of these three depressions.

36. The table above shows the depth below sea level of some of the deepest depressions in the world. These depths are written as negative integers because they are below sea level. Write an equation that shows the sum of the depth of the lowest depression in the ocean floor and the depth of the deepest part of Lake Baikal in Russia.

Lesson 10-3 Objective 2: Use models to add integers with unlike signs.

Dynamic Item

37. Write the numerical expression for the model. Find the sum. Let one white tile equal +1 and one black tile equal –1.

■ ■ ■ + □ □
■ ■ ■   □ □

[A] 6 + 4; 2 [B] –6 + 4; –10 [C] 6 + 4; 10 [D] –6 + 4; –2

Dynamic Item

38. Write the numerical expression for the model. Find the sum. Let one white tile equal +1 and one black tile equal –1.

■ + □
■ ■   □

39. Write a word problem for the equation represented by the number line shown below.

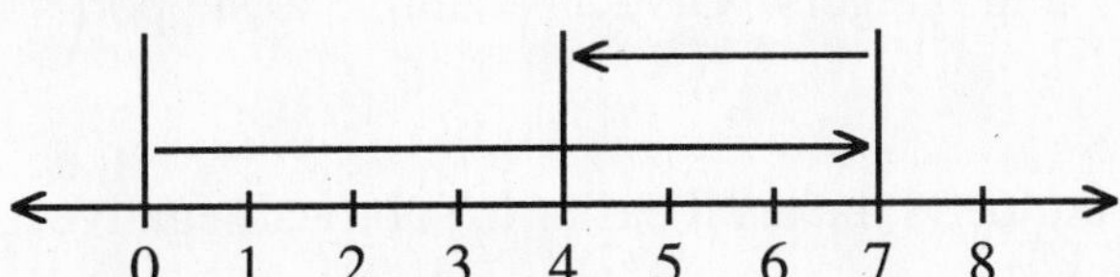

40. The sum of two integers is 0. What can you conclude about the two integers? Give examples to support your conclusion.

41. Write a word problem involving the sum of a positive and a negative integer.

42. The expression $a + b + (-5)$ represents a positive integer. Choose the possible values for a and b.

[A] $a = 4$ and $b = 1$ [B] $a = 6$ and $b = -1$

[C] $a = -2$ and $b = 4$ [D] $a = -4$ and $b = 10$

43. Write the numerical expression represented in the model below. Find the sum.

□ □ □ + ▩ ▩ ▩ ▩
□ □ □   ▩ ▩ ▩ ▩

[A] 6 + (-8); -2 [B] -6 + (-8); -14 [C] -6 + 8; -2 [D] 6 + 8; 14

CHAPTER 10

44. The highest temperature recorded in Maine was 105° F. The lowest temperature recorded was -48° F. Write an addition sentence showing the sum of the two temperatures. Find the sum.

45. A football team gained 10 yards, lost 3 yards, gained 9 yards, and lost 2 yards. Write the total gain or loss of yards as an integer.

Lesson 10-4 Objective 1: Model the subtraction of integers.

Dynamic Item

46. Which model shows the difference 1 – 7?

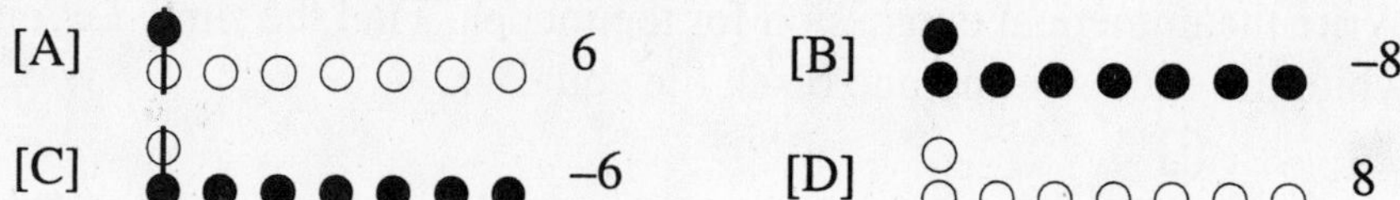

Dynamic Item

47. Draw a model to find the difference 6 – 9.

48. Write a rule for subtracting integers. Give an example to support your rule.

49. Explain how adding zero pairs makes it easier to subtract negative numbers. Give an example.

50. Describe a problem that can be solved using the model below. Explain how to solve the problem.

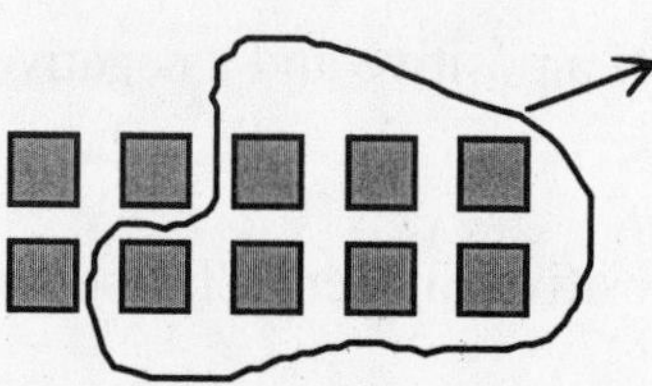

51. Use positive and negative integers to write two different subtraction number sentences that have a difference of -6.

52. Choose the numerical expression that equals -6.

[A] -8 - 2 [B] 5 - (-1) [C] -3 - 9 [D] -4 - 2

53. The temperature for a city in January ranges from about 9° F below zero to 25° F above zero. What is the difference in temperature?

CHAPTER 10

54. Use the integers -4, 3, 2, -1, 0 and 8 to find two integers that when subtracted give the greatest difference and the least difference.

55. Karen was balancing her checkbook. The starting balance was $58. She wrote checks for $28, $16, and $39. How much money does Karen need to deposit into her checking account to cover her checks?

56. The integers -9, -7, -4, -2, and 6 are arranged in the three figures below. The difference of the numbers inside the square is 2 or 10. The difference of the numbers inside the circle is 5 or -3. There are three numbers inside the rectangle. The difference of the numbers inside of the rectangle is -13 or 1. What are the numbers inside each figure?

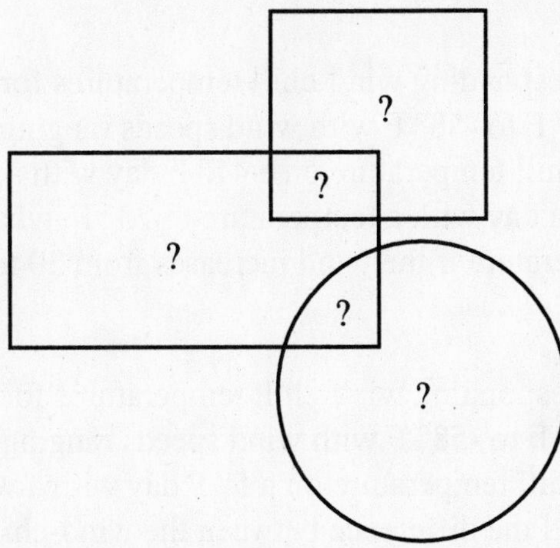

Wind Speed (mi/h)	Temperature °F												
	50	41	32	23	14	5	-4	-13	-22	-31	-40	-49	-58
	Wind-chill Temperature °F												
5	48	39	28	19	10	1	-9	-18	-27	-36	-51	-56	-65
10	41	30	18	7	-4	-15	-26	-36	-49	-60	-71	-81	-92
20	32	19	7	-6	-18	-31	-44	-58	-71	-83	-96	-108	-121
30	28	14	1	-13	-27	-40	-54	-69	-81	-96	-108	-123	-137
40	27	12	-2	-17	-31	-45	-60	-74	-89	-103	-116	-130	-144
50	25	10	-4	-18	-33	-47	-62	-76	-90	-105	-119	-134	-148

Source: *The Old Farmer's Almanac 1994*

57. The table above gives the corresponding wind-chill temperatures for temperatures ranging from 50° F to -58° F with wind speeds ranging from 5 mi/h to 50 mi/h. The wind-chill temperature on a 41° F day with a wind speed of 40 mi/h is 12° F. On a day with a temperature of 23° F, what is the change in wind-chill temperature if the wind increases from 30 to 40 mi/h?

58. The table above gives the corresponding wind-chill temperatures for temperatures ranging from 50° F to -58° F with wind speeds ranging from 5 mi/h to 50 mi/h. The wind-chill temperature on a 5° F day with a wind speed of 30 mi/h is -40° F. Find the difference between the wind-chill temperatures on a 14° F day and a 41° F day with the same wind speed of 20 mi/h.

Lesson 10-4 Objective 2: Use models to solve equations with integers.

59. The expression $a - b - 5$ represents a negative integer. Choose possible values of a and b.

[A] $a = 4$ and $b = -1$ [B] $a = 3$ and $b = -3$

[C] $a = 2$ and $b = -3$ [D] $a = -2$ and $b = -7$

Lesson 10-5 Objective: Solve problems using multiple strategies.

60. The mean of five numbers is greater than 38 but less than 42. Four of the numbers are 44, 39, 36, and 35. Which of these numbers cannot be the other number?

[A] 36 [B] 55 [C] 50 [D] 44

61. Which of the following is the largest length?

[A] 68 in. [B] $5\frac{3}{4}$ ft [C] $2\frac{2}{3}$ yd [D] 3 yd 8 in.

62. Jena works for a department store. She is paid $5.20 per hour for the first 35 hours worked. Any hours worked thereafter she is paid $7.80 per hour. How much does Jena earn if she works 42 hours?

63. The sum of two numbers is –2. The difference of the two numbers is 4. What are the two numbers?

64. The Robinsons bought 5 tickets to a concert in the park. Adult tickets cost $11.75 each. Child tickets cost $8.50 each. If the Robinsons spent $52.25 in all, how many adult and children tickets did they buy?

65. A student has 3 one-dollar bills, 2 five-dollar bills and 6 ten-dollar bills in his pocket. What is the probability that he will reach into his pocket and select a one-dollar bill?

66. There are 8 roads from June's house to Cara's house and 5 roads from Cara's house to Don's house. How many possible routes can June take to get to Don's house if she goes to Cara's house first?

67. You open a book and the product of the page numbers is 7140. What pages have you opened the book to?

68.

Day	Food Eaten (grams)
0	0.0
1	1.0
2	3.2
3	6.5
4	10.6
5	15.4

Source: The Study of Biology, Prentice Hall

The table above gives the number of grams of food eaten by a baby chick on the first five days of life. Construct a line graph using the data in the table. Based on the graph, predict the amount of grain needed to feed a chick on the sixth and seventh days.

Lesson 10-6 Objective 1: Make a function table.

Dynamic Item

69. Complete the function table:

Input	Output
9	13
10	14
11	?
12	16
13	?
14	?

Dynamic Item

70. Make a function table for decades (output) as a function of centuries (input). (Start with 1 and go to 6.)

71. Use the table below.
a. What number belongs in the blank cell or box?
b. How are the numbers in column B related to the numbers in column A?
c. If h stands for the number of hours worked, what variable expression represents the amount earned?

	A	B
1	Number of Hours Worked	Amount Earned
2	1	4.50
3	2	9.00
4	3	13.50
5	4	?

72. a. Copy and complete the table below.
b. If b stands for the number of games bowled, what variable expression represents the total cost for bowling?
c. Graph the data.

	A	B	C
1	Number of Games Bowled	Cost for Games	Cost for Rental of Shoes
2	1	$4.00	$1.00
3	2	$8.00	$1.00
4	3	$12.00	$1.00
5	4	?	$1.00
6	5	?	$1.00

Lesson 10-6 Objective 2: Graph functions.

Dynamic Item

73. From the graph of values, determine the function rule.

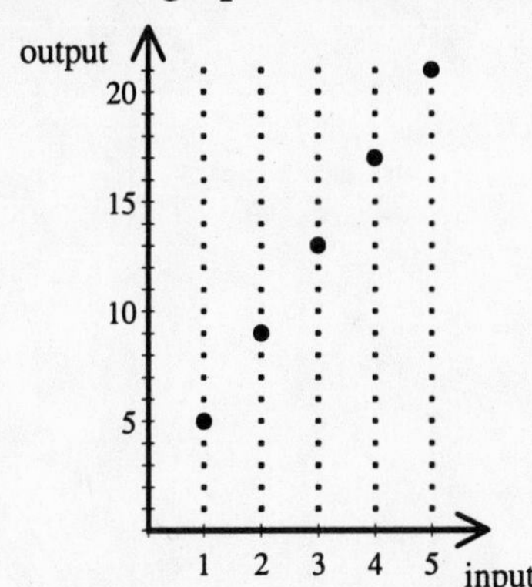

[A] output = 3 · input + 2 [B] output = 4 · input + 1

[C] output = 1 · input − 4 [D] output = 2 · input − 3

Dynamic Item

74. Graph the function for:

Input	(pounds)	1	2	3	4	5	6
Output	(ounces)	16	32	48	64	80	96

75. a. Explain the difference between collinear and noncollinear points.
b. Are the points (2, 5), (3, 6), and (4, 7) collinear or noncollinear? Explain.
c. Are the points (2, 8), (3, 27), and (4, 64) collinear or noncollinear? Explain.

76. In your own words, what is meant by the phrase, "graphing functional data"?

77. The drama club sells carnations for its annual holiday fund-raiser. Help the drama club decide which company to use. Which graph below represents the company that would be the most economical for the club to hire?

[A]

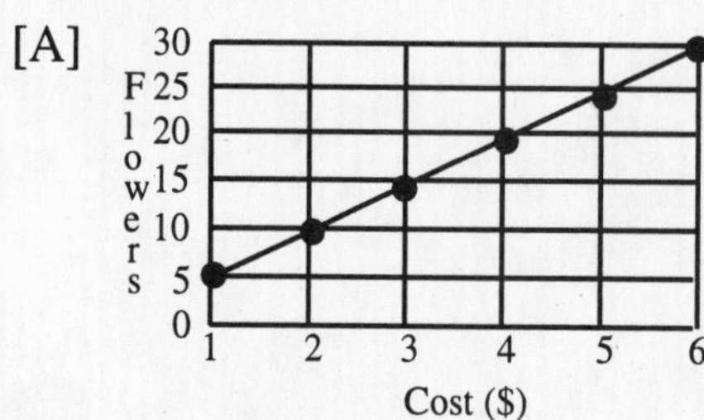

[B]

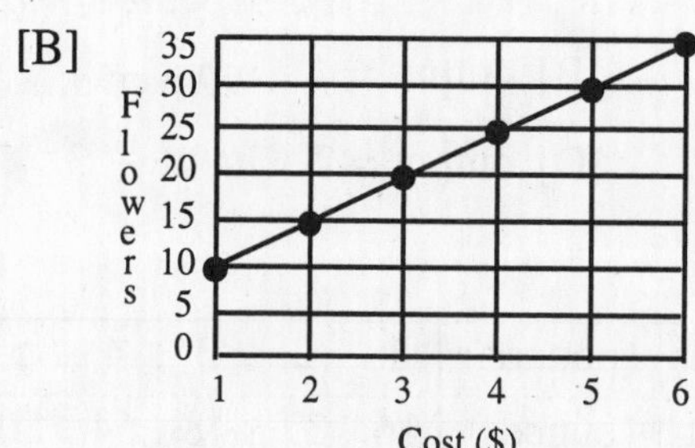

[C]

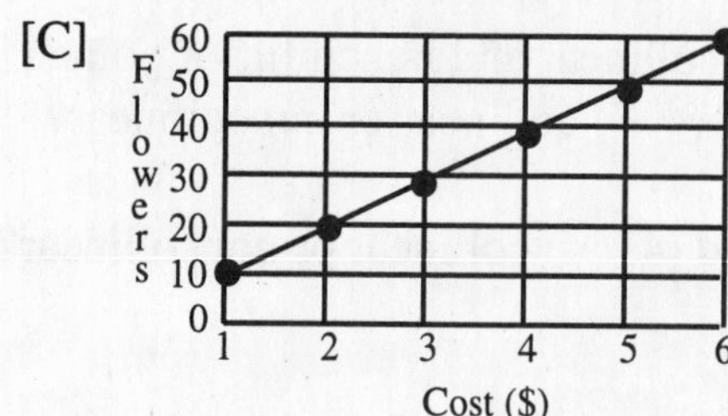

[D]

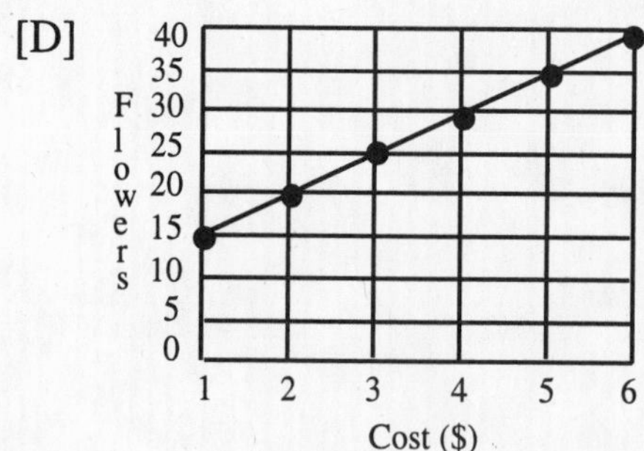

78. Choose the variable expression that best describes the graph below.

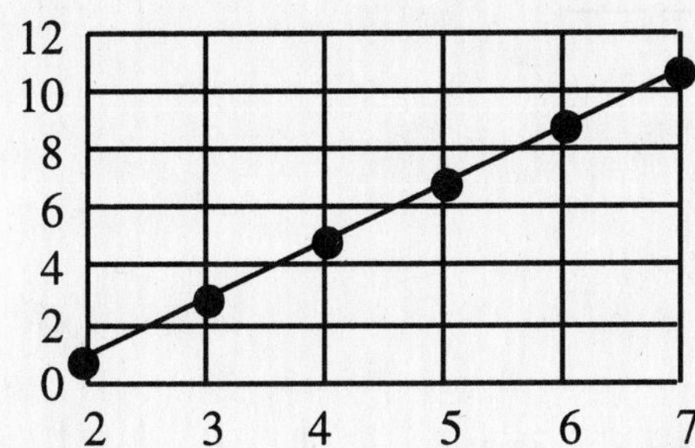

[A] $x^2 - 3$ [B] $2x + 3$ [C] $2x - 3$ [D] $x^2 + 3$

79. Choose the graph below that best represents the data in the table.

Number of Hours	Miles Driven
1	38
2	53
3	68
4	83
5	98

[A]

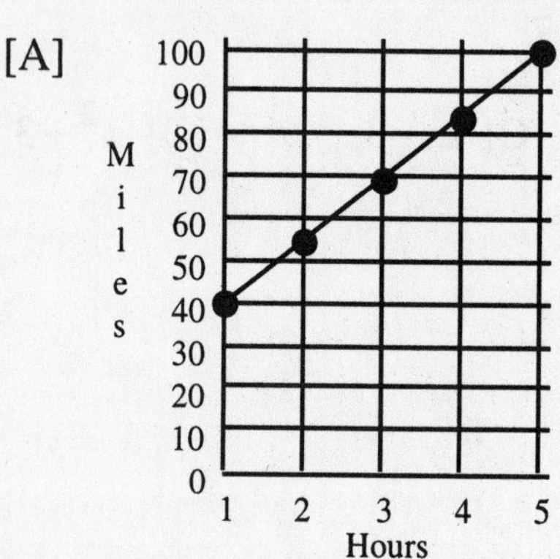

[B]

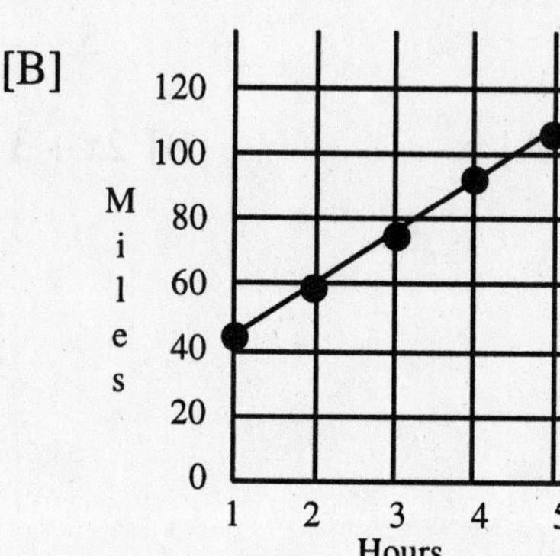

[C]

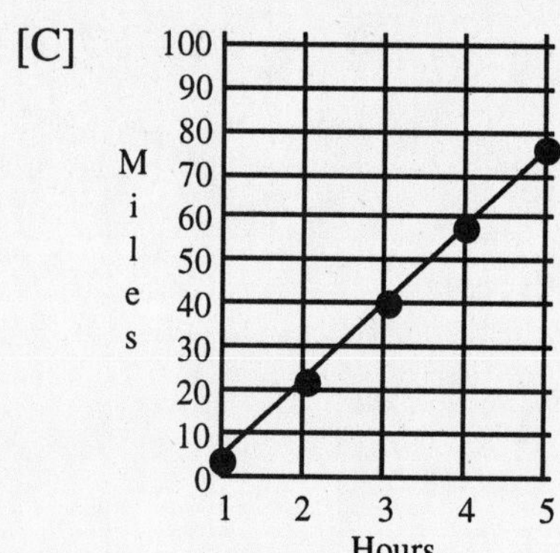

[D]

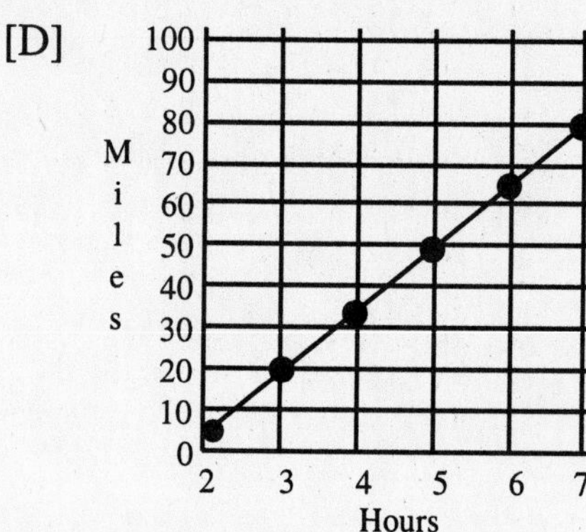

CHAPTER 10

80. a. How is the location of point Q determined?
b. Copy the graph shown below. Plot the point (2, 9).
c. Plot the following points on the same graph: (1, 4.5), (3, 13.5). Draw a line through the points on your graph. Are the points collinear or noncollinear?

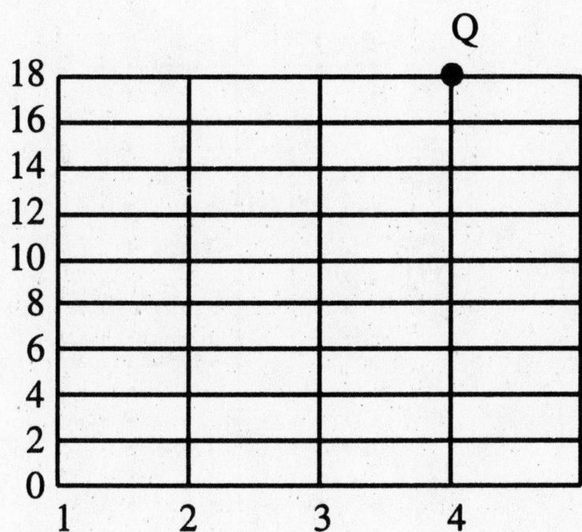

81. a. Copy and complete the table shown below.
b. Graph the data.

1	2
2	5
3	10
4	17
5	?

82. Venus is the closest planet to Earth. It passes between the Earth and the Sun every 584 days. Following each pass between the Earth and the Sun, Venus rotates 5 times on its axis. Create a spreadsheet and then a graph to show how many times Venus rotates on its axis for 1 – 5 passes between the Earth and the Sun.

83. Did you know that most people blink their eyes 25 times in one minute? Create a spreadsheet and a graph using five points to show how many times a person blinks their eyes.

Lesson 10-7 Objective 1: Use a coordinate plane to graph points.

Dynamic Item

84. Which of the following is the graph of the point $C(-2, -4)$?

[A] 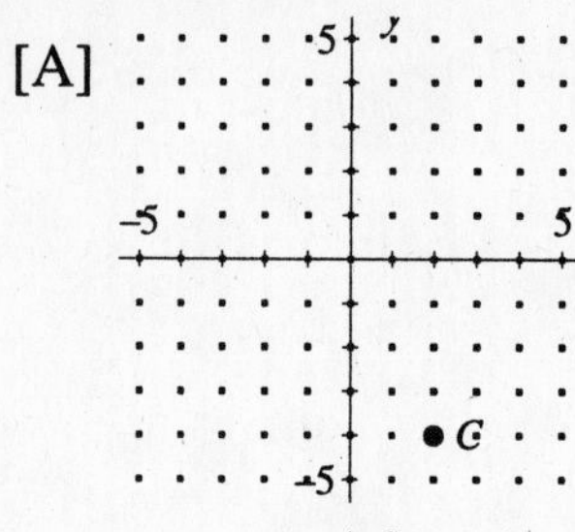

[B] 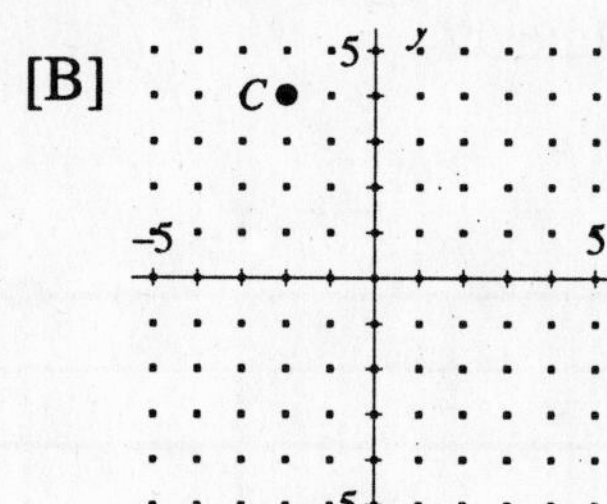

[C] 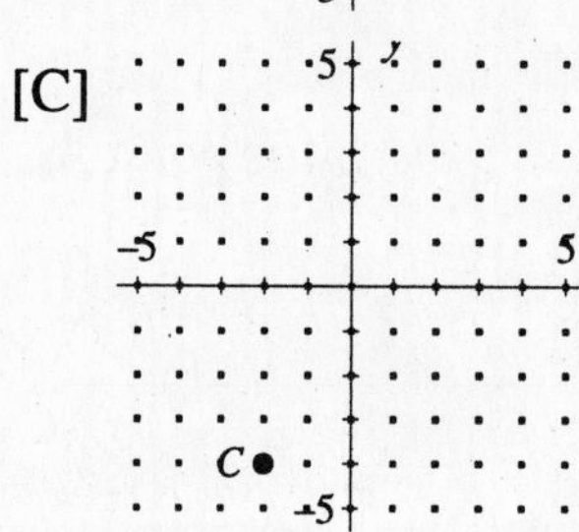

[D] 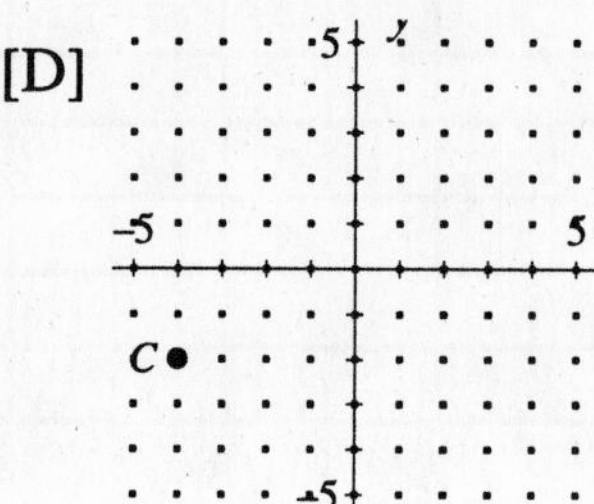

Dynamic Item

85. Graph the point $C(-2, 1)$.

86. Is the point with coordinates (–2, –4) the same point as the point with coordinates (–4, –2)? Explain.

87. Robert was explaining to Thomas how to graph the point (–2, 4) on a coordinate plane. He told Thomas to start at -2 and move two units to the left. Then move 4 units up from the *x*-axis. Do you agree with Robert's explanation? Explain.

88. Which of the following points can be found in the third quadrant?

[A] $T(6, -2)$ [B] $W(-6, -2)$ [C] $D(-6, 0)$ [D] $R(0, -6)$

89. Which of the following sets of ordered pairs are not coordinates of the vertices of an isosceles triangle?

[A] (–3, –3), (0, 0), (2, –3) [B] (–4, 5), (–4, 0), (0, 0)

[C] (5, –4), (1, 2), (6, –4) [D] (3, 6), (2, 2), (4, 2)

90. Graph a square on a coordinate plane so that it has a line of symmetry through (1, 2) and (4, 2).

91. Three vertices of a rectangle have coordinates (–1, 2), (5, 2), and (–1, 6). What are the coordinates of the fourth vertex?

Lesson 10-7 Objective 2: Name the coordinate points and the quadrants of the coordinate plane.

Dynamic Item

92. In which quadrant is the point with coordinates (–7, 3)?

[A] fourth quadrant [B] first quadrant

[C] second quadrant [D] third quadrant

Dynamic Item

93. What are the coordinates of point *A*? In which quadrant is point *A* located?

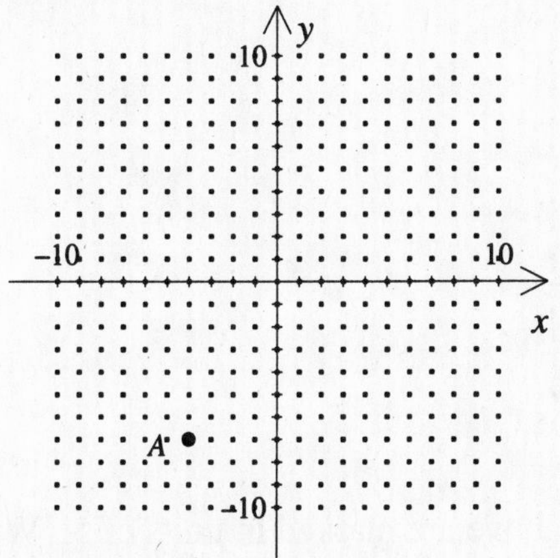

94. Name the coordinates of the point which is three units to the left of the *y*-axis and down 5 units from the *x*-axis.

95. Name the coordinates of four points in the coordinate plane that are 4 units from the origin.

96. Graph the coordinates for each figure. Are the figures similar? Congruent?

Figure 1: *A*(2, 1), *B*(3, 2), *C*(6, 2), *D*(7, 1)
Figure 2: *E*(2, 5), *F*(3, 4), *G*(6, 4), *H*(7, 5)

97. Graph and connect the points for the figure described by the ordered pairs. Name the figure. *R*(1, 1), *S*(–2, 2), *T*(–3, –2), *U*(–3, 0), *W*(–1, 0)

CHAPTER 10

98.

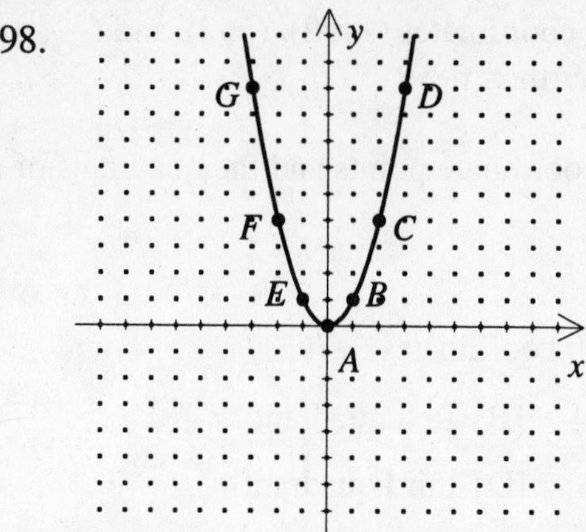

Suppose the axes of the graph above are marked in units of one. Write the coordinates of each point.

99.

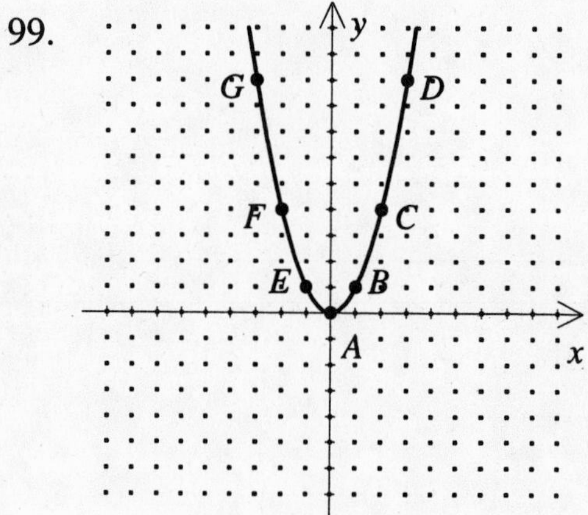

Suppose the axes of the graph above are marked in units of 5. Write the coordinates of each point.

Lesson 10-8 Objective 1: Find profit and loss.

100. Explain what we mean by the words income and expense.

101. You decide to buy a local business and you are interested in the Not Just Yogurt Shop. You meet with the owner and ask the following questions. Which of these questions is unnecessary if you ask the other three questions?

[A] Did the shop have a profit or a loss for the year?

[B] What were the monthly losses for the year?

[C] What were the monthly profits for the year?

[D] What is the amount that you want for the sale of your shop?

102. The table below shows the monthly income and expenses for The 123 Company for September through December. What is the total profit or loss over the four months for The 123 Company?

Income and Expenses for The 123 Company

Month	Income	Expense ($)	Profit / Loss ($)
September	$15,389	–9,785	
October	$12,500	–10,520	
November	$11,989	–10,980	
December	$9,862	–11,230	

[A] $7225 [B] $42,515 [C] $49,740 [D] –$7225

103. Make up a name of a company and a seasonal product that it produces. Create a table for the company that shows the monthly income, expenses, and balances for a year. Explain factors during the year that affected losses or profits.

	A	B	C	D
1	Week	Income	Expenses	Balances
2	1	$3289	–$1210	?
3	2	?	–$2980	$7935
4	3	$3692	–$2549	?
5	4	$4202	?	$3011
6	Totals:	?	?	?

104. Refer to the spreadsheet above. What formula would you enter in cells B3 and C5 to find each value?

105. Refer to the spreadsheet above. What formula would you enter in cells B7 and C7 if you wanted to find the average income and the average expenses for the month?

106. Copy and complete the spreadsheet above. Did the company show a profit or a loss for the month?

107. The table below shows the monthly income and expenses for The 123 Company for September through December. Make a line graph to display the monthly profit/loss. What conclusions can you make from the graph?

Income and Expenses for The 123 Company

Month	Income	Expense ($)	Profit / Loss ($)
September	$15,389	–9,785	5,604
October	$12,500	–10,520	1,980
November	$11,989	–10,980	1,009
December	$9,862	–11,230	–1,368

Profits and Losses for R. A. F. Company

Month	Balance (profit / loss)
January	$985
February	–$402
March	$350
April	–$1235
May	–$860
June	$0
July	$3250
August	$3900
September	–$1512
October	$966
November	$1525
December	$1683

108. The table above for R.A.F. Company shows the monthly balances for a year. Explain how you can find out whether the company had a profit or a loss at the end of the year.

109. The table above for R.A.F. Company shows the monthly balances for a year. In which month did the R.A.F. Company earn and spend the same amount of money?

Lesson 10-8 Objective 2: Draw and interpret graphs involving integers.

Profits and Losses for R. A. F. Company

Month	Balance (profit / loss)
January	$985
February	–$402
March	$350
April	–$1235
May	–$860
June	$0
July	$3250
August	$3900
September	–$1512
October	$966
November	$1525
December	$1683

110. Use the table above. Draw a line graph of the monthly balances for the R.A.F. Company. Can you think of some reasons why the R.A.F. Company's profits or losses fluctuated from one month to another? Make up a story that traces the financial condition of the company during the year.

111. Use the table above. The owner of the R.A.F. Company wanted to find the range of the balances for the year. What is the range of the balances?

CHAPTER 10

Chapter 11: Exploring Probability

Lesson 11-1 Objective 1: Find experimental probability.

Dynamic Item

1. A number cube is rolled 340 times and the results recorded as follows: there were 53 ones, 58 twos, 47 threes, 56 fours, 55 fives, and 71 sixes. What is the experimental probability of rolling a two or a three?

   [A] 0.69 [B] 0.59 [C] 0.31 [D] 0.41

Dynamic Item

2. In your last 35 basketball games, you attempted 140 free throws and made 70. What is the experimental probability of you making a free throw in your next game?

3. Can you play a fair game using the spinner below? Explain why or why not. Give an example to back your response.

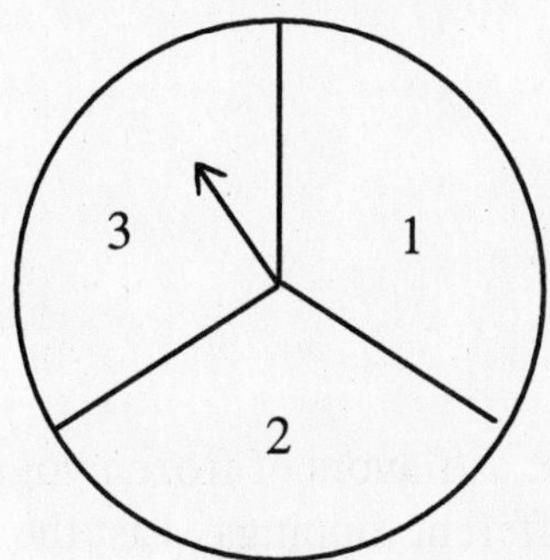

4. Tasha and Lee played a series of games against each other. Tasha won three more than twice as many games as Lee. Lee won 15 games. Find the Probability(Tasha wins).

   [A] $\frac{33}{48}$ [B] $\frac{15}{48}$ [C] $\frac{2}{15}$ [D] $\frac{15}{33}$

5. Suppose you put 2 baseballs, 2 blocks, and 2 rolls of breath mints inside a bag. You reach inside the bag and choose an object. Is it equally likely that you will pick a baseball or a block? Explain.

6. Patrick says that the probability of rolling a 7 on a number cube is $\frac{1}{6}$, since each number is equally likely to occur. Danny says that the probability of rolling a 7 is 0. Who do you agree with? Explain your reasoning.

7. Kate said to Liam, "If you roll a 5 on a number cube, you win. If I get a head on a coin toss, I win." Is the game fair or unfair? Explain.

CHAPTER 11

Lesson 11-1 Objective 2: Find possible outcomes.

Dynamic Item

8. 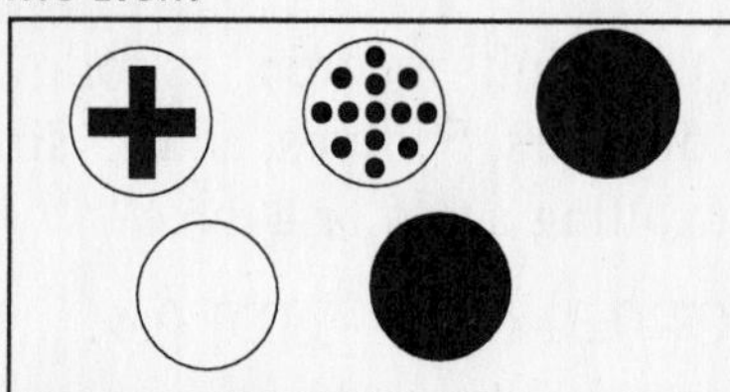

The box contains 5 counters. They are the same size and shape but have different patterns. Which is a possible outcome if 3 counters are selected from the box at one time?

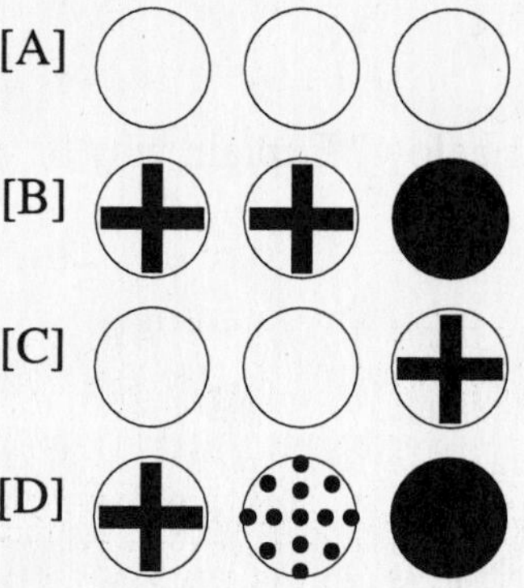

Dynamic Item

9. A yogurt shop offers vanilla and peppermint as flavors of frozen yogurt and caramel, strawberries, and pecans as different toppings. List the possible choices for a single serving of frozen yogurt with one topping.

10. Marcus said to Angela "Let's play a game. If I toss two number cubes and the product is even, I win. If the product is odd, you win." Is the game fair? Explain.

11. When is a game fair and when is it unfair? Give an example of each.

12. Describe a game using two different objects where the outcomes are equally likely.

13. Ruth tosses a number cube. Find the number of possible outcomes for getting an odd number or a number greater than 3.

[A] 6 [B] 3 [C] 5 [D] 1

14. The numbers 1 - 9 are written on index cards and placed face down on a table. If an odd number is turned over you receive one point. If an even number is turned over you receive two points. The first person to reach 10 points wins. Write a rule to make the game fair.

15. Marta has a bag filled with 5 red, 7 green, and 4 blue marbles. List the possible outcomes for drawing two marbles.

Lesson 11-2 Objective: Solve problems by simulation.

16. Thirty people attended the class play. During intermission the cast gave out door prizes. Each person counted off by ones beginning with number one. Each person who counted a multiple of 2 stood up and received a school banner. Then the people who were still seated counted by ones again. Each person who counted a multiple of two stood up and received a school calendar. This process was repeated one more time to give out football tickets. How many people were seated after the third counting?

    [A] 7 [B] 8 [C] 4 [D] 2

17. Albert has five coins in his pocket. The coins are dimes and nickels. How many possible coin combinations can Albert have in his pocket?

    [A] 6 [B] 10 [C] 8 [D] 4

18. Anthony, Tom, Anne, Carol, Earl and Martin are seated in this order around a circular table. Each seat is spaced evenly apart. Who is seated directly across from Earl?

19. The volleyball team practices every day after school at 3:30. The team has divided themselves into four groups of five. Each player in a group passes the ball once to everyone else. How many passes are made in each group? in all the groups together?

20. Write all the possible numbers that can be formed using the numbers 1, 2, and 3. Do not repeat numbers. Which numbers are divisible by 4?

21. Arrange the numbered squares below into 3 columns so that the sum of each column is the same. What is the sum of each column?

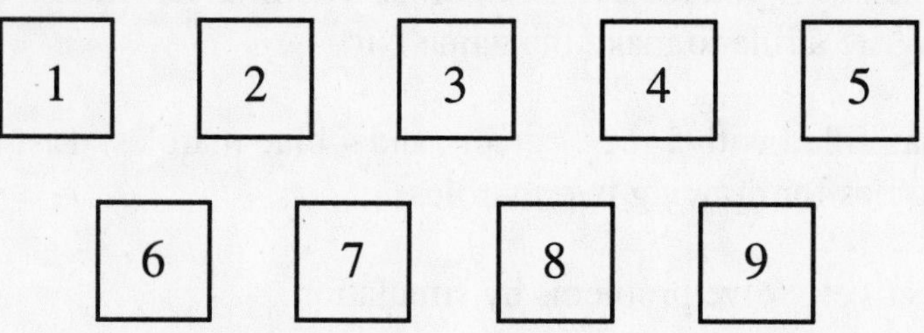

22. Jake has six colored markers. He uses three different colored markers to draw a picture. What are the possible color combinations Jake can use for his drawing?

23. Gary forgot his bicycle lock combination. He knows it is a 3-digit number and none of the numbers are the same. He also remembers that the product of the digits is 80 and the sum of the digits is 15. What numbers should he try? How many possible numbers might he have to try?

24. Frank was thinking of a number. He multiplied it by 2 and then added 5 to the product. He multiplied the result by 5 to get 235. What number was Frank thinking of?

25. Move two consecutive coins at one time. For example, move coins 2 and 3 or 3 and 4 below. How many moves will it take to arrange the coins so that the order is 1, 3, 5, 4, 2?

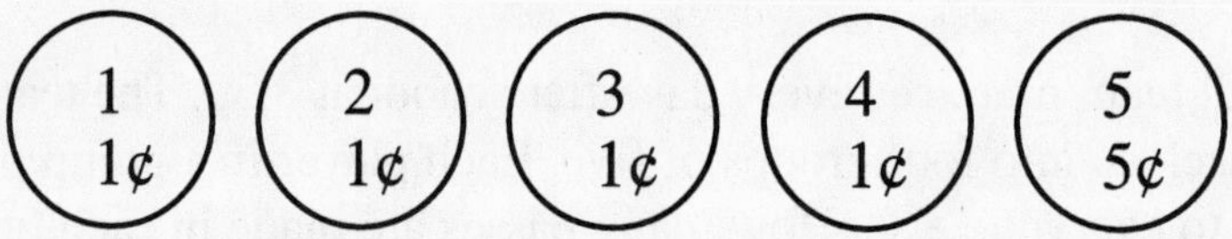

Lesson 11-3 Objective: Use random numbers to simulate probability problems.

Dynamic Item

26. In a list of random 1s and 2s, the digit 1 represents a coin toss landing heads. What series of digits would represent the coin tosses tails, heads, heads, heads?

[A] 1112 [B] 2221 [C] 1222 [D] 2111

Dynamic Item

27. You have a computer-generated list of random digits 0 - 9. What is the probability that you will see a 0 in the first space?

    List of Random Digits 0 - 9
    6 1 9 8 6 2 3 0 4 7 2 8 2 2 7 0 1
    3 6 3 9 3 9 0 2 6 5 8 3 1 0 8 8 6
    8 4 2 9 7 5 0 1 8 2 3 9 5 4 7 0 6

28. Suppose you toss three coins. What is the probability that all three coins will land on tails? Describe how this problem can be simulated using random digits.

29. How can a computer be used to explore experimental probability?

30. Write a problem using the random list of numbers below generated from a computer program.

    1 3 1 1 2 1 2 2 3 3
    1 1 2 2 2 2 3 1 1 3
    3 3 1 2 3 2 1 3 3 2

31. Ten Sing-A-Long videos are given out at random to charity donors. For every $20 ticket you purchase you receive a Sing-A-Long video . How many tickets would you have to purchase to obtain all ten videos? Describe how this problem can be simulated using random digits.

32. You use a computer to list 600,000 random digits from 5-9. About how many times will the number 8 be listed?

33. A box contains one red cube, one blue cube, one orange cube and one yellow cube. Ten cubes are drawn from the box, one at a time. Describe how this experiment can be simulated using a computer. Then simulate the experiment.

34. Suppose a factory produces steel. On a production line, $\frac{1}{10}$ of the steel pieces are light weight, $\frac{7}{10}$ of the steel pieces are medium weight, and $\frac{2}{10}$ are heavy weight. Describe how a computer can be used to simulate a random sample of 30 pieces of steel.

35. Marsha programmed a computer to list 4's and 5's. It lists three 4's in a row. Is the program more likely to list a 4 or a 5 next?

36. When you toss two dice, how likely is it that the sum will be odd? To simulate this problem use the list below. Make a table showing the number of odd sums, the number of times the dice were tossed, and the probability of an odd sum.
5, 3, 11, 2, 7, 9, 8, 4, 10, 5
6, 11, 12, 6, 5, 3, 7, 2, 8, 3
4, 5, 8, 10, 7, 11, 9, 9, 12, 3
6, 11, 2, 5, 8, 10

37. The numbers 1-6 are written on index cards and placed in a box. A card is drawn and then put back in the box. How would you use a computer program to finding the experimental probability of drawing the same card twice?

38. Adam took a true/false test. He did not feel well the night before and could not study. Adam did not know the answers to any of the ten questions. What is the probability that he will get 7 out of 10 questions correct by guessing randomly? Model this situation using random digits.

Lesson 11-4 Objective 1: Find the theoretical probability of an event.

Dynamic Item

39. A number cube is tossed. Find the probability of obtaining a number greater than 1.

[A] $\frac{1}{2}$ [B] $\frac{5}{6}$ [C] 1 [D] $\frac{1}{6}$

Dynamic Item

40. A bag contains 5 red, 6 white, and 7 blue marbles. Find the probability of obtaining a blue marble in a single draw.

41. Explain how to find the probability of an event.

42. Explain what you must know about the outcomes of an experiment before you can find the probability of a certain event.

43. Make up three different examples of situations which have a probability of $\frac{2}{3}$.

44. Donato's little brother Joseph is too small to see inside his sock drawer. Joseph has 2 pairs of white socks, 4 pairs of black socks, and 1 pair of blue socks inside his drawer. If the socks are not paired together, what is the probability that Joseph will reach inside his drawer and pick a black sock?

[A] $\frac{3}{7}$ [B] $\frac{2}{7}$ [C] $\frac{4}{7}$ [D] $\frac{6}{7}$

45. Refer to the Venn diagram below. What is the probability that a student plays football or baseball?

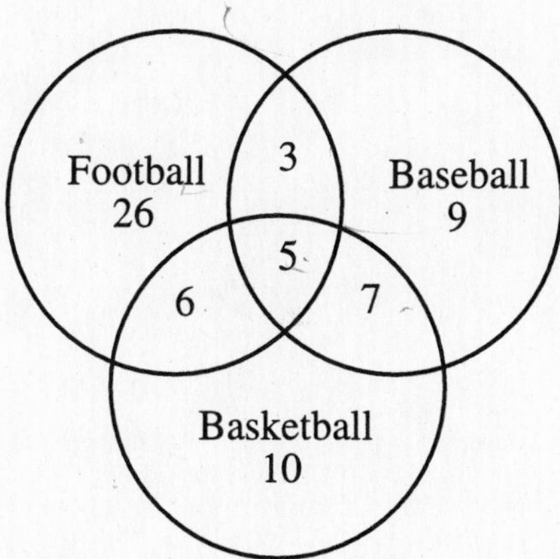

[A] $\frac{3}{5}$ [B] $\frac{7}{10}$ [C] $\frac{7}{16}$ [D] $\frac{28}{33}$

46. An octahedron is an eight sided number cube. The number cube has eight faces that are equilateral triangles. Each face is numbered 1, 2, 3, or 4. Probability of (1) = Probability of (2) = Probability of (3) = Probability of (4). How many faces are numbered 3?

47. During a tennis practice, Harriet was working on her first serve. She made 19 out of 57 tries. What is the probability she will make her first serve in the upcoming match? Express you answer as a decimal.

48. Ty conducted a poll on favorite ice cream flavors. He surveyed 100 people. Eighty-two people like chocolate and 62 like vanilla. What is the probability that a person likes both?

49. Refer to the Venn diagram below. If three more people who play football are added to the survey, what is the new probability that a student plays football?

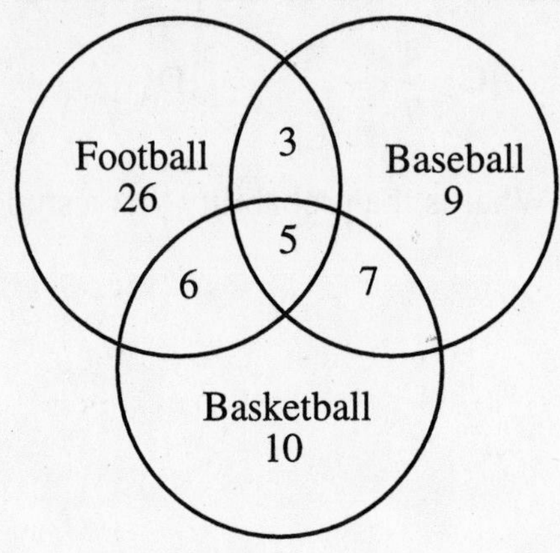

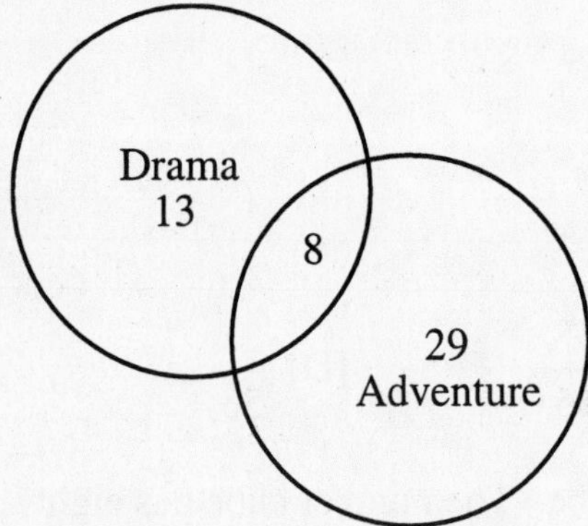

50. Refer to the Venn diagram above. Hedi surveyed her class to see which type of book students enjoy reading: drama or adventure. Find the probability that a student enjoys reading drama.

51. Refer to the Venn diagram above. Find the probability that a student enjoys reading only adventure.

Lesson 11-4 Objective 2: Define types of events.

52. Estimate the probability that each of these events will occur.
a. There is no school on July 4.
b. Your birthday will fall on a weekday.
c. You will become the president of the United States.
d. A friend will roll a number cube twice and get the same number.
e. The temperature in Laredo, Texas is below freezing on August 18.

Lesson 11-5 Objective 1: Use tree diagrams to find possible outcomes and probabilities.

Dynamic Item

53. Elaine went to the mall to buy a shirt for a friend. Her choices for the shirt are striped and plaid. Both of the choices come in purple, blue, and green. Draw a tree diagram that represents her choices.

Dynamic Item

54. At Larry's Pizza Parlor you have a choice of a small or a large pizza and olives is the only topping available. Use a tree diagram to show how many different pizzas are possible.

55. What is a tree diagram and how can a tree diagram be used to find the probability of an event?

56. Describe a problem that can be solved using the tree diagram below.

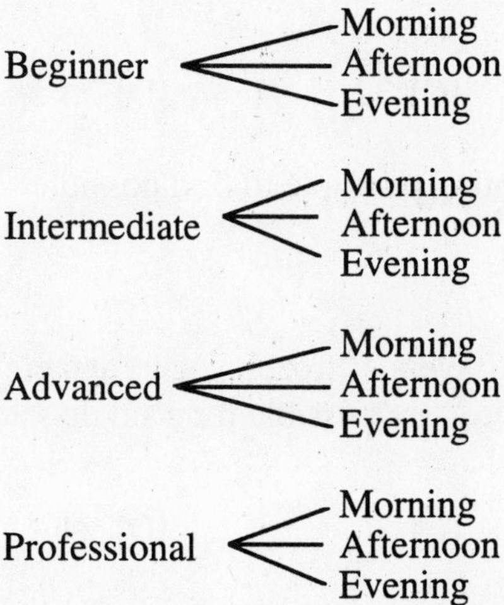

57. Coach Horack creates a roster before each softball game. He has four possible pitchers, three possible catchers, and two possible players for each of the other seven positions. How many different rosters can the coach possibly make?

[A] $4+3+2+2+2+2+2+2+2=21$

[B] $4\times3\times2\times2\times2\times2\times2\times2\times2=1{,}536$

[C] $4+3+2=9$ [D] $4\times3\times2=24$

CHAPTER 11

58. The Osaka Restaurant offers a dinner special on Wednesday for $12.00. The special includes a choice of a main dish, an appetizer, and sushi. The choices are listed in the table below. How many different dinner combinations does the Wednesday night special give customers?

Osaka Restaurant
Wednesday Dinner Special

Appetizer:	Miso Soup Salad
Main Dish:	Negimaki Sukiyaki Tempura Katsu
Sushi:	Saki Ika Ebi Hamachi

[A] 8 [B] 10 [C] 32 [D] 24

Lesson 11-5 Objective 2: Use the counting principle to find possible outcomes and probabilities.

Dynamic Item

59. A yogurt shop offers four different flavors of frozen yogurt and eight different toppings. How many choices are possible for a single serving of frozen yogurt with one topping?

[A] 32 [B] 12 [C] 36 [D] 24

Dynamic Item

60. A lunch menu consists of 5 different kinds of sandwiches, 2 different kinds of soup, and 4 different drinks. How many choices are there for ordering a sandwich, a bowl of soup, and a drink?

61. Describe the counting principle in your own words.

62. Ms. Rose wrote the name of four books on the chalkboard. She told her class that each student is to read any one of the books and then write a report, give an oral summary, or make a poster about the book. How many combinations of books and projects might Ms. Rose receive?

63. On Friday nights the local diner serves three main entrees, each with a choice of vegetable. The entrees are beef, chicken, and fish and the vegetables are spinach, broccoli, and carrots. How many possible dinner combinations does the diner serve? List them.

64. Amanda's class is taking a trip to the Science Museum. There will not be enough time to see everything. Each student must first choose one of four interactive exhibits to see, then one of three films, and finally one of two guided tours. How many possible combinations might students choose from? List three combinations.

65. Raven is deciding how to decorate her room. Her available choices are shown in the chart below. Assuming that both types of wallpaper go with all the colors of paint and that all combinations of paint and wallpaper are equally likely to be selected, what is the probability that Raven will choose floral wallpaper? What is the probability of choosing purple paint with floral wallpaper?

Paint	Wallpaper
yellow	striped
pink	floral
cream	
purple	
blue	
gray	

66. Tamara likes to mix and match her 4 scarves, 3 pairs of gloves, and 2 hats. The colors are described in the table below. On Monday, she randomly grabs a scarf, hat, and a pair of gloves. What is the probability of Tamara choosing a red hat and black gloves?

Scarves	Gloves	Hats
red	black	white
white	brown	red
brown	red	
black		

67. Richelle is in charge of fundraising for a charity. She must organize several fundraising events throughout the year and encourage volunteers to run the events. This year she has planned an event for each season. Use the table below. How many possible combinations of events are there? Explain whether you think it would be easier for Richelle to use a tree diagram or the counting principle to find all the possible combinations.

Summer	Fall	Winter	Spring
car wash	walk - a - thon	book sale	can drive
bake sale	dance - a - thon	craft fair	carnival
auction	music show	wrapping paper sale	
telethon		donation drive	

68. The tables below show the busiest airports, shipping ports, and rapid rail systems in the United States. Suppose you are doing a report in which you have to research one entry from each table. You have no preference for any choices over any other choices. What is the probability that you would select Chicago O'Hare Intl. Airport, the port of Houston, TX, and the Metro Boston TA?

Busiest Airports
1. Chicago O' Hare Intl.
2. Dallas / Ft. Worth Intl.
3. Los Angeles Intl.
4. Hartsfield Atlanta Intl.
5. J.F. Kennedy Intl., NY

Busiest Shipping Ports
1. New Orleans, LA
2. New York, NY
3. Houston, TX

Busiest Rapid Rail Systems
1. New York City TA
2. Washington Metro Area TA
3. Chicago TA
4. Metro Boston TA

Source: The Universal Almanac, (c) 1992

Lesson 11-6 Objective 1: Identify independent events.

Dynamic Item

69. Which events are independent?

[A] You draw 2 colored cards at the same time and get one red and one green.

[B] You draw a card from a deck, replace it and draw a second.

[C] You draw a card and don't replace it. Then you draw another.

[D] You swim 10 laps in 15 min today and do the same tomorrow.

Dynamic Item

70. Are the following events independent?
You draw a red card from a deck with an equal number of red and blue cards and, before replacing it, draw another red card.

71. Explain what it means for two events to be independent.

72. Determine whether each of the following pairs of events are independent. If not, explain why not.

a. The names of all the people at a party are put into a hat for a raffle. The first name picked wins the grand prize and is not eligible for any other prizes. The second name picked wins the runner-up prize.
b. There are ten rubber balls in a bin. Each ball is a different color. Loni is the first to take a ball and selects a blue one. Erica is the second to take a ball and selects a red one.
c. It has been sunny and clear for the last two Sundays. The forecast for next Sunday is sunshine.
d. Jordan stayed up late last night watching television. Jordan did poorly on his quiz this morning.
e. Carlos tosses a coin that comes up heads. Jennifer tosses a coin that also comes up heads.

Lesson 11-6 Objective 2: Use multiplication to find probabilities of independent events.

Dynamic Item

73. Two urns each contain black balls and blue balls. Urn I contains 2 black balls and 3 blue balls and Urn II contains 3 black balls and 4 blue balls. A ball is drawn from each urn. What is the probability that both balls are blue?

[A] $\frac{1}{5}$ [B] $\frac{6}{35}$ [C] $\frac{12}{35}$ [D] $\frac{1}{7}$

Dynamic Item

74. A coin is tossed and a number cube is rolled. What is the probability that the coin shows tails and the number cube shows 4?

[A] $\frac{1}{12}$ [B] $\frac{1}{6}$ [C] $\frac{1}{4}$ [D] $\frac{2}{3}$

75. Sandra rolls a 5 on a number cube. When she rolls it a second time she rolls another 5. Find the probability of this happening by using two different methods. Explain why both methods work.

76. Mrs. Burns entered her name in two separate contests at a club dinner. Twenty people entered the first contest. The probability that she would win both contests was $\frac{1}{300}$. How many people entered the second contest?

[A] 15 [B] 280 [C] 600 [D] 150

77. Elijah and Angelina are playing a game that has two piles of cards. Each of the 12 cards in one pile lists one month of the year. Each of the 7 cards in the other pile lists a day of the week. On each person's turn, the player randomly chooses one card from each pile. What is the probability of choosing a card with a month beginning with the letter J and a card with a day beginning with the letter T?

[A] $\frac{1}{14}$ [B] $\frac{1}{84}$ [C] $\frac{3}{42}$ [D] $\frac{1}{42}$

78. Danny and Jorge are choosing who will go first in a game. They will decide by each holding out either one or two fingers at exactly the same time. If the number of fingers held out is even, Danny will go first and if it is odd, Jorge will go first. What is the probability that Danny will hold out one finger and Jorge will hold out two fingers?

79. Jan's mother bought snacks and drinks for the basketball team. In one box she put 4 apples, 3 oranges, a peach, and a grapefruit. In another box she put 2 containers of apple juice, 4 containers of water, 2 containers of orange juice, and one container of cranberry juice. The first girl chooses randomly. What is the probability that she will choose an orange and cranberry juice?

80. Mr. Duncan put the following in each of two boxes: 2 blue erasers, 3 red erasers, and 5 white erasers. One eraser is picked randomly from each box. What is the probability of choosing:
a. 1 blue and 1 red eraser?
b. 1 red and 1 white eraser?
c. 2 blue erasers?

81. Ted has 4 baseball hats and 2 jackets. Use the table below. If he chooses randomly, what is the probability that he will choose a white jacket and green hat?

Hats	Jackets
blue	white
black	blue
red	
green	

82. Susie is holding two bunches of flowers. In one hand, she has four pink and six blue daisies and in the other hand she has two pink and eight blue daisies. She asks Jill to close her eyes and choose one flower from each bunch. What is the probability that Jill picks two blue daisies?

83. The lists below show the 10 most popular spectator sports and the five most popular participation sports. One sport is chosen randomly from each list. What is the probability of choosing hockey and swimming?

Most Popular Spectator Sports	Most Popular Participation Sports
Baseball	
Thoroughbred racing	Swimming
Greyhound racing	Exercise walking
Harness racing	Bicycle riding
Basketball	Fishing
Football	Camping
Hockey	
Auto racing	
Tennis	
Boxing	

84. The charts below show nine of the tallest buildings in the world and six of the tallest mountains in the world. One entry is picked randomly from each list. What is the probability of choosing a building and a mountain that are both located in the United States?

Tall Buildings		
1.	Sears Tower	Chicago
2.	World Trade Center, North	New York
3.	World Trade Center, South	New York
4.	Empire State	New York
5.	Central Plaza	Hong Kong
6.	Bank of China Tower	Hong Kong
7.	Amoco	Chicago
8.	John Hancock	Chicago
9.	Chrysler Building	New York

Tall Mountains		
1.	Everest	China
2.	Mana	India
3.	Cachi	Argentina
4.	McKinley	US
5.	Ampato	Peru
6.	Paleromo	Argentina

Source: The Universal Almanac (c) 1992

Lesson 11-7 Objective 1: Use a tree diagram or a list to find number of arrangements.

85. The Medeiros family wanted to display the school pictures of their three children on the wall of their living room. They want to hang the pictures horizontally in a row. Explain how to determine the number of possible arrangements.

CHAPTER 11

86. Write a problem that can be solved using the tree diagram below. Explain how you can solve the problem another way.

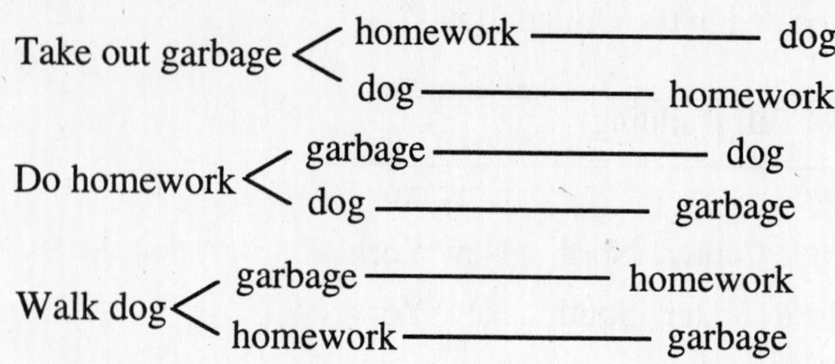

87. Jimmy invited 15 friends to a party. All of his guests arrived separately. Explain which method is the easiest to use to determine the number of possible orders in which his guests can arrive. Why?

88. Predict how many possible arrangements there are for the numbers 3, 4, 5. Then make an organized list showing them.

Lesson 11-7 Objective 2: Use the counting principle to find number of arrangements.

Dynamic Item

89. How many different arrangements can be made with the letters in the word TOPIC?

[A] 25 [B] 10 [C] 20 [D] 120

Dynamic Item

90. How many different ways can you arrange five people shoulder-to-shoulder in a line?

91. Five animals are being adopted from an animal shelter. The new owners can pick up their pets the next day. In how many different orders can five animals leave the shelter?

[A] 5 [B] 120 [C] 24 [D] 6

92. There are 6 different magazines in a waiting room. Virgil flips through each of them in random order. In how many different orders can he select the magazines?

[A] 120 [B] 720 [C] 6 [D] 12

93. Mrs. Melon's drama class is putting on a talent show. There are 5 acts in the show. The acts appear in random order. In how many different ways can Mrs. Melon arrange the order of the acts?

94. There are 8 horses in a race. In how many different orders can the horses finish the race?

95. Joyce's family is having a family photograph taken. The four children will sit shoulder-to-shoulder on the floor in front of their parents. In how many different arrangements can the children sit?

96. Shana is arranging 6 compact disks on a shelf. She places them randomly. How many different arrangements are possible?

97. Below are listed 8 of the most popular theme and amusement parks. How many more arrangements of the list are possible?
Walt Disney World
Disneyland
Knott's Berry Farm
Universal Studios
Sea World
Kings Island
Six Flags Magic Mountain
Busch Gardens

98. Mei-Ling has the information about deserts shown in the chart below. She has given only the names of the deserts to her friend and has asked her friend to guess the size order of the deserts. Her friend makes every possible incorrect guess before getting the answer. How many incorrect guesses were made?

Desert	sq km	Location
Sahara	9,065,000	N. Africa
Gobi	1,295,000	Mongolia
Kalahar	582,800	S. Africa
Chihuahuan	362,000	United States

Source: The Universal Almanac (c) 1992

CHAPTER 11

Lesson 11-8 Objective 1: Identify samples from a given population.

99. In order to make accurate predictions, a sample must be representative of a whole population. Explain in your own words what this statement means. Be sure to define the terms sample and population.

100. Explain whether or not each sample described is random and/or representative of the population.

a. To find the average age of drivers in a particular city, all the names of people with driver's licenses are put into a file. One hundred names are picked from the file as the sample.
b. To find the average income of an adult in the United States, 250 workers in Tennessee are questioned.
c. To find the average number of shoppers in a particular store, shoppers are counted on two consecutive Saturday mornings.

101. About 46 percent of the atmosphere is made up of oxygen molecules. You sample 100 random molecules of atmosphere. How many do you think will be oxygen molecules? What is the size of the sample?

Lesson 11-8 Objective 2: Make predictions about a population based on a sample.

Dynamic Item

102. In a random sample of 400 customers at a fast food restaurant, it was determined that 124 customers ordered a salad. If the restaurant typically has 1000 customers in a day, how many of these customers will probably order a salad?

[A] 4960 [B] 344 [C] 250 [D] 310

Dynamic Item

103. In a random sample of 300 customers at a fast-food restaurant, it was determined that 114 customers ordered a salad. If the restaurant typically has 1000 customers in a day, how many of these customers will probably order a salad?

104. A new movie opened the other day. So far, 500,000 people have seen it. The producers of the movie need to know if the people liked it. They ask 5,000 people who saw the movie at random and 3,500 enjoyed the movie. Predict the total number of people that enjoyed the movie.

[A] 175,000 [B] 350,000 [C] 14,300 [D] 33,300

105. A survey showed that 56% of car owners prefer four-door cars, 31% prefer two-door cars, and 13% have no preference. You ask 500 people. How many do you think will prefer four-door cars?

[A] 44 [B] 444 [C] 56 [D] 280

106. Twenty-five percent of the population have pets. What is the probability that the next person you speak with will have a pet? (Source: Roper Reports)

107. Out of 600 students, 150 eat hot cereal each morning. There are 4,800 students in Fun Valley. Estimate how many students you think eat hot cereal each morning.

108. Marisa is researching information about martial artists. She found that 6 out of 10 martial artists practice every day. There are 100 martial artists at a school. Predict how many practice every day. What is the sample size?

109. Jenna took a survey to find out how many sixth graders know what they would like to do when they get older. The results are shown in the table below. You ask 250 sixth graders if they know what career they want to pursue. Predict how many would say yes and how many would say no. Will your prediction always hold true? Explain.

Know for sure	28%
Do not know	52%
Have an idea	20%

110. The owners of an amusement park have hired you to find out if visitors will return to their park. You find that 450,000 people visit the park during a given week. When you ask 1,000 people at random whether or not they will return, 750 say yes, 150 say no, and 100 say they are unsure. Organize the results of your survey into a chart. Summarize your findings and explain to the owners how you are able to predict the total number of visitors that plan to return to the park.

111. Mary works in a factory that produces 1,000 telephones each day. When 50 telephones were sampled, it was found that 2 were defective. Estimate how many telephones are defective each day.

112. A Nielsen survey in 1990 produced the following results.

Highest-Rated Network Television Series

Show	Rating
1. Roseanne	23.4
2. Cosby Show	23.1
3. Cheers	22.9
4. A Different World	21.1
5. America' s Funniest Home Videos	21
6. Golden Girls	20.1
7. 60 Minutes	19.7

The ratings are produced by following the viewing habits of 4,000 households. Each rating is the percent of all households that are believed to watch a given show. a. What is the total sample size? There are 35,000 households with television sets in a particular city. b. How many households in the particular city watched America's Funniest Home Videos?

Number of Digits	Frequency
1	1
2	3
3	3
4	3
5	2
6	1

[1]

[2] D

[3] Answers may vary. Sample: A frequency table is a list of data that shows the number of times each response or item occurs. A line plot is used to organize data. A line plot displays data on a horizontal line.

[4] Answers may vary. Sample: No. The range is the difference between the greatest value and the least value in a set of numerical data. Since the number of oranges is neither the greatest nor the least value in the set of data, the range would not be affected.

[5] D

[6] Answer may vary. Sample: The bookstore can use the information in the frequency table to determine which type of book sells the most. It can also help the bookstore keep track of inventory.

[7] a. e: 17; i: 16; o: 26; u: 0
b. The data show the number of times each vowel occurs in the word.

Year	Frequency
1989	𝍸
1990	||||
1991	𝍸 ||
1992	|||
1993	||

[8]

[9] C

range = 10

[10] 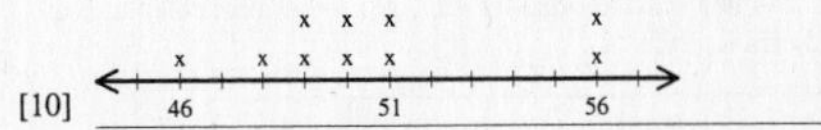

[11] C

[12] Answers may vary. Sample: How many more students were born on a Monday than a Friday?

[13] a. 12 or 58;. b. Answers may vary. Sample: Subtract 40 from the greatest number in the set of data (52 – 40 = 12). The range would then be 52 – 12 = 40. Or add 40 to the least number in writing in the set of data (40 + 18 = 58). The range would then be 58 – 18 = 40.

a.

Jan.	Feb.	March	April	May	June	July	Aug.	Sept.	Oct.	Nov.	Dec.
									x		
		x							x	x	
x	x	x	x						x	x	
x	x	x	x			x	x		x	x	x
x	x	x	x	x		x	x	x	x	x	x
x	x	x	x	x	x	x	x	x	x	x	x

[14] b. October

a.

Football	Soccer	Baseball	Basketball	Other
x				
x				
x		x		
x		x		
x		x		
x		x	x	
x		x	x	
x		x	x	
x		x	x	
x		x	x	
x	x	x	x	
x	x	x	x	
x	x	x	x	x
x	x	x	x	x

b. 7
c.No. The range is the difference between the greatest value and the least value of a set of numerical data. This set of data is not numerical, it is

[15] categorical.

[16] 7 claps

[17] B

[18] Nick

[19] 10

[20] A

[21] 64

[22] 6 sheets

[23] 25 paints; 32 paint brushes; 30 smocks

[24] Tony: $7.75; Jim: $10.75

[25] A

[26] 53

[27] mode; You can tell which items are the most common just by glancing at the table.

[28] Median. Extremes in height will affect the mean.

[29] Mode; The mode is most useful in determining the most frequent category.

[30] 7

[31] 3 in.

[32] C

[33] 60

[34] a. mean: $3\frac{1}{2}$; mode: 4
b. The mode, because it is the number that occurred most often.

[35] Answers may vary. Sample: If the number changed is greater than the original number, the mean will be larger. If the number changed is smaller than the original number then the mean will be smaller.

[36] The mean can be most affected since one very large or very small number can change the mean a great deal.

[37] A

[38] A

[39] B

[40] Answers may vary. Sample: The median family income is $28,500.

[41] B

[42] 1093

[43] a.(B5 + C5 + D5 + E5)/4 = 90
b. No. Hector's mean score will stay the same. His mean score will only decrease if he scores below 90 in game 5.

[44] Answers may vary. Sample: In row 1 enter the following: cell A1 Employee Number; cell B1 Employee Name; cell C1 Hourly Rate; cell D1 Hours Worked. Enter the given information under the appropriate heading.

Chapter 1: Using Statistics to Analyze Data

[45] Answers may vary. Sample: A computer spreadsheet is a table made on a computer. The data in a spreadsheet is organized in rows and columns. A spreadsheet can be useful to organize data and to perform calculations quickly and efficiently.

	A	B	C	D	E
1	Student	Test 1	Test 2	Test 3	Test 4
2	Mark F.	90	82	95	93
3	Julie A.	92	91	85	88
4	Dimi C.	87	84	91	90
5	Paul R.	95	73	84	88
6	Patel H.	86	87	88	91

[46] The spreadsheet is organized according to student test grades. It shows the four test results for five students.

[47] B

[48] D6 + C6

[49] B

[50] =(A2 + B2 + C2 + D2 + E2 + F2)/6

[51] cell C6: $8600; cell D6: $14,000; cell E6: $9,866.67

[52] 29° F

[53] a. the value in cell F5 will get larger;
b. the value in cell F5 will get smaller;
c. the value in cell F5 will stay the same since the formula in F5 does not contain the cell B2.

[54] B

[55] B

[56] No. A line graph shows change over a period of time. This data does not show a change over a period of time. A circle graph would be the most appropriate since the data show parts of a whole.

[57] D

Chapter 1: Using Statistics to Analyze Data

[58] Answers may vary. Sample: The line graph shows how the world population has changed over the years between 1840 and 1990. The world population slowly increased from 1840 to 1940 and has drastically increased from 1940-1990.

[59] Check students' work.

[60] 4 days

[61] $16 per hour

[62] a. Utah; b. Look for the most bars with the same height. In this case, NY and TX both scored approximately 95. No other score appeared twice.

[63] a. 25; b. Answers may vary. Sample: The team showed a steady improvement from 1990-1993.

[64] D

[65] 3

[66] The graphs are similar in that they both display data. A bar graph is used to compare amounts where a circle graph compares parts to a whole. In some cases data can be displayed either in a bar graph or circle graph depending on what information you want to be translated from the graph.

[67] A

[68] A circle graph does not show any indication of change over a period of time. A circle graph shows parts of a whole.

[69] $0.20

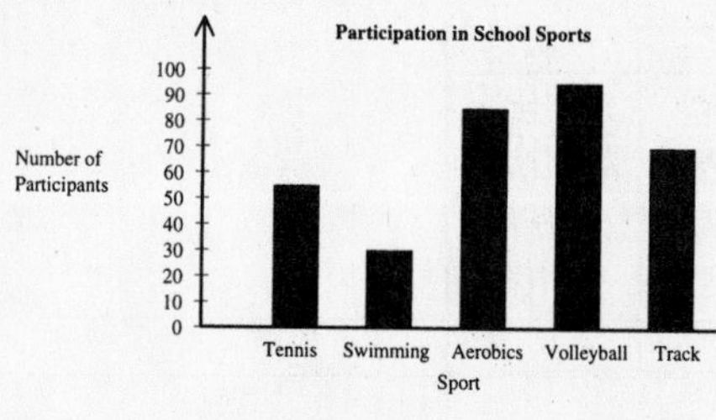

[70]

Chapter 1: Using Statistics to Analyze Data

[71] The bars in a bar graph represent the amount of each item in a set of data.

[72] The graph would have too many numbers on the scale which can make the graph difficult to read. A scale of 0–300 using intervals of 50 would be more appropriate.

[73] B

[74] B

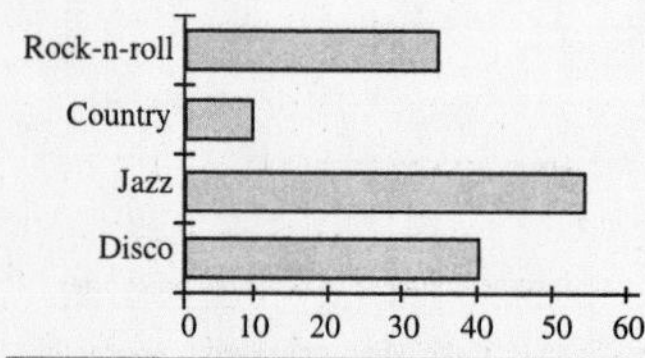

[75]

[76] Answers may vary slightly. The y-axis should be labeled from 0 to 12 at intervals of 2. There should be three bars of heights 11.8, 7, and 7, labeled mean, median, and mode, respectively.

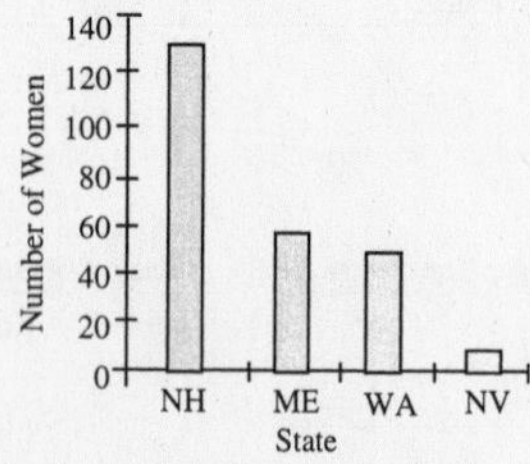

[77] average: 62 women

[78] C

Chapter 1: Using Statistics to Analyze Data

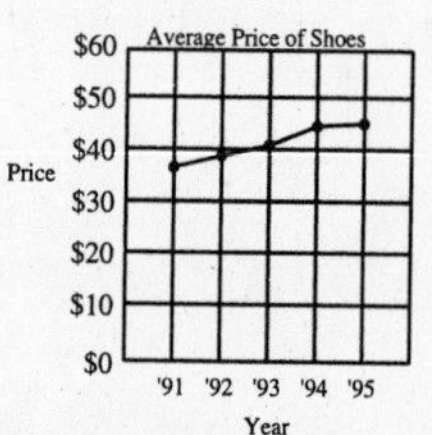

[79] greatest increase from 1992 to 1994

[80] Draw the horizontal and vertical axes. Determine the scale and the intervals for the vertical axis. Label the horizontal and vertical axes. Give the bar graph a title. Draw a bar to show each item in the set of data.

[81] Answers may vary. Sample: The data can be displayed in a line graph. First draw the horizontal and vertical axes. Then determine the scale and the interval to use on the vertical axis. The scale for this data can be $25,500 – $29,000 using intervals of $500. Finally, plot the data on the graph.

[82] The y-axis should be labeled from 0 to 30 at intervals of 5. The x-axis should be labeled with the years 1990 through 1993. Data points should be at (1990, 10), (1991, 30), (1992, 20), (1993, 10). A line connects the four points. Changing the scale and the interval on a graph does not affect the data. It only affects the appearance of the graph.

[83] The y-axis should be labeled 0 to 14 miles at 2-mile intervals. The x-axis should be labeled Mon. through Fri. Data points: (Mon., 5), (Tues., 13), (Wed., 0), (Thurs., 13), (Fri., 9). A line connects the five points. Marta averaged 8 mi each day.

[84] The second graph; the scale on the vertical axis distorts the relative heights of points on the graph.

[85] D

[86] Answers may vary. Sample: Draw a line graph with a scale of $60,000-$140,000 using intervals of 2000 on the vertical axis. Place the years on the horizontal axis very close together.

Chapter 1: Using Statistics to Analyze Data

[87] Graph II

To show a dramatic decrease in profit over the past four years, show a gap
on the vertical scale. Use a scale that begins with $60,000 using intervals
[88] of $5000. Space the items on the horizontal axis very close together.

The farther apart the data items are on the horizontal axis, the slower the
increase or decrease is shown in the data. Drastic increases or decreases
can be shown by placing the data items closer together on the horizontal
[89] axis.

The intervals of the scale on the vertical axis are unequal; the scale on the
[90] vertical axis shows a gap.

The first graph; the scale on the horizontal axis distorts the relative lengths
[91] of the bars on the graph.

Answers may vary. Sample: No; The price of a pair of jeans in 1993 is
[92] more than the price of a pair of jeans in 1990.

The graph is misleading because at first glance it looks as if the VCR
Instant View is twice as popular as the VCR Clear View. The graph is
[93] misleading because the vertical axis shows a gap in the scale.

Since graphs can be misleading, it is important to examine the scale on the
axes. Different scales and intervals can affect the appearance of a set of
data. A scale starting at zero will give a more accurate representation of
[94] the data as opposed to a scale with a gap.

[95] A

Answers may vary. Sample: Show a gap in the scale on the vertical axis.
[96] Have the scale begin with 10 instead of 0. Use intervals of 1 instead of 5.

Chapter 2: Patterns and Algebraic Thinking

[1] D

[2] 19, 16, 13

a.

b. 25
c. Answers may vary. Sample: The fifth triangle would have 1 triangle in
the 1st row, 3 triangles in the 2nd row, 5 triangles in the 3rd row, 7
triangles in the 4th row, 9 triangles in the 5th row, and 11 triangles in the
[3] 6th row.

[4] B

[5] C

Answers may vary. Sample:

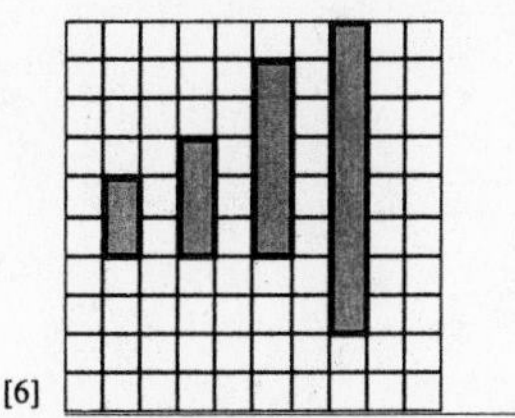

[6]

[7] 2, 5.5, 9, 12.5, 16

a. 0.21, 0.12, 0.03
[8] b. Each term in the number pattern is subtracted by 0.09.

Chapter 2: Patterns and Algebraic Thinking

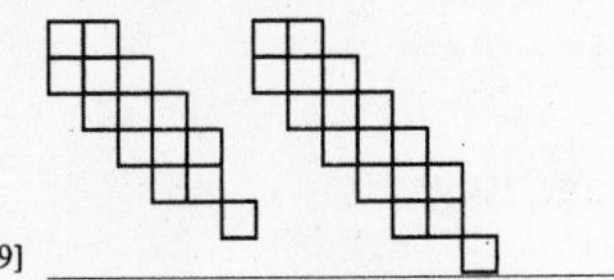

[9]

[10] ‡ooo, o‡, ‡ooo, oo‡, ‡ooo, ooo‡, ‡ooo

a. After 21 days the bamboo will be 63 ft high. After 28 days the bamboo
will be 84 ft high.
b. 90 ft
c. 30 ft

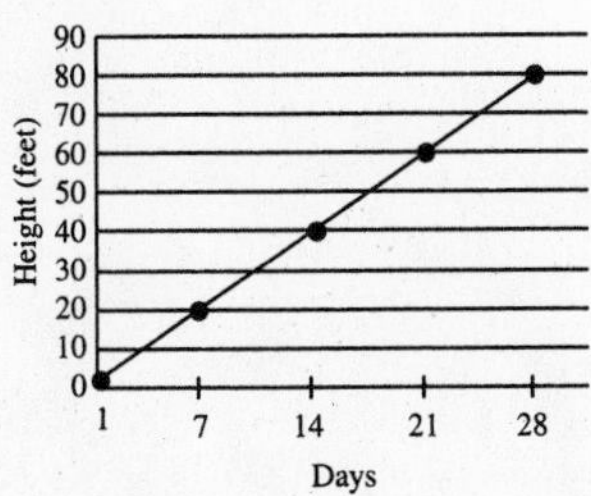

[11]

a. Possible description: Begin with 2 and repeatedly multiply by 4.
[12] b. Possible next terms: 512, 2048, 8192, 32,768

a. 48, 96, 192
b. Multiply the previous number by 2 to find each term in the number
[13] pattern.

a. The numbers in Column II are equal to the numbers in Column I. The
numbers in Column III are twice the numbers in Column I.
[14] b. Each number in Column III is twice that of Column I.

[15] B

[16] 21

Chapter 2: Patterns and Algebraic Thinking

5, 2, 4. Answers may vary, but should include that the number of diagonals
[17] equals the number of sides minus 3.

[18] D

[19] B

[20] 64

[21] 12

15 and 16; 25 and 26. Answer may vary. Sample: Guess a number whose
square is close to the product. When you are close, try adding 1 to the
[22] number and check the product.

[23] $3.50

[24] 20

[25] 50

[26] 49

[27] D

[28] 56

Answers will vary. Sample: The order of operations is a set of rules for
evaluating mathematical expressions. This set of rules guarantees that
everyone will get the same value for an expression by describing which
operations within an expression should be computed first . The first step to
finding the value of an expression is to do all the operations within
parentheses. The second step is to do all the multiplication and division
from left to right. The last step is to do the addition and subtraction from
[29] left to right.

According to the order of operations, multiplication should be performed
[30] first and then subtraction.

Answers will vary. Sample: The first step to finding the value of the
expression is to do the multiplication from left to right first. Thus $3 \times 1 =$
3 and $3 \times 4 = 12$. The resulting expression is $6 + 12$. The next step is to
do the addition. The answer is 18. Felicia must have added $6 + 3$ before
doing the multiplication. Her resulting expression was then $9 \times 1 \times 4$,
[31] which equals 36. Felicia violated the order of operations.

Chapter 2: Patterns and Algebraic Thinking

[32] $(133) \div 2 + 1 = 6$. Answers describing how to change the value will vary. Check expressions for accuracy. An example would be $133 \div (2+1) = 12$.

[33] Answers may vary but should have a value of 34. Sample: $20 \times 2 + 5 \,1\,1$.

[34] A

[35] <

[36] D

[37] D

[38] Answers will vary. The value of the given expression is 2. Any expression that has the same value is correct. Check student answers for accuracy.

[39] >. The left side of the equation is equal to 41. The right side of the equation is equal to 20. Thus the left side is greater than the right side.

[40] Answers may vary. Sample: $4 \cdot 2 - 1 + 6$

[41] Answers may vary. Sample: $8 \times 2 - (4+3) + (18 \div 6)$

[42]

[43] Answers may vary. Sample: $4x + 3$

[44] D

[45] 5

[46]

a.

42	7	32
17	27	37
22	47	12

b. Yes. The the rows, columns, and diagonals have the same sum.

c. $5x + 2$

d. Answers may vary. Sample answer for $x + 2$:

10	3	8
5	7	9
6	11	4

Chapter 2: Patterns and Algebraic Thinking

[47] Answers may vary. Sample: Substitute 5 for a, and 2 for b into the variable expression. Follow the rule for order of operations. First square the 5 to get 25. Then multiply 3 times 2 to get 6. Add 25 and 6 to get 31.

[48] D

[49] A

[50] Answers may vary. Samples: $a = 5, b = 2$; $a = 6, b = 5$; $a = 7, b = 8$

[51] 7

[52] $a = 8$; $b = 6$; $c = 9$

[53] 16

[54] B

[55] a number p multiplied by ten

[56] No. The quotient of 21 and x means $21 \div x$, and x divided by 21 means $x \div 21$.

[57] Answers may vary. Sample: The sum of x and 10. Ten more than x.

[58] A

[59] a) $8x$ b) $x - 7$ c) $x + 3$ d) $\frac{44}{x}$

[60] $x + 2$; Since x is an even number, the next greater even number is two numbers away.

[61] A

[62] A

[63] $x - 5$

[64] $2a + 2b$

[65] x^2

[66] Answers may use different letters for the variables. Sample: $x^3 + 5$; 13

[67] Answers may use different letters for the variable. Sample: Carmen's Age = $2A + 2$

Chapter 2: Patterns and Algebraic Thinking

[68] Lemon: \$0.35; Eggs: \$1.05; Noodles: \$1.25

[69] $x \div 5$

[70] True. The expression 5 + 12 and the number 17 have the same value.

[71] Answers may vary. Sample: An expression may only contain variables, numerals, and operational symbols. An expression does not contain an equal sign. For example $x + 3$. An equation is a mathematical sentence that contains an equal sign. For example: $x + 3 = 5$.

[72] D

[73] 24

[74] B

[75] C

[76] $x + 4 = 6$

[77] a. $x = 5$
b. $a = 6$
c. $z = 7$

[78] $b - a$

[79] $a + 3 + 4 = 15$ or $a + 1 + 6 = 15$ or $a + 5 + 2 = 15$; $a = 8$
$3 + 5 + b = 15$ or $6 + b + 2 = 15$; $b = 7$

[80] a. $x = 102$; b. $y = 16{,}193$; c. $z = 464.1$

[81] $0.99x + 0.05x$; 10 bottles = \$10.40

[82] 5.5

[83] 3

[84] a. $x = 2$; b. $y = 3$; c. $z = 3$

[85] $9 = 3x$; $x = 3$

[86] D

[87] 5

[88] Answers may vary. Sample: Both equations use inverse operations to find the solution. The equation $4x = 16$ uses division to solve. The equation $x + 6 = 12$ uses subtraction to solve.

Chapter 2: Patterns and Algebraic Thinking

[89] Answers may vary. The value of x is greater than 3.

[90] D

[91] Answers may vary. Sample answer given. $14x = 168$

[92] a. $x = 12$; b. $y = 1.6$; c. $z = 4$

[93] $x(1.85) = 1{,}822$; $x = 984.86$ (or 985, if rounding)

[94] $15x = \$63.75$; $x = \$4.25$

[95] 1

[96] $a = 20$

[97] $x = 9$

Chapter 3: Adding and Subtracting Decimals

[1] A

[2] Student model should show 0.06 shaded.

[3] Sentences may vary but should contain the words "three tenths."

[4] Explanations should include that the number one can be divided into 10 parts or 100 parts. Three-tenths would be 3 of the "10" parts. Thirty hundredths would be 30 of the "100" parts.

[5] One dime is equal to 0.10 dollar. Ten dimes are equal to one dollar.

[6] C

[7] A

[8] B

[9] Answers may vary. Example: A model should show 48 of 100 squares shaded.

[10] false; check student's explanation

[11] C

[12] 4 slices

[13] $2\frac{1}{2}$

[14] D

[15] 2,208,915,418

[16] For each place moved from right to left in the place value chart, the value of the digits increases by a factor of 10.

[17] A number in expanded form shows the place value of each digit. A number written in standard form is the numbers written in expanded form combined together.

[18] A

[19] $90 + 2 + 0.4 + 0.02 + 0.007$

[20] D

[21] D

Chapter 3: Adding and Subtracting Decimals

[22] Answers will vary.

[23] thousandths

[24] 4.62

[25] Check students' drawings.

[26] 0.022

[27] Check students' drawings. The 3 should be under the ones column, the 5 under the tenths, and the 2 under the hundredths.

[28] Thousands, Hundreds, Tens, Ones, Tenths, Hundredths, Thousandths, Ten Thousandths, Hundred Thousandths, Millionths.

[29] Oxygen: $90 + 7 + 0.5$; ninety-seven and five tenths;
Sodium: $0.1 + 0.06 + 0.005$; one hundred sixty-five thousandths;
Phosphorus: $1 + 0.8$; one and eight tenths;
Cobalt: $0.0002 + 0.00004$; twenty-four hundred thousandths

[30] Answers may vary. Sample: Frank Thomas from the Chicago White Sox had the best batting average out of the five players given in the chart.

[31] C

[32] D

[33] Check students' drawings, which should show that $0.51 > 0.32$.

[34] Check students' drawings.

[35] Check students' drawings.

[36] $A > B$; C is greater than A and B

[37] C

[38] $3.419 = 3.419000$

[39] Answers may vary. Samples: using models; using place value to compare numbers from left to right; using a number line.

[40] Answers may vary. Sample: to determine which baseball player has the best batting average; to determine who has the most money.

[41] $0.30 > 0.03$

[42] Answers may vary. Sample: 0.26

Chapter 3: Adding and Subtracting Decimals

[43] 0.285

[44] D

[45] D

[46] D

[47] 19 and 6

[48] 5 and 8 years old

[49] Exact location of the numbers will vary. Sample suggested. Row 1: 1 and 4 Row 2: 3 and 2 Row 3: 5 Row 4: 8 and 9 Row 5: 6 and 7

[50] 129 students and 9 adults

[51] Answers may vary. Samples: 1 apple and 12 oranges, 4 apples and 10 oranges, 7 apples and 8 oranges

[52] a. S; b. Q; c. T

[53] New York, Los Angeles, Chicago, Houston, Philadelphia, San Diego, Detroit, Dallas.

[54] B

[55] B

[56] D

[57] Check students' drawings. Their answer should be 0.8.

[58] Check students' drawings. Their answer should be 1.2.

[59] Answers may vary. Sample: 5 tenths and 13 hundredths

[60] 5.61

[61] C

[62] Answers may vary. Sample: Write the difference vertically and align the decimal points. Subtract from right to left. First subtract the tenths column and then the ones column.

[63] 1.1

[64] 0.62

Chapter 3: Adding and Subtracting Decimals

[65] $81.87

[66] Answers may vary. Sample: 1 baseball jersey $25.95; 1 baseball glove $35.95; 1 batting glove $6.99; and 1 baseball cap $15.99; $84.88

[67] Answers may vary. Sample: Estimate $3.99 as $4.00. Add. $1.85 + $4.00 = $5.85; Subtract. $5.85 - $0.01 = $5.84.

[68] D

[69] 350

[70] C

[71] 0.5

[72] 7.000

[73] B

[74] D

[75] Answers may vary. Sample: Add the front-end digits. Adjust by estimating the sums of the remaining digits. Add the results.

[76] D

[77] Answers may vary. Samples: to make sure you have enough money to go grocery shopping; to measure distances; to measure an object's dimensions.

[78] a: 3.211 and 9.75; b. 15.08 and 9.75; or 7.09 and 2.31

[79] $13

[80] Answers may vary. Sample: two 4 oz glasses of OJ; 1 plain granola bar; and $\frac{1}{2}$ cup of sherbet: total 2.3 oz.

[81] Answers may vary. Sample: Round each number to the nearest dollar and add. Use front-end estimation.

[82] $7.00

[83] $2.00

[84] D

[85] 84.544

ANSWERS

Chapter 3: Adding and Subtracting Decimals

[86] a. True. For example: 0.9 – 0.5 = 0.4; 0.4 < 1
b. False. For example: 0.9 + 0.5 = 1.4; 1.4 > 1; The sum of two decimals less than 1 is sometimes less than one.

[87] B

[88] D

[89] $5.14

[90] $2,111.42

[91] 0.3

[92] B

[93] 728.62

[94] C

[95] $1.61

[96] For every additional one ounce a letter weighs, the postage rate increases by $0.23.

[97] Answers may vary depending on estimating technique used. Sample: $7.00

[98] $23.01

[99] Juan added instead of subtracting.

[100] A

[101] 1.6 cm

[102] Count how many steps it takes you to walk across the room. Then multiply that number by 25 to estimate the length of the room.

[103] A

[104] Answers may vary. Sample: To measure a segment, align 0 on the ruler with one end of the segment, then read the length.

[105] Check students' work.

[106] 40 cm

[107] Verify students' answers.

Chapter 3: Adding and Subtracting Decimals

[108] 11.9 cm

[109] A

[110] millimeters

[111] Answers may vary, but should include that centimeters are used to measure short lengths. Meters would be more appropriate.

[112] a: m; b: cm; c: km; d: mm

[113] Check students' work.

[114] C

[115] A

[116] true

[117] B

[118] true

[119] Check students' work.

[120] B

[121] 3 kg

[122] A

[123] D

[124] Answers may vary. Sample: gram, because dry cereal isn't very heavy.

[125] liter

[126] Answers may vary. Sample: cough medicine, because you only take a little bit at a time.

[127] D

[128] Answers may vary. Sample: metric, because all the units can be compared by multiplying or dividing by powers of 10.

[129] 2 L Answers may vary. Sample: 2 L is the same as 2000 mL.

[130] D

Chapter 3: Adding and Subtracting Decimals

[131] C

[132] Answers may vary. Sample: the amount of time between two events.

[133] Your answer should include the amount of time each activity takes, as well as the total elapsed time.

[134] A

[135] 3 hr 10 min

[136] 7 hr 35 min

[137] December 6th; 2:00 p.m.

[138] 2 hr 45 min

[139] Route 2

[140] 4:00 p.m.

[141] B

[142] Sheep

[143] C

[144] Answers may vary. Sample:

ACTIVITIES	START TIME	END TIME
Math	8:15	8:55
Social Studies	9:00	9:40
English	9:45	10:25
Gym	10:30	11:10
Music	11:15	11:55
Lunch	12:00	12:40
Reading	12:45	1:25
Art	1:30	2:10
Science	2:15	3:00

Chapter 3: Adding and Subtracting Decimals

[145]

ACTIVITIES	START TIME	END TIME
Walk home from school	3:00	3:15
Have a snack	3:15	3:30
Walk the dog	3:30	3:40
Do homework	3:40	4:40
Eat dinner	4:40	5:05
Change into dance uniform	5:05	5:15
Walk to dance class	5:15	5:30

Chapter 4: Multiplying and Dividing Decimals

[1] B

[2] 1200; answers may vary

[3] Answers will vary. Sample: Compatible numbers are numbers that are easy to multiply or divide mentally. For example, compatible numbers for 5.2 × 2.98 might be 5 and 3.

[4] D

[5] Answers will vary. Sample: It is easier to use compatible numbers. Rounding each factor to the nearest whole number leaves 14 × 48, which is simpler than the original expression, but still difficult to compute. Changing the factors to compatible numbers might produce 15 × 50, which is the easiest of the three expressions to compute.

[6] Answers may vary. Accept all logical answers. Sample: Caterina's estimate will be closer to the actual product because the rounded factors are closer to the actual factors than the compatible numbers. The greater the difference between the factors used and the original factors, the greater the difference between the estimated product and the actual product.

[7] Answers may vary slightly. Samples given.
a. $7. (2 × 1.71) + (3 × 1.11) becomes (2 × 2) + (3 × 1) = 7.
b. $8. (2 × 2.29) + (2 × 1.95) becomes (2 × 2) + (2 × 2) = 8.
c. $4.43. 0.43 + (2 × 1.02) + (2 × 1.11) becomes 0.43 + (2 × 1) + (2 × 1) = 4.43.

[8] a. 16 km. (4 × 3.8) becomes (4 × 4) = 16.
b. 9 km. (.09) becomes (1), (3.8) becomes (4), 4 – 1 = 3 3 × 3 = 9.
c. $\frac{1}{2}$ km. (1.2 ÷ 2) becomes (1 ÷ 2) = $\frac{1}{2}$.

[9] Answers will vary. Sample: There are about 18 grams of fat in 3.2 cookies. Students need to multiply the number of grams of fat, 5.7, by the number of cookies, 3.2. Rounding the factors to the nearest whole number or changing them to compatible numbers leaves 6 and 3. Thus the estimated product is 18.

Chapter 4: Multiplying and Dividing Decimals

[10] Answers may vary. Sample: The total number of hours can be found by multiplying the number of hours each week, 68.82, by the number of weeks, 2.76. The estimate can be found by changing the factors to compatible numbers. The compatible numbers are 70 and 3. The estimated product is 210.

[11] A

[12] Answers may vary. Sample: 16

[13] Answers will vary. Sample: Numbers involved in multiplication or division can be changed into compatible numbers to make the computation easier. The product or quotient calculated with those compatible numbers is then an estimate and not the actual answer.

[14] B

[15] $12. Students should change the amount saved into a number that is compatible with 12 months. Thus if the amount saved is changed to 144, the expression becomes $144 ÷ 12 = the amount saved each month ($12).

[16] Answers may vary. Sample: The answer can be found by dividing the weight of the box, 33.92, by the weight of each book, 2.65. The estimate can be found by changing the dividend and divisor to compatible numbers. The compatible numbers are 30 and 3. The estimated quotient is 10.

[17] A

[18] 8^3

[19] Do all work within the parentheses first. Do all work with exponents: 2^3 = 8. Continue to complete all work within the parentheses: 23 - 8 = 15. Then add in order from left to right: 3 + 15 = 18.

[20] a. 1,024
b. Each term increases by one power of 4.

[21] No. Answers may vary. Sample:$(2^2 + 3^2) = 13$; $(2 + 3)^2 = 25$; The sum of the squares of two numbers does not equal the square of the sum of two numbers.

[22] base: 5; exponent: 9

[23] 4^6

[24] 2^7

Chapter 4: Multiplying and Dividing Decimals

[25] The last digits form a repeating pattern of 7, 9, 3, 1.

[26] 18 cm^2

[27] B

[28] –69

[29] D

[30] A

[31] 56

[32] D

[33] any two; (6 × 7) + (3 × 7), 7 × (6 + 3), 63

[34] Answers will vary slightly. Sample: The area of the pool is equal to the length of the pool times the width of the pool (Length × Width = Area). The problem gives the area of the pool and the width. Thus, Length × 50 ft = 5000 sq. ft. Dividing the area (5000) by the width (50), gives the length (100). The length is 100 ft.

[35] Answers will vary. Sample: Area is the total number of square units that cover the rectangle. The area of the rectangle is the product of its length times its width.

[36] B

[37] (4×2)+(4×5) and 4×(2+5). The total area is 28 square units.

[38] The expression is 5×(3+9). There are 60 players. The rectangle should have a width of 5 and a total length of 12. There should be a line inside, making 2 rectangles of size 5×3 and 5×9.

[39] 1200 square meters. Explanations will vary. Sample given. The figure shows two rectangles. The area of the entire theater can be calculated by adding the areas of each of the two sections. The expression for this addition is (30×15)+(30×25). Using the distributive property, this expression can be rewritten as 30×(15+25) = 30×40 = 1200.

[40] 1000 m^2. The expression is 40×25 = (40×20)+(40×5) = 800+200 = 1000.

[41] D

Chapter 4: Multiplying and Dividing Decimals

[42] 24

[43] The missing numbers are 4, 5, 13. Explanations will vary. Sample: According to the distributive property, the value of a number multiplied by two numbers added in parentheses is equal to the sum of the factor multiplied by each of the numbers separately. Thus on the right-hand side of the equation, you know that 5 is being multiplied by each of the numbers in parentheses on the left-hand side of the equation.

[44] Check students' work.

[45] C

[46] The expression that will give the number of seats is 7×102. Using the distributive property, the expression becomes (7×100)+(7×2) = 700+14 = 714.

[47] Answers will vary. Sample: The model for the first expression has one grid with an area shaded that is 3 boxes by 2 boxes. The total number of shaded boxes is 6, so the product is 0.06. The model for the second expression consists of two grids with an area shaded that is 3 boxes by 20 boxes. The total number of shaded boxes is 60, so the product is 0.6. The products contain the same numeral, 6, but the second product is ten times larger than the first.

[48] C

[49] B

[50] 5.2 miles

[51] Answers will vary. Sample: Use decimal square grids in which each box represents one tenth. Only one grid is necessary to model the multiplication of two decimal numbers that are less than one. Count up 5 rows from the bottom and 2 columns over. Shade in all the boxes in this area. Count the number of shaded boxes to get the product. There are 10 shaded boxes, each of which represents one tenth. Ten times one tenth equals 0.1. The product is 0.1. Students may also suggest shading one number horizontally on the grid and the other vertically. The intersection of the two shaded areas is the product.

[52] Answers will vary according to the situation described. The sentence to go with the model is 0.3×0.8.

ANSWERS

[53] Answers will vary. Sample: Students should include that models are a visual way to find products by counting shaded boxes in a grid. They should also note that drawing models can be a slow process when many products need to be found.

[54] Models may vary somewhat. Sample: a 10×10 grid with a shaded section 6 units by 3 units.

[55] The model should show three grids with a shaded section that is 22 boxes by 6 boxes. The product is 1.32. Thus 0.6 kg is equal to 1.32 pounds.

[56] Models may vary. Sample shown.

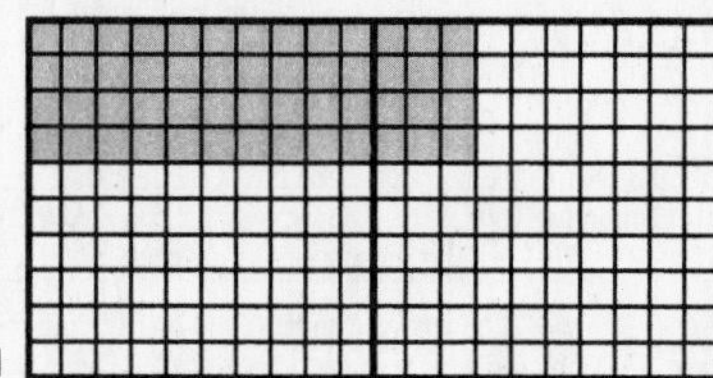

[57] (b) or (f). Explanations may vary. Sample: You know that at least one of the factors must be greater than 2 because Alex used 3 grids. One grid is for decimals between 0 and 1. Two grids are for decimals between 1 and 2. And three grids are for decimals between 2 and 3. The only two choices with at least one factor that is greater than 2 are b and f.

[58] C

[59] 1.6

[60] 1,104; 110.4; 11.04; 110.4; The number of decimal places in the product is equal to the number of decimal places in the factors of the expression.

[61] $420

[62] $53.75. The equation is $215 \times 0.25 = 53.75$

[63] 0.45 inches. The expression is 15×0.03.

[64] 39.2 m/sec. The expression is 4×9.8.

[65] From top to bottom the missing numbers in the Factor 2 column are: 100; 10; 1000. Students should see that multiplying a decimal factor of ten equates to moving the decimal to the right. The number of places the decimal is moved is equal to the number of zeros in the factor. From top to bottom the missing numbers in the product column are: 24; 2,400; 24.

[66] A

[67] 0.51

[68] Answers will vary. Sample: The answer actually has four decimal places as would be expected. However, the fourth decimal place is a zero and is dropped from the calculator's answer.

[69] Answers will vary. Sample: The total number of decimal places in the factors being multiplied equals the number of decimal places in the product. Students should note that sometimes the last decimal places is a zero that is not written.

[70] C

[71] Answers will vary. Sample: Gwen can round the factors to the nearest whole numbers and then multiply the rounded factors. For this example she would multiply $3 \times 12 = 36$. The estimate gives her an idea of what her answer should look like. Then when she multiplies the decimal factors, she should be less confused as to where the decimal should be. In this case the numerals of the decimal product are 3844. Even if she is unsure where the decimal belongs, she knows that the answer should be close to 36. Thus the decimal belongs between the 8 and the 4. The answer is 38.44.

[72] Rhinoceros takes 648 days. The expression is 2.4×270. A swan takes 43.2 days. The expression is 0.16×270.

[73] A cheetah can run 69.9 mi/h. The expression is 2.33×30. A spider can crawl 1.17 mi/h. The expression is 0.039×30.

[74] Answers will vary. Sample: The dividend, 0.6, is represented by 6 shaded columns. The divisor, 0.3, is represented by 3 shaded columns. The brackets show that there are 2 groups of 3 columns in the 6 columns. Thus the quotient is 2.

[75] B

[76] Answers will vary. Sample: Several answers can be correct. For example, the sentence could be $0.4 \div 0.2 = 2$. Two groups of 2 columns can be circled on the grid. Or the answer could be $0.4 \div 0.02 = 20$. Twenty groups of 2 squares can be circled on the grid. Check answers for accuracy.

[77] 1.5 mi/h. The sentence is $0.3 \div 0.2 = 1.5$. The model should show a 10×10 grid with 30 boxes shaded and divided into one and a half groups of twenty boxes (i.e., one group of twenty boxes and one group of ten boxes).

[78] Yes. Dividing by hundredths is just like dividing by tenths except that each box in the grid represents $\frac{1}{100}$ instead of $\frac{1}{10}$.

[79] D

[80] The mathematical sentence is $0.8 \div 0.04 = 20$. Answers will vary as to the problem. Check student answers for accuracy.

[81] She bought 4 peaches. The model should show a 10×12 shaded grid divided into 4 parts vertically.

[82] He can water 5 plants. The model should show a 10×6 shaded grid, which is split into 5 sections of 12 units.

[83] $0.8 \div 0.16 = 5$. The dividend, 0.8, represents the amount of apples being divided. The divisor, 0.16, represents the size of each group into which the apples are being divided. The quotient, 5, represents the number of groups of apples. The model should show a 10×8 shaded grid divided into 5 sections of 16 units each.

[84] 50 km/h. The sentence is $2 \div 0.04 = 50$. The model should show two grids with 50 groups each containing 4 boxes.

[85] B

[86] 0.7

[87] $0.15

[88] Answers will vary. Sample: To divide a decimal by a whole number, place the decimal point in the quotient above the decimal point in the dividend. Then divide as you would with whole numbers. So

$$\begin{array}{r} 1.56 \\ 3\overline{)4.68} \end{array}$$

[89] Moving the decimal one place to the right multiplies 0.8 by 10. Two places equates to multiplying by 100. Three places equates to multiplying by 1000.

[90] D

[91] A

[92] $7.55

[93] 9.75

[94] Sample answer: $0.52 \div 8$

[95] Sample: I would use mental math because $45 \div 15 = 3$, so $0.045 \div 15 = 0.003$.

[96] 0.3 pounds

[97] B

[98] 8.5

[99] Answers may vary. Sample: The 2 numbers in each expression have the same number of decimal places. All three expressions have the same numerals but, different values. The quotients for all three expressions are the same, 8. Students might suggest that if a number is divided by another number with the same number of decimal places, it is as if there were no decimals.

[100] Answers will vary. Sample: When you divide a decimal by a decimal, you have to change the divisor to a whole number. To do this, move the decimal point in the divisor to the right until the divisor is a whole number. Count the number of places the decimal moved. Then move the decimal point in the dividend the same number of places to the right. Place the decimal in the quotient above the moved decimal point in the dividend and divide as with whole numbers. For example,

$$\begin{array}{r} 16.5 \\ 5\overline{)82.5} \end{array}$$

Chapter 4: Multiplying and Dividing Decimals

[101] D

[102] Answers will vary. Sample: Students should suggest mental math or pencil and paper because 15 goes easily into 45. All that is required for division is to move the decimal point to the proper position. Because the divisor must be multiplied by 100 to get a whole number, the dividend must also be multiplied by 100. Thus the dividend will have one decimal place and so must the quotient. The divisor, 15, goes into 45 three times and the quotient must have one decimal place, so the quotient is 0.3.

[103] 0.165 cm

[104] 2.05 mi/h

[105] D

[106] Answers will vary. Sample: More, because $275 \div 12 > 20$.

[107] Answers will vary. Sample: $0.05 \div 0.2 = 0.25$. I used mental math to multiply 0.25 by 0.2.

[108] The first step is to multiply both the divisor and the dividend by 10, so that the divisor is a whole number.

[109] There are 33 students in his class.

[110] Stephanie's weight

[111] 12 years. You don't need the information about the average speed.

[112] C

[113] C

[114] The problem cannot be solved without knowing the total number of calendars sold.

[115] The amount he paid and the change he received help to find the price. The number of videos he rented, however, is necessary to answer the question.

[116] A

[117] $384. All information except the total money taken in and the expenses incurred is extraneous.

[118] $56. Blue paint = 2 gallons at $9 each = $18. White paint = 2 gallons at $7 each = $14. Yellow paint = 3 gallons at $8 each = $24.

[119] Each skate weighs 2.8 lb. The price and the color of the skates are unnecessary.

[120] The problem cannot be solved without knowing the number of students.

[121] Bernadette needs to work 5 weeks. She earns $40 per week (8 hours × $5/hr.) The information about which days she works and that her sister works at the store as well is unnecessary.

[122] The problem cannot be solved without knowing how much money Melony paid.

[123] C

[124] 1.25 m

[125] 7×10 kg; Answers may vary. Sample: I used mental math to change all the masses to kilograms.

[126] 0.89 kg

[127] 0.2375 kg

[128] 0.920 km

[129] Soup A; 205 mg more

[130] 3.7 cm > 45 mm. Answers may vary. Sample: 3.7 cm = 37 mm, 37 mm < 45 mm

[131] Soup A . Answers may vary. Sample: because 0.004 kg = 4 g, and 750 mg = 0.75 g.

[132] Harry

[133] 7 rolls

[134] A

[135] 420 mm

Chapter 5: Investigating Fractions

[1] D

[2] 90, 170, 295

[3] Divisibility is the ability of one whole number to divide into another with no remainder. There are rules for finding divisibility by 1, 2, 3, 4, 5, 9, and 10.

[4] D

[5] B

[6] The rule for divisibility by 4 is that if the number formed by the last two digits is divisible by 4, the number is divisible by 4. In the first number in the chart, the last two digits are 24. Because 24 is divisible by 4, the number is divisible by 4. NOTE: Students should be finding the number formed by the last two digits, not the sum of the digits. Additional examples will vary.

[7] No, 192 is not divisible by 10. The guests will fit evenly if she assigns 8, 6, 4, 3, 2, or 1 to each table.

[8] Yes. The number 85 ends in 5, so it is divisible by 5.

[9] Numbers that are divisible by both 2 and 3 are divisible by 6. Additional examples will vary.

[10] Because 135 is divisible by 9, Jamie can divide his hotels evenly among his properties. Jamie can place 15 hotels on each property. But 93 is not divisible by 10, so Carmela cannot divide her hotels evenly among her properties.

[11] Yes. Although 87 is not divisible by 5, $87 is divisible by 5. They each could have contributed $17.40.

[12] C

[13] 5,265

[14] No. The sum of the digits rule works for 3 and 9, but it does not work for all numbers. For example, the sum of the digits for 23 is divisible by 5, but 23 is not divisible by 5. Examples may vary.

[15] Answers will vary. Because 3 is a factor of 9, any number that is divisible by 9 is also divisible by 3. Other examples will vary. For example, any number that is divisible by 4 is also divisible by 2 or any number that is divisible by 14 is also divisible by 7.

[16] Answers will vary. No, the dolls will not fit evenly if she places 9 on each shelf because 140 is not divisible by 9. The dolls will fit evenly if she places 10, 7, 5, 4, 2 or 1 on each shelf. Students might suggest the highest number to allow for the lowest number of shelves.

[17] Yes. Students should suggest that the sum of the digits of the length of the race equals 24, which is divisible by 3. Thus the length is divisible by 3.

[18] C

[19] 8, 10, 12, 26

[20] A prime number is a number that has exactly two factors, one and itself. A composite number is a number that has more than two factors.

[21] Answers may vary. Sample: Zero is not prime because it has an infinite number of factors. Zero is not composite because it does not have more than two factors.

[22] D

[23] No. $A \times B$ has A and B as factors in addition to 1. Examples will vary.

[24] $14.00 is a reasonable answer. Subtract $11.00 from $24.00, leaving $13.00 for 2 pairs of socks and 1 T-shirt. Socks could cost $3.00 and T-shirts could cost $7.00. Other answers could be $22.00 (socks: $1.00, T-shirt: $11.00) or $6.00 (socks: $5.00, T-shirt: $3.00)

[25] 11 years old

[26] A

[27] Answers may vary, but final numbers should match sample.

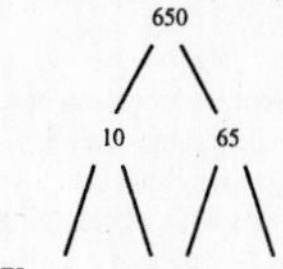

ANSWERS

[28] Answers may vary. Seven: one row of seven tiles. Eighteen: Three rectangles with the dimensions 1 × 18, 9 × 2, and 3 × 6. The dimensions of the rectangles are factors of the number. Because 7 tiles result in only one rectangle, the dimensions of which are 1 and 7, it can be determined that 7 is a prime number. Eighteen, however, has several factors and is therefore a composite number.

[29] C

[30] Answers may vary. He could have made 80 groups of 1, 16 groups of 5, or 40 groups of 2. Students need to find the factors of 80 and select one of the combinations that includes a prime number.

[31] Three different rectangles can be drawn. The dimensions of the rectangles are 5 × 4, 2 × 10, and 1× 20. Check student diagrams for accuracy.

[32] 10, 14, 35, and 70

[33] Answers will vary. There could be forty-two groups of one, twenty-one groups of two, fourteen groups of three, or six groups of seven.

[34] C

[35] 30

[36] The greatest number that is a factor of each number. For example, the greatest common factor of 12 and 18 is 6.

[37] Answers may vary. The greatest common factor can be found by one of two methods. The first is to make a list of the factors for each number. The factors that the numbers have in common can then be circled. The common factor with the highest value is the greatest common factor. The other method is to construct a factor tree and write the prime factorization for each number. The common factors can then be circled as before, but this time the common factors are multiplied together to find the greatest common factor.

[38] $.13

[39] 30 cm × 30 cm

[40] C

[41] C

[42] 12

Chapter 5: Investigating Fractions

[43] Answers may vary. Students should recognize that the greatest common factor of two prime numbers is always one. The reason is that the only factors of a prime number are one and itself. Thus the only factor common between two different prime numbers is one.

[44] A

[45] C

[46] Answers may vary. Three possibilities are 28, 36, and 44.

[47] 6 cm. Six is the greatest common factor of 42, 78, and 108.

[48] 12

[49] 15. Students must find the greatest common factor of 30 and 45 (the sum of the musicians and cheerleaders).

[50] 25 baskets

[51] 3 vases. Students must find the GCF of 15, 18, and 24.

[52] 2

[53] A

[54] Diagrams may vary.

[55] Answers may vary. A fraction bar is a rectangle broken up into equal size sections. When a fraction bar is used to model a fraction, the number of sections is equal to the denominator of the fraction. The number of sections that are shaded is equal to the numerator of the fraction.

[56] Equivalent fractions are fractions that represent the same part of the whole. Examples will vary.

[57] $\frac{1}{3}$

[58] $\frac{2}{5}$. You should draw a fraction bar with five sections, two of which are shaded.

Chapter 5: Investigating Fractions

[59] $\frac{4}{9}$. Draw a fraction bar with nine sections, four of which are shaded.

[60] $\frac{5}{10}$

[61] $\frac{3}{9}$. Fraction bars should have nine sections, three of which are shaded. Equivalent fractions are also correct.

[62] $\frac{4}{6}$. The fraction bar should have six sections, four of which are shaded. Equivalent fractions are also correct.

[63] $\frac{11}{20}$; Models will vary.

[64] $\frac{1}{2}$

[65] A

[66] Close to zero: $\frac{2}{45}$; $\frac{7}{60}$; $\frac{4}{56}$. Close to one half: $\frac{45}{100}$; $\frac{15}{38}$. Close to one: $\frac{76}{80}$; $\frac{9}{10}$; $\frac{32}{35}$.

[67] a. $\frac{12}{25}$ b. $\frac{6}{13}$ c. $\frac{8}{14}$ d. $\frac{24}{50}$

[68] A

[69] $\frac{9}{10}$, $\frac{18}{20}$, $\frac{36}{40}$

[70] Answers may vary. One explanation is that equivalent fractions can be found by multiplying or dividing the numerator and denominator of a fraction by the same non zero number. Some students may suggest drawing fraction bars and inserting or deleting sections without changing the shaded region.

[71] $\frac{3}{6}$, $\frac{6}{12}$, $\frac{12}{24}$

[72] Answers may vary. Samples are $\frac{2}{16}$ and $\frac{1}{8}$.

Chapter 5: Investigating Fractions

[73] Answers may vary. Obvious answers are $\frac{6}{60}$, $\frac{1}{10}$, $\frac{2}{20}$.

[74] Answers may vary. Obvious answers are $\frac{28}{60}$, $\frac{14}{30}$, $\frac{7}{15}$.

[75] A

[76] $\frac{2}{3}$

[77] Answers may vary. A fraction is in simplest form when the only common factor between the numerator and denominator is one. The simplest form of a fraction can be found by dividing the numerator and denominator by their greatest common factor.

[78] A

[79] A

[80] The fraction is $\frac{2{,}500}{10{,}000}$. The simplest form of the fraction is $\frac{1}{4}$.

[81] $\$10$ is $\frac{10}{100} = \frac{1}{10}$. $\$20$ is $\frac{20}{100} = \frac{1}{5}$. $\$50$ is $\frac{50}{100} = \frac{1}{2}$.

[82] Answers may vary. Correct answers are a camel and a tiger, a goat and a tiger, or a lion and a tiger.

[83] Answers may vary. Students should estimate that Antarctica is about 20% of the circle graph. The fraction is $\frac{20}{100}$, or $\frac{1}{5}$.

[84] D

[85] Write the mixed number as a sum. Express the whole number as a fraction. Write an equivalent fraction for the whole number fraction and then add the numerators.

[86] A

[87] 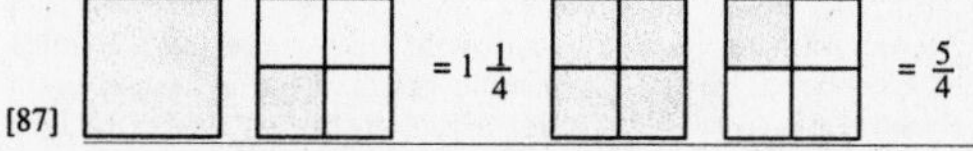

ANSWERS

[88] Sample answers: $\frac{6}{1}, \frac{12}{2}, \frac{18}{3}$

[89] $\frac{11}{4}$

[90] $\frac{17}{4} \times \frac{29}{8} \times \frac{9}{4}$

[91] $\frac{52}{14}$; $3\frac{10}{14}$

[92] B

[93] $7\frac{1}{2}$

[94] The model should show 2 filled-in squares and a third square divided into 4 sections, three of which are filled in.

[95] $9\frac{3}{4}$

[96] $12\frac{3}{4}$

[97] $2\frac{1}{2}$ pizzas

[98] A

[99] 2,574

[100] No. The next time Mike will receive a shipment of games and bicycles will be in 18 days. The LCM of 6 and 9 is 18.

[101] A

[102] B

[103] Answers may vary. Samples: 5, 10 or 20.

[104] The 30th, 60th, and 90th persons were chosen to clean up both.

[105] 1968, 1972, 1976, 1980, 1984, 1988, 1992; 11

[106] 6

Chapter 5: Investigating Fractions

[107] 60, 120, 180, 240; 60 is the smallest.

[108] September 6, 12, 18, 24, 30.

[109] D

[110] 72

[111] To find GCF and LCM of two numbers, factor each number as a product of primes. The product of the common primes is the GCF. The LCM is the least number that is a common multiple of two or more given numbers.

[112] D

[113] Find the lowest number where the column of multiples of 4 crosses the diagonal of the multiples of 7.

[114] >

[115] Yes; When two fractions have the same numerator and different denominators, the fraction with the larger denominator is less.

[116] Determine the common denominator between the fractions by finding the least common multiple of the numbers in the denominator. Write equivalent fractions using the least common multiple denominator. Compare the numerators.

[117] B

[118] Check students' models. $2\frac{3}{4} > \frac{12}{5}\left(2\frac{2}{5}\right)$

[119] rectangle

[120] 10; The number of questions on the exam should be a multiple of 10, since the LCD of the three fractions is 10.

[121] A

[122] $\frac{1}{4}, \frac{1}{2}, \frac{3}{4}$

[123] $1\frac{1}{2}, 1\frac{5}{8}, 1\frac{2}{3}$

[124] $\frac{1}{2}, \frac{2}{4}, \frac{2}{5}, \frac{3}{6}, \frac{3}{7}, \frac{3}{8}, \frac{4}{8}$

Chapter 5: Investigating Fractions

[125] $\frac{7}{8}$

[126] Greg; Juan

[127] Yellow Rainbow; Loving You

[128] C

[129] $\frac{9}{20}$

[130] Answers may vary. Sample: A terminating decimal is a decimal with a finite number of decimal places. A repeating decimal is a decimal that repeats and does not end. A bar is used to show which digit or digits repeat. A terminating decimal can be expressed as a fraction.

[131] Edward

[132] $\frac{31}{100} \times \frac{37}{100}$

[133] 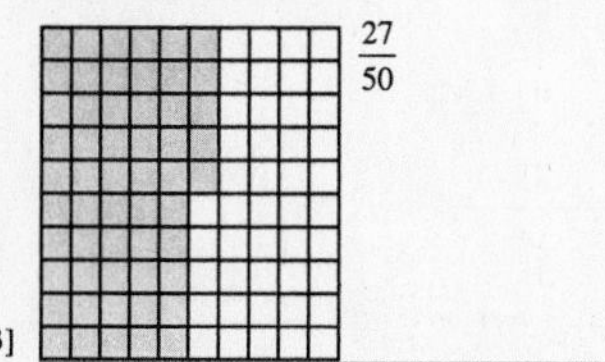 $\frac{27}{50}$

[134] Tuesday

[135] $\frac{9}{11}$

[136] C

[137] 2.45

[138] The decimal equivalent is equal to the numerator multiplied by 0.09.

[139] C

[140] D

Chapter 5: Investigating Fractions

[141] Answers may vary. Sample: Fractions can be used to follow a recipe, to measure the dimensions of a room, or to follow the stock exchange. Decimals can be used for money amounts, batting averages, or the measuring of rain fall.

[142] 0.16

[143] $\frac{5}{8}$

[144] 50

[145] $383.18

[146] D

[147] D

[148] 680 ft.

[149] 4 or 12

[150] 97

[151] $305.24

[152] 108

[153] week: 6, 12, 18, 24, 30

[154] 56 in.

[155] 103.5 in.^{2}

ANSWERS

[1] $1\frac{1}{2}$

[2] 1

[3] about 2 cups

[4] Answers may vary. Students should explain that a fraction can be rounded by deciding whether it is closest to 0, $\frac{1}{2}$, or 1 and then writing the fraction as that number. This can be very helpful when estimating sums or differences because numbers can be rounded before they are added and subtracted. The numbers 0, $\frac{1}{2}$, and 1 are easily added and subtracted.

[5] Answers may vary. Check to see that fractions add to two when rounded. For example, $\frac{5}{8}, \frac{4}{5}, \frac{1}{9}$, and $\frac{3}{7}$ round to $\frac{1}{2}$, 1, 0, and $\frac{1}{2}$, the sum of which is 2. Students should show similar logic in their explanations.

[6] B

[7] 1

[8] Answers may vary. Students may explain that they should first round each mixed number to the nearest whole number. Thus $31\frac{6}{7}$ rounds to 32 and $10\frac{1}{8}$ rounds to 10. The whole numbers can then be subtracted. So 32 - 10 = 22.

[9] Answers may vary. Students should begin by rounding the lengths of time required to print each type of page to the nearest whole number (1, 2, and 3 minutes). They must then determine what combination of pages might require 11 minutes. For example, four normal pages would require about 4 minutes, two pages with charts would require about 4 minutes, and one page with a graph would require about 3 minutes. Thus a report of seven pages, two of which have charts and one of which has a graph, would take 11 minutes. Check student answers for accuracy.

[10] A

[11] B

[12] \$8. Students should round each weight to the nearest whole number, thus 2 lb, 4 lb, and 4 lb. Next they must add the rounded weights, 10 lb, and multiply the total number of pounds by the price per pound. Thus $10 \text{ lb} \times \$0.80/\text{lb} = \$8$.

[13] The puppy gained about 29 lb between its first and last visit. Students should round the weight at the first visit to 7 lb and the weight at the last visit to 36 lb. The difference between the two weights can then be easily found. The puppy gained about 7 lb between its second and third visits. Students should round the weight at the third visit to 26 lb and subtract the rounded weight of the second visit, 19 lb.

[14] From left to right: 16° C, 3° C, 3° C, 2° C, 5° C. Students may round each temperature to the nearest whole number, then subtract the previous temperature to find the temperature change. If students round to the nearest half, answers will be: 16° C, 3° C, $2\frac{1}{2}$° C, 4° C.

[15] D

[16] $1\frac{2}{5}$

[17] Answers may vary. Explain that fraction bars can be drawn parallel to one another so that the shaded portions on each do not overlap. A third fraction bar can then be drawn that aligns with the first fraction bar. By shading the number of sections that matches the first and second fraction bars, the third fraction bar will give the sum of the first two. This is true only when the fraction bars have the same number of sections, thus the fractions have the same denominators.

[18] Answers may vary. Because the fractions have like denominators, the answer will have the same denominator. To complete the sentence, add the numerators (2 + 4 = 6), and place the sum in the numerator of the answer. Thus the sum of the fractions is $\frac{6}{9}$.

[19] Answers may vary. Draw a model that can be described by the equation $\frac{1}{4}+\frac{3}{4}=\frac{4}{4}$ (or 1). Draw either fraction bars or circles to model the sentence. Either type of model should show one of four shaded sections added to three of four shaded sections to produce four out of four shaded sections.

[20] A

[21] $\frac{1}{3}$ of the throws

[22] $\frac{1}{2}$ of her money

[23] A

[24] $\frac{1}{5}$

[25] A

[26] The equation is $\frac{10}{10}-\frac{4}{10}=\frac{6}{10}$ or $\frac{3}{5}$.

[27] $\frac{7}{12}$. The equation is $\frac{4}{12}+\frac{3}{12}=\frac{7}{12}$.

[28] Day 4. Subtract the distance on each day from the distance the next day to see the changes. The greatest change from one day to the next is $\frac{3}{8}$ mile on Day 4.

[29] Mathematics; $\frac{1}{5}$h

[30] $\frac{1}{8}$ mi

[31] Answers may vary. Create problems that can be solved by the equation $\frac{5}{6}-\frac{2}{6}=\frac{3}{6}\left(\text{or } \frac{1}{2}\right)$. For example, a sample problem might be that five out of a group of six students read a particular book. Two of those students that read the book did not enjoy it. What fraction of the group read and enjoyed the book?

[32] Answers will vary. The first method is to use fraction bars that describe the fractions given then to find a fraction bar with an area equal to the sum or difference. The second method is to find equivalent fractions with the same denominator, model them with fraction bars, then find the sum or difference.

[33] Answers will vary. Students should suggest that estimation is important because it gives you an idea of what the answer should be close to. In this way, you will know if the answer you calculate is correct. Otherwise, you can make a mistake and not realize that your answer is incorrect.

[34] D

[35] $1\frac{7}{20}$ pounds

[36] $\frac{1}{2}$ gallon

[37] B

[38] $\frac{23}{20}$ or $1\frac{3}{20}$

[39] She has traveled $\frac{7}{10}$ of the track and has $\frac{3}{10}$ of the track to go. If the track is three miles, she must go 0.9 mile more.

[40] $19\frac{1}{24}$ gallons

[41] $\frac{5}{12}$ h or 25 min.

[42] $\frac{5}{8}$ cup

[43] $\frac{1}{3}+\frac{1}{2}+\frac{3}{4}=\frac{19}{12}=1\frac{7}{12}$

ANSWERS

Chapter 6: Using Fractions

[44] Students must first add the number of games won to the number of games tied. They must then place this number over the total number of games played to show the fraction of games that were won or tied. To write their equations they must subtract this fraction from the total number of games played over itself.

Bruins: $\frac{80}{80}-\frac{56}{80}=\frac{24}{80}$. Penguins: $\frac{80}{80}-\frac{47}{80}=\frac{33}{80}$.
Flames: $\frac{80}{80}-\frac{54}{80}=\frac{26}{80}$. Whalers: $\frac{80}{80}-\frac{42}{80}=\frac{38}{80}$.

The Boston Bruins have the smallest fraction of lost games. The Hartford Whalers have the largest. Student answers regarding predictions will vary. Most students will predict the Calgary Flames have the smallest fraction, however they should realize that although the Bruins won fewer games than the Flames, they also lost fewer games because they had more ties.

[45] A

[46] $\frac{7}{40}$

[47] Answers may vary. When the sum of the fraction parts is an improper fraction, the fraction must be renamed as a mixed number. The mixed number can then be added easily to the whole number to find the answer. Examples will vary.

[48] B

[49] $10\frac{5}{6}$ yd

[50] No. The sum of the two mixed numbers is $4\frac{1}{12}$ c, which is slightly greater than four.

[51] Answers may vary. Students should explain that the whole numbers can be added first to get the sum 10. Next the fractions can be mentally placed into two groups, one with a denominator of 3 and one with a denominator of 5. The groups are $\frac{2}{3}+\frac{1}{3}$ and $\frac{1}{5}+\frac{3}{5}$. The sum of each group can then be found, $\frac{3}{3}$, which equals 1, and $\frac{4}{5}$. Finally, these numbers are added to the sum of the whole numbers to get the answer $11\frac{4}{5}$.

Chapter 6: Using Fractions

[52] D

[53] $18\frac{1}{8}$ in.

[54] C

[55] $10\frac{8}{13}$

[56] 87 ft. Students must first find the total length of the three sides of the parking lot. They can add in two sets of mixed numbers or add all three numbers at once. The sum of $22\frac{1}{2}+22\frac{1}{2}+40\frac{3}{4}=85\frac{3}{4}$. They must then find the next largest whole number that is divisible by 3. That number is 87.

[57] $53\frac{29}{30}$ mi

[58] 4 rolls

[59] C

[60] $3\frac{3}{5}$

[61] C

[62] Wednesday; $1\frac{1}{4}$ in.

[63] $1\frac{1}{8}$ lb

[64] $2\frac{1}{6}$ yd

[65] January; $1\frac{3}{8}$" more than February

[66] C

[67] $1\frac{3}{4}$

Chapter 6: Using Fractions

[68] The next number is $13\frac{7}{12}$. Each number is $2\frac{3}{4}$ greater than the previous number. Explanations may vary.

[69] $1\frac{7}{24}$ ft

[70] From smallest to largest: garlic, grapefruit, potato, onion, pineapple, celery, turnip, pumpkin. Weight differences:
$\frac{1}{2}$ lb; $3\frac{15}{16}$ lb; $3\frac{3}{16}$ lb; $6\frac{5}{8}$ lb; $28\frac{9}{16}$ lb; $2\frac{11}{16}$ lb; $767\frac{3}{4}$ lb
Organization of charts will vary. Check for accuracy.

[71] Monday; $\frac{1}{6}$ hour longer

[72] $\frac{7}{12}$ cup

[73] D

[74] Answers may vary.

[75] A

[76] D

[77] $414

[78] 560

[79] $54\frac{1}{2}$ meters. Students need to find the total perimeter of the fence and subtract the length of the house.

[80] Five red strips and four black strips.

[81] 2 miles

[82] $19.94

[83] 56

[84] $\frac{3}{8}$

[85] C

Chapter 6: Using Fractions

[86] $\frac{3}{10}$

[87] Answers may vary. The answer is $\frac{1}{3}\times\frac{1}{2}$. To multiply fractions, multiply across the numerators and then multiply across the denominators. So the answer is $\frac{1}{6}$.

[88] Answers may vary. Multiplying any number by a proper fraction means that you are finding a portion of that number. Because a portion is always smaller than the original number, the product of any number multiplied by a fraction is always smaller than the number. Thus the product of two fractions that are smaller than 1 will always be smaller than one.

[89] The multiplication sentence is $\frac{1}{3}\times\frac{3}{5}=\frac{3}{15}$. Problems that can be described using the model will vary. Check for accuracy.

[90] B

[91] $\frac{3}{8}$. The equation is $\frac{1}{2}\times\frac{3}{4}=\frac{3}{8}$.

[92] $\frac{1}{14}$. The equation is $\frac{5}{7}\times\frac{1}{10}=\frac{5}{70}$, or $\frac{1}{14}$.

[93] C

[94] $\frac{2}{9}$

[95] The Gobi desert is one-seventh the size of the Sahara. $\frac{1}{7}\times 3{,}500{,}000$ is 500,000.

[96] (a) $\frac{2}{7}$; $\frac{1}{2}\times\frac{2}{7}=\frac{1}{7}$. (b) $\frac{5}{7}$; $\frac{1}{5}\times\frac{5}{7}=\frac{1}{7}$.

[97] 16 muffins are left

[98] $4\frac{1}{2}$ yd

[99] The product must be less than the whole number you started with.

[100] C

Chapter 6: Using Fractions

[101] 8

[102] Yes. The carpet is $4\frac{1}{5}$ yd^2.

[103] D

[104] A

[105] A

[106] $20\frac{2}{5}$

[107] $10\frac{2}{5}$. Students must first find the area of each crate $\left(\frac{8}{5}\times\frac{13}{6}=3\frac{7}{15}\right)$ and then add it together three times or simply multiply by three.

[108] 2 cups

[109] $\frac{5}{8}$ of a pound

[110] C

[111] Answers will vary.

[112] No; $6\frac{2}{3}\times 15\frac{3}{4}=105$

[113] D

[114] $\frac{1}{3}$

[115] Answers may vary. The reciprocal of a fraction is found by inverting the fraction. When a fraction is multiplied by its reciprocal, the product is one. Reciprocals are used when dividing by fractions because dividing by a fraction is the same as multiplying by the reciprocal of that fraction.

[116] Answers may vary. Students may describe the steps of each type of division. Students should suggest that dividing a whole number by a whole number is actually the same as multiplying by the reciprocal of that number. For example, $6\div 3$ is $6\times\frac{1}{3}$. Examples will vary.

Chapter 6: Using Fractions

[117] Answers may vary. Check for accuracy. An example would be that at a certain beach, lifeguards remain at each post for $\frac{1}{3}$ hr before switching to another. How many posts would a lifeguard have in 9 hours? The answer is 27. Check for similar logic.

[118] B

[119] $\frac{1}{8}$

[120] B

[121] $\frac{77}{270}$

[122] Answers may vary. First change the mixed number to an improper fraction, $\frac{5}{4}$. Next, find the reciprocal of the fraction, $\frac{4}{5}$. Then multiply the whole number by the reciprocal. Students should simplify before multiplying. Thus $40\times\frac{4}{5}=40\times 4\times\frac{1}{5}=160\times\frac{1}{5}=160\div 5=32$.

[123] C

[124] 6. Explanations will vary.

[125] $16\frac{2}{3}$

[126] 5

[127] 5

[128] $2\frac{6}{17}$. Students must divide the number of hours in a day on the Earth (24) by the number of hours in a day on Saturn $\left(10\frac{1}{5}\right)$. $24\div 10\frac{1}{5}=24\div\frac{51}{5}=24\times\frac{5}{51}=\frac{120}{51}=2\frac{18}{51}=2\frac{6}{17}$

[129] D

[130] $3\frac{1}{4}$ quarts

Chapter 6: Using Fractions

[131] Answers may vary. Students should explain that they must multiply the number of yards by 36 inches. They should know to multiply rather than divide because they are converting from a larger unit, yards, to a smaller unit, inches. Thus they are looking for a larger number than the one being converted. Since there are 36 inches in one yard, there are 90 inches in $2\frac{1}{2}$ yards.

[132] Answers may vary. Because not all items are measured in the same units, you need to be able to change from one unit to another.

[133] Answers may vary. Check problems for logic. Sample: Jennifer has $3\frac{1}{4}$ pounds of apples. How many ounces of apples does she have? The answer is 52 ounces.

[134] A

[135] A

[136] $\frac{1}{5}$ mile

[137] Yes. Convert 3 gallons to 12 quarts to 24 pints to 48 cups. Since Timmy needs only 42 cups, he has more than enough juice.

[138] a) no
b) 5 feet

[139] $3\frac{3}{4}$. Convert 252 ounces to $15\frac{3}{4}$ pounds. Then divide the number of pounds in the package by the number of pounds the pet eats each week.

[140] 3 quarts. Divide 6 pints $\div$ 2 pints/quart = 3 quarts.

[141] 6600 feet

[142] No. Multiply $2\frac{1}{4}$ tons by 2000 pounds/ton to find the total number of pounds the bridge can hold. The bridge can hold up to 4,500 pounds, thus the truck cannot cross the bridge.

[143] Yes. She needs $2\frac{3}{5}\times 8$ oz/c $=20\frac{4}{5}$ oz. She has 22 oz.

Chapter 7: Ratios, Proportions, and Percents

[1] $\frac{11}{13}$

[2] D

[3] A ratio is a comparison of two numbers. Examples will vary.

[4] One ratio describes pies to apples (3:7). Another ratio describes apples to pies (7:3). A third ratio describes pies to the total number of objects (3:10). And the fourth ratio describes apples to the total number of objects (7:10).

[5] D

[6] D

[7] $\frac{3}{5}$

[8] Yes, he is correct. There are 12 inches in 1 foot and there are 3 feet in 1 yard. The ratio of inches to yards is 36:1.

[9] 4:2

[10] Students' drawings may vary but should contain 5 socks and 2 shoes.

[11] 3:1

[12] a. 5:2 b. 2:3 c. 3:5

[13] a. square to triangle; b. octagon to decagon; c. pentagon to hexagon

[14] 64:14 (Can also be written as 32:7); 187:11 (Can also be written as 17:1); 303:225

[15] A

[16] Answers may include 1 : 8, 2 : 16, 3 : 24, etc

[17] If one ratio is equal to another, each term in one ratio can be either multiplied or divided by the same non-zero number to produce the numbers in the other ratio.

[18] A

[19] A

[20] Answers will vary. Samples: a. 3:4 and 18:24; b. 1:5 and 6:30; c. 7.5 and 28:20.

Chapter 7: Ratios, Proportions, and Percents

[21] $\frac{1}{4}; \frac{1}{2}$

[22] a. $\frac{2}{1}$; b. $\frac{3}{4}$; c. $\frac{2}{3}$

[23] a. 3,000; b. 12.5; c. 600

[24] Equal ratios have the same simplest form. All three answers are equal ratios and are therefore all correct.

[25] C

[26] 16 pens per box

[27] Answers will vary. Sample: A rate is a ratio that compares two measures with different units. Example: miles per hour. A unit rate is a rate that compares one unit to another unit with a quantity of one.

[28] Jim is incorrect. Grace got a better deal. She paid $1.20/notebook while Jim paid $1.30/notebook. The answer can be determined by finding and comparing the unit rate paid by each person.

[29] a. 27.7 mi/h; b. $0.33/peach; c. 3 steps/s

[30] She ran at 0.18 mi/min

[31] D

[32] no

[33] Answers will vary. Sample: A proportion is a statement showing that two ratios are equal. The cross products of a proportion are equal.

[34] Answers will vary. Sample: The product of the first numerator, 3, and the second denominator, 15, is 45. The product of the first denominator, 5, and the second numerator, 9, is 45. Because the cross products are equal, the statement is a proportion and a proportion is an equation stating that two ratios are equal. Thus the statement is true.

[35] b and c

[36] No. The cross products are not equal.

[37] B

[38] $\frac{1}{2}$

Chapter 7: Ratios, Proportions, and Percents

[39] Yes. The weight of the water when the tank is full will be 240 pounds $\left(\frac{5}{40} = \frac{30}{x}\right)$. The weight of the water plus the weight of the tank will be 260 pounds.

[40] C

[41] B

[42] 36

[43] Kevin read 4 books in 6 weeks or 2 books in 3 weeks. Multiplication or division can be used to find the proportion. Because Kevin read fewer books, the numerator of the proportion must be smaller than the numerator in Mary's rate. Thus the proportion can be found by division.

[44] 4, $\left(\frac{33.5}{1} = \frac{134}{x}\right)$

[45] 18 in.

[46] Swimming

[47] B

[48] 120

[49] D

[50] 260 dimes

[51] 17

[52] 180 gallons

[53] Over 30 million

[54] 6 more spelling words

[55] Explanations may vary. The sum is 2,550.

[56] B

[57] B

[58] printer 1: 25 min; printer 2: 10 min; printer 3: 6.25 min; printer 4: 5 min

[59] B

Chapter 7: Ratios, Proportions, and Percents

[60] 9 cm

[61] Answers may vary. Sample 1 cm = 15 m. Any equal ratio is also correct.

[62] Answers will vary. Sample: The figure can be enlarged as long as all of the details are enlarged by the same amount. The scale must be changed as well by either increasing the scale measure or decreasing the actual measure.

[63] Answers will vary. The scale must be one that allows 20 ft to be represented in 8 in. Sample: He could use 2 in. = 5 ft.

[64] $\frac{1\text{ cm}}{3\text{ m}}; \frac{0.5\text{ cm}}{5\text{ m}}$

[65] A

Let x be the length of the room.

$$\frac{9}{15} = \frac{14.4}{x}$$
$$9x = 15 \times 14.4$$
$$\frac{9x}{9} = \frac{216}{9}$$
$$x = 24$$

[66] The room is 24 feet long.

[67] Answers may vary. Sample: Write the scale as a ratio. Set this ratio equal to the ratio of the size of the drawing to the actual size of the object. Write the cross products and solve.

[68] B

[69] B

[70] B

[71] 9 m

[72] Draw a rectangle with lengths 4 cm and 2.5 cm. The scale should be 1 mm = 20 cm.

[73] 9.525 cm

[74] A

Chapter 7: Ratios, Proportions, and Percents

[75] 74%

[76] Answers will vary. Sample: A percent is a number that is compared to 100.

[77] Answers will vary. Sample: A percent is a number that is compared to 100. Therefore if you are told that a given percent (60%, for example) answered no, it means that out of 100 people, 60 said no. You can then subtract 60 from 100 to determine the number of people that did not say no. In this example, 40 people did not say no.

[78] D

[79] A

[80] Answers may vary. Sample: She has $30 (30% of $100) and needs $30 more to have $60, which is 60% of 100.

[81] Answers will vary. Sample: To determine the percent left, Mario must find the total amount of money he spent ($42 + $24 + $6 = $72). Then he must subtract the total from the original $100 ($100 − $72 = $28). He must then figure out what percent of 100 is the remaining amount. Twenty-eight is 28% of 100.

[82] 29%

[83] 88%

[84] Students should shade 28 squares.

[85] 30%; 54%

[86] 57%

[87] A

[88] 0.24

[89] Answers may vary. Sample: To write a percent as a fraction, write the percent as the numerator and the denominator as 100. Then simplify the fraction by dividing the numerator and denominator by the GCF.

[90] Answers will vary. Sample: A percent can be written as a decimal or a fraction. All three forms are equivalent. The quantity, 18, appears in all three forms.

Chapter 7: Ratios, Proportions, and Percents

[91] $\frac{12}{25}$; 0.48; 48%

[92] $\frac{57}{125}$, 0.456, $\frac{21}{250}$, 0.084, $\frac{47}{1000}$, 0.047

[93] 42%; 0.42, $\frac{21}{50}$

[94] Row 1: $\frac{17}{50}$, 34%; Row 2: 0.33, 33%; Row 3: $\frac{31}{100}$, 0.31; Row 4: $\frac{8}{25}$, 32%; Row 5: 0.3, 30%

[95] D

[96] D

[97] A

[98] D

[99] Answers will vary. Sample: Percents can be written as fractions and decimals. A percent, such as 67%, can be written as a fraction by writing the percent as a fraction with a denominator of 100. Therefore both students are correct.

[100] 0.35, 35%

[101] 0.62, $\frac{31}{50}$

[102] 75%, 25%

[103] C

[104] A model should be drawn with 10 equal sections. Each section is 10%. If the entire model were shaded the cost would be $7.00. Each section represents a cost of $0.70. Students should shade 2 sections or 20% for an estimated price of $1.40.

[105] Student should draw a model with 10 equal sections. Each section is 10%. If the entire model were shaded it would represent 60. Each section represents 6. Students should shade 1 section, or 10%, to represent 6.

[106] Models may vary. Sample: 5 x 5 grid slightly more than 5 squares shaded.

Chapter 7: Ratios, Proportions, and Percents

[107] A

[108] Answers may vary. 6

[109] Answers will vary. Sample: The second sale is better. The first sale price can be found by multiplying the percent by the original price. The second sale price can be found by multiplying the percent off by the original price and then subtracting the product from the original price. The first ad says that jewelry is 80% of the original price, which means that it has been marked down by 20% $(100\% - 80\% = 20\%)$. The second ad says that the jewelry has been marked down 25%, which is 75% of the original price $(100\% - 25\% = 75\%)$.

[110] Answers will vary depending on estimating technique used. Samples: 720, 666, 684, 665.

[111] B

[112] Answers will vary. Sample: Round the price of the coat to $57. Write the percent as a fraction, $\frac{80}{100} = \frac{4}{5}$. Multiply $\frac{4}{5}$ by $57 to get $45.60. The sale price of the coat is $45.60 so Azeeb can afford the coat. (Students might also correctly suggest setting up a model).

[113] 35

[114] 48 min or 0.8 h

[115] 15% of 89

[116] Answers will vary. Sample: Round $199 to $200. Write the tax as a fraction in simplest form, $\frac{3}{50}$. Multiply the fraction by the price of the television. The tax will be $12.

[117] A

[118] 30.29

[119] Answers will vary. Sample: Some percents, such as 50%, can be written as fractions that are easy to multiply by other numbers $\left(\frac{1}{2}\right)$. Other percents, such as 13%, cannot be written as nicely and are easier to work with as decimals.

[120] D

Chapter 7: Ratios, Proportions, and Percents

[121] $451

[122] D

[123] 156

[124] B

[125] A

[126] Answers will vary. Sample: Enrico received responses from 10 people (20% x 50). He wants responses from at least 18 people. Thus he needs responses from 8 more people.

[127] 42.75 g

[128] 13 games. Since you are talking about games won, you must round up.

[129] 6 students

[130] 21 red; 20 yellow; 13 white; 5 orange; 11 combination. Answers require rounding because flowers are not divisible.

[131] 20 people; 61 people; 5 people

[132] C

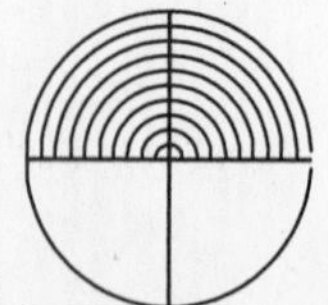

[133]

[134] Answers will vary. Sample: Express each percent in the table as a decimal. Multiply the decimal by 360, the number of degrees in a circle. Round the answer to the nearest degree. Then use a protractor to draw an angle inside a circle that has the measure you just calculated. Follow this procedure for all the data in the table.

Chapter 7: Ratios, Proportions, and Percents

[135] Answers may vary slightly. No. The interior angles of all circles, regardless of size, add up to 360°. Therefore, both Gerry and Richard will multiply the decimal forms of the percents in the table by 360° to find the angle measures of each section of their graphs. The lengths of the sides of the angles in Gerry's circle will be longer than those in Richard's circle, but the angle measures will all be the same.

[136] B

[137] B

[138] Answers may vary. Sample: Susie should convert the percents into decimals and multiply each of them by 360° to determine the number of degrees in each section of the circle graph. Her circle should be broken into 5 sections with measures of 46.8°, 154.8°, 122.4°, and 7.2°.

[139] Answers will vary. Students must realize that the total of the percents must add to 100. Therefore, the combined percent of students who vacuum and put away groceries must be 19%. Any combination of percents that add to 19 will be correct.

[140] Car, 14%; walk, 24%; bus, 62%

[141] Check students' graphs.

[142] Check students' graphs.

[143] Check students' graphs.

ANSWERS

Chapter 8: Tools of Geometry

[1] B

A

[2]

[3] Answers may vary. Sample: A plane is the most encompassing of the geometric figures described. All of the other figures exist within planes. Lines are the next most encompassing figure, then rays, line segments, and finally points. Any figure that is more narrowly defined, such as a point, can exist within any figure that is more widely defined.

[4] Different planes. A plane is a flat surface that extends indefinitely in all directions. The wall is in a plane that extends vertically from the surface of the Earth. The wall's shadow is in a plane that is parallel to the Earth's surface.

[5] Lines continue without end in each direction. The arrows in the diagram indicate that the geometric figures are lines. Thus each line extends beyond that which is shown and the two lines will eventually intersect.

[6] C

[7] D

[8] Answers may vary. Sample: L, M, N; K, O, N; ON and OL.

[9] The diagram should resemble a simple house. Some students may draw the same shape at a slant. It can still be correct.

[10] Answers will vary but students should suggest that points are used to indicate cities or other locations on the map. Line segments are used to connect various locations. Because the map is drawn on a flat surface, the map itself could be considered to be part of a plane. Yes, more than two cities could have collinear locations.

[11] $\overleftrightarrow{PL}$

[12] A

[13] AB and FE; BC and GF; CD and HG; DE and AH

Chapter 8: Tools of Geometry

[14] a. Park Avenue and Criss-Cross Street
b. Sunny Court and Acorn Way
c. Sunny Court, Park Avenue, and Acorn Way
d. Sunny Court, Criss-Cross Street, and Acorn Way

[15] Answers may vary. Sample:

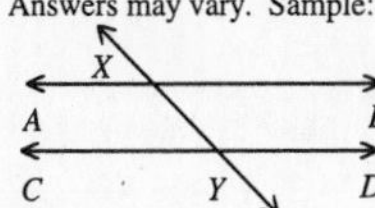

[16] A

[17]

[18] Answers may vary. Sample: The center point of the protractor should be placed on the vertex of the angle in such a way that one side of the angle passes through zero on the protractor scale. The scale should be read where the second side of the angle passes through the scale.

[19] B

[20] A

[21] Answers may vary. Sample: All of the sides of a square are equal in length. Therefore, no matter what the size of the square, the sides will always meet at the same angle. Triangles, however, can take on various shapes and sizes, thus creating many different combinations of angles.

[22] Answers may vary. Sample: Student diagrams should show the walk beginning at an angle of 0°. The diagram should show a gradual increase in angle. Students should indicate that the walk becomes more difficult as the angle increases. A greater angle means a steeper incline.

Chapter 8: Tools of Geometry

[23] Answers may vary. Check students' answers for accuracy. Sample: Draw one side of the angle using the straightedge of the protractor. Place the center point of the protractor at what will be the vertex of the angle in such a way that the line drawn passes through the zero point on the protractor's scale. Draw a mark outside the scale of the protractor at the desired measurement. Then use the straightedge to connect the vertex to the mark. Make sure to use the proper scale on the protractor.

[24] Answers may vary. An obtuse angle, $\angle ABC$ will be greater than 90°. An acute angle, $\angle DEF$ will be less than 90°.

[25] 49°; Answers may vary. Sample: Students must realize that $\angle ABE$ has a measure of 180°. Therefore, the sum of the three angles must equal 180°. So, $180° - 72° - 59° = x$. $x = 49°$.

[26] a. 90°; b. 180°; c. 90°; d. 60°; e. 165°

[27] 12°, 88°, 123°; students should use 0° and 90° as reference points to estimate the measurements. Answers may be slightly off.

[28] C

[29] B

[30] There are four right angles in a baseball diamond. The angle made by the ball would be acute. Even though students cannot yet calculate angles, they should realize that the height of the mound is small when compared with the distance to home plate. Thus the angle must be small. Check student diagrams for accuracy.

[31] $\angle MLO$, $\angle MLN$, $\angle NLO$

[32] A

[33] 1,2 or 2,3 or 3,4 or 4,1 or 7,8 or 5,6 or 6,7 or 5,8

[34] Answers may vary. Exterior: $\angle ABC$, $\angle ABD$, $\angle GEF$, or $\angle FEH$. Interior: $\angle CBE$, $\angle DBE$, $\angle BEH$, or $\angle BEG$.

[35] ∠FEH, ∠GEB

[36] 135°

[37] 45°

Chapter 8: Tools of Geometry

[38]

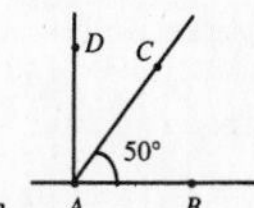

[39] Answers may vary. Sample: ∠1 and ∠3.

[40] Measures: 30° and 60°; the sum of the measures must be 90°, and 60 is twice 30.

[41] Sample: Congruent angles have the same measure. You could tell by using a protractor or tracing one and putting it on top of the other. If it fits, the angles are congruent.

[42] True. The sum of complementary angles is 90°, so both angles must be less than 90°.

[43] D

[44] right

[45] An isosceles triangle has two congruent sides. An equilateral triangle has three congruent sides. An equilateral triangle is therefore also an isosceles triangle because it fits the definition of having two congruent sides. An isosceles triangle, however, is not necessarily an equilateral triangle.

[46] The triangle is obtuse. The sum of the three angles must equal 180°, so the remaining angle must be 101°. Because one angle is obtuse, the triangle is obtuse.

[47] Equilateral triangles not only have congruent sides, but also congruent angles. They are also called equiangular.

[48] B

[49] A

[50] C

[51] scalene

[52] Triangles should have no congruent sides and one 90° angle.

[53] Triangles should have three acute angles and two congruent sides.

[54] Triangles should have three congruent sides.

Chapter 8: Tools of Geometry

[55] a. isosceles; b. equilateral

[56] a. 6, 8; b. 2, 5; c. 2, 4, 5; d. 1, 3, 4, 7, 8; e. 3, 7; f. 1, 3, 7, 9

[57] C

[58] hexagon

[59] In a convex polygon, the number of angles matches the number of sides . In a nonconvex polygon, the same is true. However, some of the angles are outside the figure.

[60] C

[61] Figure I is not a polygon because it has no segments. Figure II is a polygon, but it is not convex. Figure III is not a polygon because it is not closed. Figure IV is a convex polygon.

[62] No. It is impossible to draw a 3-sided polygon that is not convex.

[63] D

[64] Answers may vary. Sample: Check to see that students are using the prefixes properly so that they will become more comfortable using them to describe polygons.

[65] Answers may vary. Sample: Students should explain that polygons are closed figures made up of segments. Polygons can be separated from each other according to the number of sides they have and whether or not they are convex.

[66] Answers may vary, but students should note the different number of sides and angles of differences. The fact that they are all convex polygons should be included among the similarities.

[67] Answers may vary, but students should note the different number of sides and angles as differences. The fact that they are all convex polygons should be included among the similarities.

[68] Check student's diagrams. Diagrams should be of a convex hexagon.

[69] Check student's diagrams. Diagrams should be of convex octagons.

[70] No . If a polygon is convex, a line connecting two points inside the polygon cannot intersect the polygon. Yes. If a polygon is not convex it is possible for a line segment connecting two points to intersect the polygon.

Chapter 8: Tools of Geometry

[71] quadrilateral, parallelogram, rhombus

[72] square

[73] D

[74] Answers may vary. Sample: Check student diagrams for accuracy. Triangles arranged in different combinations can produce all of the figures described.

[75] The figure should have two pairs of parallel sides, but it should not have right angles or four congruent sides.

[76] Figure should be a trapezoid.

[77] C

[78] All the figures are convex polygons with four sides. A square is a figure with four congruent sides and four right angles. A square is similar to a rhombus in that rhombuses also have four congruent sides. Unlike squares, however, rhombuses do not necessarily have four right angles. Like squares, rectangles have four right angles, but unlike squares, rectangles need not have four congruent sides. Parallelograms have two pairs of parallel sides, but unlike rectangles and squares, parallelograms do not need right angles. Trapezoids have only one pair of parallel sides and are therefore different from the other figures.

[79] A square has two pairs of parallel sides and four congruent sides, as does a rhombus. A square also has four right angles. Although a rhombus can have right angles, it does not always have right angles and therefore is not always a square.

[80] C

[81] Answers may vary. Sample: Students should be creative in their answers. Charts should show that quadrilaterals includes all of the other terms. It should also show that rectangles and rhombuses are types of parallelograms and that squares are rhombuses and rectangles. Finally, it should show that trapezoids are a separate category or quadrilaterals that are not directly related to parallelograms.

[82] a. 4 quadrilaterals; b. 1 square

[83] The figure is a quadrilateral, a polygon, and a trapezoid. Because all trapezoids are quadrilateral polygons, the best name for the figure is trapezoid.

Chapter 8: Tools of Geometry

[84] The figure is a polygon, quadrilateral, square, rectangle, and parallelogram. Because all squares are polygons, quadrilaterals, rectangles, and parallelograms, the best name for the figure is a square.

[85] 9

[86] D

[87] A

[88] 8

[89]
RB 2
6
H&C 7
9
2
PB&J 7

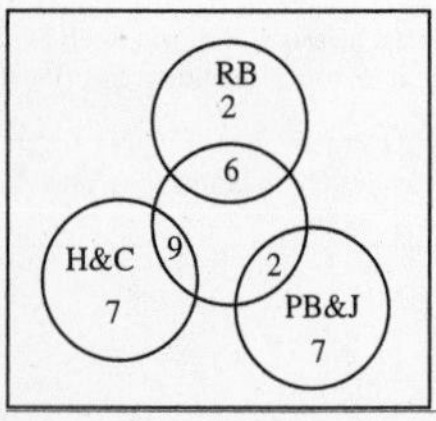

[90] 4

[91] 4;
B.ball 12
Math 5
3
1
5
4
4 Karate

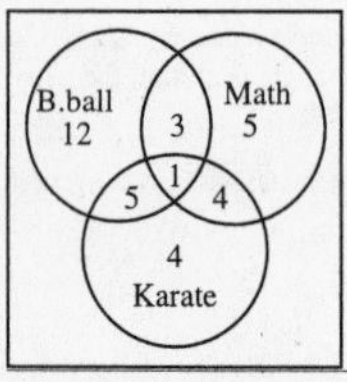

[92] Answers may vary. Samples: 11, 23, 35, 47.

[93] 9; **a.** \$20-1, \$5-1, \$1-1; **b.** \$10-1, \$1-16; **c.** \$10-1, \$5-1, \$1-11; **d.** \$10-1, \$5-3, \$1-1; **e.** \$10-2, \$5-1, \$1-1; **f.** \$5-1, \$1-21; **g.** \$5-2, \$1-16; **h.** \$5-3, \$1-11; **i.** \$5-4, \$1-1

[94] 5

[95] Venn diagram should show an overlap of 4.

ANSWERS

Chapter 8: Tools of Geometry

[96] C

[97] A

[98] no

[99] neither

[100] Figures that are congruent have the same size and shape. Similar figures have the same shape, but not necessarily the same size.

[101] All equilateral triangles are similar because they all have the same angles. But all equilateral triangles are not congruent because they have sides of different lengths.

[102] No. No. All rectangles are neither congruent nor similar.

[103] The figures are similar because they have the same shape. They are not congruent because they are a different size.

[104] D

[105] D

[106] Similar figures have the same shape. Congruent figures have the same size and the same shape. Therefore, congruent figures are similar, but because similar figures do not have the same size they are not congruent.

[107] A. No. The figures are not the same size.
B. No. The figures are different shapes.
C. Yes. The figures are the same size and shape.

[108] A, C, and E

[109] a and f; b and g; c and h

[110] Check to make sure that student diagrams are the same shape but a different size from the original polygon.

[111] The angles of similar polygons are congruent. The sides are proportional.

[112] C

[113] true

[114] A figure that has a line of symmetry has a line that divides the figure into two congruent halves. The line is called the line of symmetry and a figure may have more than one such line.

[115] b

[116] B

[117] D

[118] Answers may vary. Check students' answers for accuracy.

[119] Although answers will differ, students should suggest folding a sheet of paper in half before cutting the design. In this way, two identical halves will be produced once the paper is unfolded.

[120] 6

[121] The figure has one vertical line of symmetry.

[122] Students should produce a mirror image of the figure.

[123] 8

[124] One, four, and five each have four lines of symmetry as do squares. Two,three, and six have fewer lines of symmetry.

[125] Numerals 1, 2, 3, 6, 7, 8, and 9 have two lines of symmetry. Numerals 4, 5, and 10 have four lines of symmetry.

[126] B

[127] D

[128] diameter

[129] Students should demonstrate an understanding of each of the terms.

[130] C

[131] D

[132] D

[133] Answers may vary. Make sure that students construct their circles and draw chords properly.

[134] Check student diagrams for accuracy.

Chapter 8: Tools of Geometry

[135] Although responses will vary, students should suggest that the bank has different slots with varying diameters. Because each type of coin is in the shape of a circle with different diameters, each coin goes into a different slot. The slots might be arranged in order of radius, half the diameter. A dime, with the smallest radius, might be at one end while quarters, with the largest radius, might be at the other.

[136] BD, BE; AC; ∠DBE and ∠EBC; DE

[137] The central angles in a circle always add up to 360°.

[138] JK, KL, and JL; KO and OL; ∠KOL

[139] Jupiter has the greatest radius, which is about 44,000 miles. Pluto has the shortest radius, which is about 700 miles.

[140] 90°

[141] Answers may vary. Sample: They both leave the original figure the same size and shape; a translation moves every part of the figure the same amount. A rotation moves some parts more than others.

[142] C

[143] Answers may vary. Sample: The line of reflection is the line over which a figure is flipped.

[144] B

[145]

[146] Answers will vary. Sample: the curved section will be at the top of the reflection, not the bottom.

[147]

Chapter 9: Geometry and Measurment

[1] A

[2] B

[3] Tennessee is 42,146 times as big as one square mile.

[4] No. The area of the picture is larger than the area of the picture frame.

[5] A

[6] C

[7] Drawings may vary. The figure should have 8 squares inclosed, which would give you an area of 16 ft^2.

[8] Drawings may vary. The area of each shape is one and a half more than the number of interior dots.

[9] 3

[10] 48 squares

[11] 6

[12] 18; You can conclude your answer is 18, because the numbers in column D multiplied by 2 gives the number of boundary dots.

[13] 640 acres

[14] The area of a shape seems to be one half of the number of boundary dots when the number of interior dots is one.

[15] 64 mm

[16] B

[17] The area will double. For example if $a = 2$ and $b = 3$. The original area is equal to 6. If a is doubled the new area will be 4×3, or 12.

[18] D

Chapter 9: Geometry and Measurment

[19] B

[20] Answers may vary. Sample answer given. Possible dimensions: 1×36; 2×18; 3×12; 4×9; 6×6.

[21] $702.00

[22] 96 m; 252 m^2

[23] 6 ft.

[24] C

[25] 225 cm^2

[26] No. The square drawn should have sides equal to 4.

[27] Perimeter: 28 cm; Area: 161 cm^2

[28] 49 ft^2 ; 7 ft x 7 ft

[29] 720 ft.

[30] 169 ft^2. Since Mr. Close's kitchen is square, the sides of the kitchen are equal in length. Divide 52 by 4 to find the length of each side. The length of each side of the kitchen is 13 ft. To find the area, square the length of one side of the kitchen. The area is equal to 13^2, or 169 ft^2.

[31] C

[32] D

[33] 27.26 m^2

[34] 6,177 m^2

[35] Answers may vary. Sample: The rectangle and the parallelogram each have an area of 27 square units. The parallelogram has a height of 3 and a base length of 9. The rectangle has a length of 9 and a width of 3.

[36] the parallelogram is a rectangle.

[37] C

[38] D

ANSWERS

[39] Students may draw a triangle with a base of 12 in. and a height of 6 in.; a rectangle with a length of 9 in. and a width of 4 in.

[40] 2106 ft^2

[41] 16 cm

[42] 140 ft^2

[43] 259 $in.^2$

[44] 14 yd^2

[45] When the base and the height are doubled, the area is four times greater.

[46] Divide the figure into two polygons, a triangle and a rectangle. Find the area of each polygon. Add the areas to find the area of the figure. The area of the figure is 34 $in.^2$.

[47] C

[48] D

[49] 9.42 cm

[50] Divide the circumference of a circle by π to find the diameter of the circle.

[51] C

[52] C

[53] 18,186 miles

[54] 5 in.

[55] 75 ft

[56] 25 petunias

[57] 207.24 in.

[58] 6 in.

[59] a. B2 × 2 × 3.14;

b. green, 31.4 cm; blue, 62.8 cm; red, 94.2 cm; orange, 125.6 cm; purple, 157 cm.

[60] Each circumference is 31.4 cm more than the previous circle. Yellow, 188.4 cm

[61] The circumference is less than 100 cm. Use estimation. Round π to 3, and 31 to 30. 30 × 3 is less than 100.

[62] D

[63] 200.96 square centimeters

[64] The area of a circle will quadruple. For example, if $r = 2$, the original area is equal to 12.56 $in.^2$. If the radius is doubled, the new area will be $4r$, or 50.24 $in.^2$. $50.24 \div 12.56 = 4$.

[65] Tuesday. The area of the 14 in. pizza is greater than the area of the 12 in. pizza. However, the 14 in. pizza was divided into more slices than the 12 in. pizza. Therefore, the size of a slice of the 12 in. pie will be larger than a slice of the 14 in. pie.

[66] Divide the circumference by π to determine the diameter of the circle. The diameter is 10 inches. One-half of the diameter is the radius. The area of the circle is $\pi(5)^2 = 78.5$ $in.^2$.

[67] B

[68] Answers may vary. Sample: To determine the size of a swimming pool cover. To determine the landing target for skydivers.

[69] Circumference: 628 ft; Area: 31,400 ft^2

[70] Circumference: 9.42 in.; Area: 7.07 $in.^2$.

[71] The area of a square is larger; 13.76 in.

[72] Radius = 2

[73] D

[74] D

[75] B

[76] 3.26 cm^2

[77] A

[78] example:

[79] A three-dimensional figure is a figure that does not lie in a single plane. Examples will vary.

[80] Answers will vary. Sample: A face is a flat polygonal surface, a base is a face that can be the bottom of the figure, an edge is a segment where two faces intersect, and a vertex is a point where two edges meet. Three-dimensional figures can be described by the number and shape of the faces and bases as well as the number of edges and vertices.

[81] B

[82] A

[83] There can be more than one net for certain figures. Examples of drawings will vary. There are six correct nets for a cube.

[84] Answers will vary. Prisms and cylinders are alike in that they both have two bases. They are different in that prisms have faces that are parallelograms as well as having edges, and vertices. Cylinders do no have polygonal faces, edges, or vertices. Pyramids and cones are alike in that they both have one base and one vertex. They are different in that in addition to the base, pyramids have edges and polygonal faces. Cones do not have edges or polygonal faces aside from the circular bases.

[85] The net should look like a square with a triangle extending from each of its four edges. The edges of the square should serve as the base of each triangle. All the triangles can be folded either up or down, as long as their points all intersect at the same vertex.

[86] a. The figure is a trapezoidal prism.
b. The faces are rectangles and the bases are trapezoids.
c. Descriptions of the relationships among the edges will vary. Students should note which edges intersect and which edges are parallel.

[87] a. The figure is a square pyramid.
b. The four faces are congruent triangles and the base is a square.
c. Descriptions about the edges will vary. You should note that four edges intersect at the top vertex and four edges form the sides of the square base.

[88] Sue Ellen drew a triangular prism. Bjorn drew a hexagonal prism. Geno drew a trapezoidal prism.

[89] The number of faces plus the number of vertices minus the number of edges always equals 2.

[90] By column: rectangular prism; triangular prism; rectangular prism; cone; sphere; cylinder; sphere. Check diagrams for accuracy.

[91] B

[92] 982 $in.^2$

[93] Answers will vary. Students might suggest unfolding the prism into a net and finding the area of the flat net. Or they might suggest finding the sum of the areas of each of the faces. Some students may also suggest finding the area of one base, one side, and one end and multiplying the sum by two.

[94] The surface area quadruples. Students should explain that as the length of each edge doubles, the area of each face quadruples. Because the area of each face is four times greater than it was when Sofia computed the area, the new surface area is four times greater than Sofia's answer. Examples will vary.

[95] C

[96] B

[97] Answers may vary. Accept all logical answers. The suggested answer is to wrap Box 1 in Wrapping B, Box 2 in Wrapping C, and Box 3 in Wrapping A. Students should explain that the answer can be found by matching the area of each sheet of wrapping paper most closely with the surface area of each box.

[98] $7.02

[99] $848. The surface area of the walls is $560 ft^2$. Applying two coats of paint is the same as doubling the surface area of the walls, so the surface area that needs to be painted is $1,120 ft^2$. The total surface area divided by the surface area covered by one gallon of paint (280 ft^2) gives the total number of gallons required. Four gallons of blue paint are required for the walls. The surface area of the ceiling is 300 ft^2, so the total surface area that has to be painted is 600 ft^2. Thus the number of gallons of white paint necessary is 2.1 which has to be rounded up to 3. The total of 7 gallons of paint at $8 each equals $56. To carpet the surface area of the floor (300† ft^2) at $5/$ft^2$ equals $1,500. The total price is then $1556.

[100] Check student's diagrams. The surface area is 2,700 cm^2.

[101] 31 stickers

[102] 22 (actually 21.6) sheets. If the box has no top, only 17 (actually 16.8) sheets are needed.

[103] High quality. The answer can be found by first determining the surface area of the four walls plus the ceiling of the shed. The surface area is 376 ft^2. The surface area can then be multiplied by the prices to find the total cost for each quality.

[104] She can get her second choice at $1.90/$ft^2$.

[105] A

[106] 96 cm^3

[107] Answers will vary. Students should explain that the volume of a rectangular prism can be found by multiplying the prism's length by its width by its height.

[108] Answers will vary. Students should explain that because volume in calculated by multiplying three values that each have the same unit, the answer must be a value with that unit cubed. Since the unit being multiplied is always one of length, three possible units of volume are m^3, cm^3, and ft^3.

[109] Answers will vary. Check student's diagrams. An example could be a rectangular prism measuring 5 cm × 3 cm × 9 cm.

Chapter 9: Geometry and Measurment

[110] Box 3 fits all the presents most efficiently. Box 1 also fits all three presents, but it is unnecessarily large and expensive.

[111] 24 cm

[112] Trunk B

[113] D

[114] 7 inches

[115] A

[116] B

[117] 24 ft^2

[118] $43.20

[119] Trunk C has the greatest volume at 7 ft^3.

[120] C

[121] 55

[122] B

[123] A

[124] 72 games

[125] Answers may vary. Sample: 13 quarters, 11 dimes, 17 nickels.

[126] 9

[127] 319 miles

[128] 7, 9, and 12

[129] 2:40 P.M.

[130] 9, 9, 14, 14, 14, 18

[131] 56

Chapter 10: Algebra: Integers and Graphing

[1] A

[2] −10 −5 0 5 10

[3] A thermometer uses a scale of positive and negative numbers as does a number line.

[4] –56 is to the left of –55 on a number line because it is less than –55. Both numbers are to the left of zero on the number line.

[5] All integer points between –5 and 5 should be included in graphs, but -5 and 5 should not be included.

[6] -8 -7 -6 -5 -4 -3 -2 -1 0 1 2 3 4 5 6 7 8

[7] C

[8] >

[9] Answers may vary. Situations might include football, banking, stock market, altitudes below sea level, temperatures below 0, etc.

[10] A

[11] C

[12] highest: 108; lowest: –52

[13] Africa

[14] Monday

[15] water and mercury; oxygen and nitrogen.

[16] iron

[17] C

[18] Answers will show that the number of white algebra tiles minus the number of black algebra tiles must equal 10.

[19] No. Adding a zero pair does not change the integer the model represents, since one negative and one positive integer is added.

Chapter 10: Algebra: Integers and Graphing

[20] Positive integers relate to points above sea level and negative integers relate to points below sea level.

[21] Answers may vary. Students' models should show -4.

[22] C

[23] D

[24] -20, 5

[25] 

[26] -282 and 282

[27] -25

[28] -60

[29] -31° F

[30] It feels colder on the 5° F day with the wind of 10 mi/h.

[31] B

[32] 3 + 2; 5

[33] The sum can be positive, negative, or zero.

[34] -8 + 4 = -4; -6 + 2 = -4

[35] -282 ft, -8,326 ft, -1,310 ft

[36] -15,000 + -2,388 = -17,388

[37] D

[38] –3 + 2; –1

[39] Answers may vary. Sample: A football team gained 7 yd on their first play. They lost 4 yd on their second play. What was the overall gain for the two plays? (a gain of 3 yd)

[40] The two integers would be opposites if the sum is 0. For example: 5 + (-5) = 0

[41] Answers may vary. Sample answer given. -10 + 5 = -5

ANSWERS

Chapter 10: Algebra: Integers and Graphing

[42] D

[43] A

[44] 105 + (-48) = 57

[45] 13 yards gained

[46] C

−3

[47]

[48] To subtract an integer, add its opposite. Sample: 8 - 3 = 8 + (-3) = 5

[49] Adding zero pairs does not change the value. It gives you enough negative tiles to take away as needed.

[50] Answers may vary. Sample: Jane owes Mike $10.00, Jane tells Mike that she will deliver his newspapers the next morning, if he will subtract $7 from the money she owes him. How much will Jane owe Mike, if she delivers the newspapers? Jane will only owe Mike $3.00. (−10 − (−7) = 3)

[51] Answers may vary. Sample: -16 - (-10) = -6 or -10 - (-4) = -6

[52] D

[53] 34° F

[54] 8 - (-4) = 12; -4 - 8 = -12

[55] $25

[56] The square: 6, -4; the circle: -2, -7; the rectangle: -9, 6, -2

[57] -4° F

[58] 37° F

[59] B

[60] A

[61] B

Chapter 10: Algebra: Integers and Graphing

[62] $236.60

[63] −8, −12

[64] 3 adults; 2 children

[65] $\frac{3}{11}$

[66] 35 possible routes

[67] 84 and 85

[68] Answers may vary. Accept reasonable estimates.

[69] 15, 17, 18

[70]

Input (centuries)	Output (decades)
1	10
2	20
3	30
4	40
5	50
6	60

[71] a. 18.00
b. $B = 4.50A$; The numbers in column B are 4.5 times the numbers in column A.
c. $4.5h$

Chapter 10: Algebra: Integers and Graphing

[72] a. $16.00; $20.00
b. 4b + 1
c.

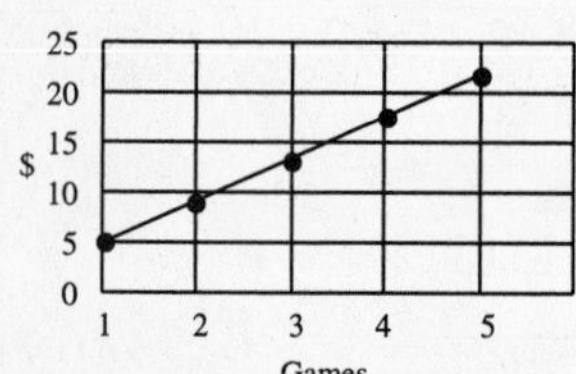

[73] B

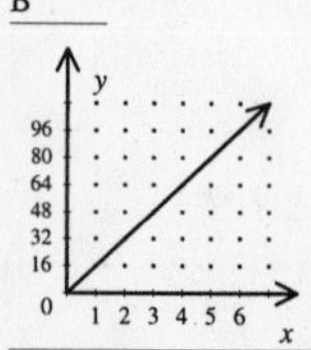

[74]

[75] a. Answers may vary. Sample: Collinear points are points on the same line. Noncollinear points are not on the same line.
b. collinear; The points form a straight line.
c. noncollinear; The points form a smooth curve, not a straight line.

[76] Answers may vary. Sample: Graphing functional data means creating a graph to show the relationship between two sets of numbers.

[77] A

[78] C

[79] A

Chapter 10: Algebra: Integers and Graphing

a. move right 4 and up 18

b.

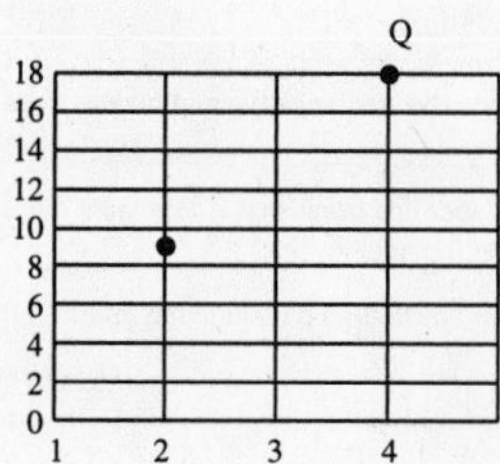

c. collinear;

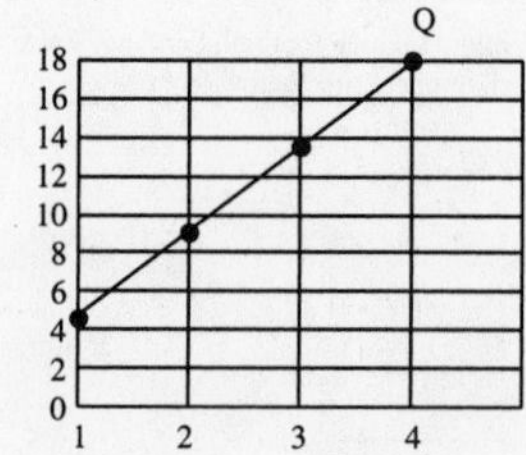

[80]

ANSWERS

a. 26

b.

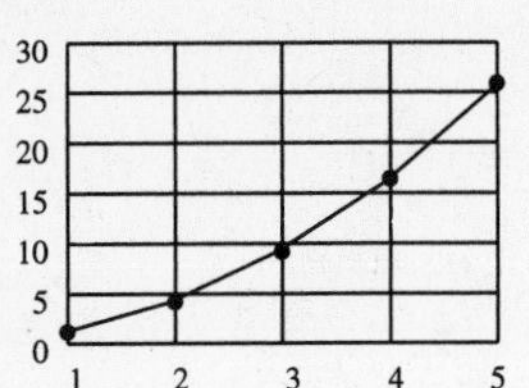

[81]

Pass	Rotations
1	5
2	10
3	15
4	20
5	25

[82]

Chapter 10: Algebra: Integers and Graphing

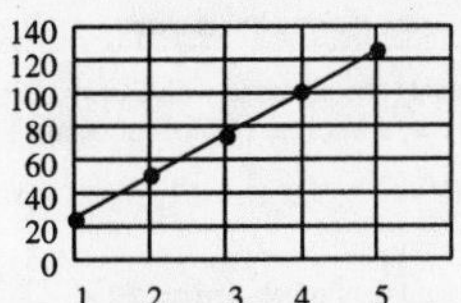

	A	B
1	Number of Minutes	Number of Blinks
2	1	25
3	2	50
4	3	75
5	4	100
6	5	125

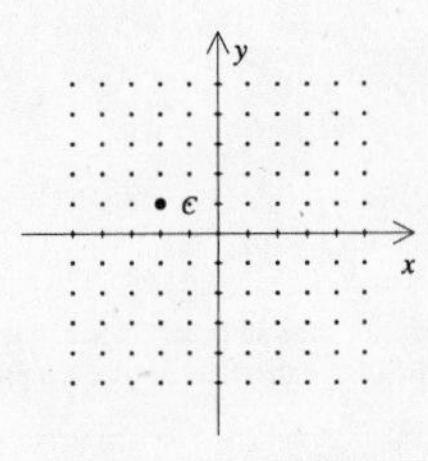

[83]

[84] C

[85]

[86] No. (–2, –4) plots a point two units to the left of the origin and 4 units down from the x-axis. The point (–4, –2) plots a point four units to the left of the origin and 2 units down from the x-axis.

[87] No. He should start at the origin when graphing an ordered pair, not at the x-coordinate.

[88] B

[89] A

Chapter 10: Algebra: Integers and Graphing

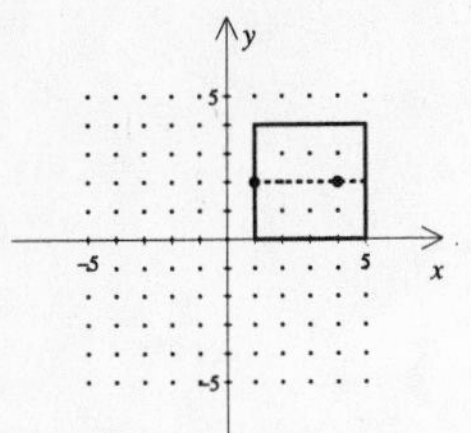

[90]

[91] (5, 6)

[92] C

[93] (–4, –7); third quadrant

[94] (–3, –5)

[95] (4, 0), (0, 4), (–4, 0), (0, –4)

[96] yes; yes

[97] Pentagon

[98] A(0,0), B(1,1), C(2,4), D(3,9), E(-1,1), F(-2,4), G(-3,9)

[99] A(0,0), B(5,5), C(10,20), D(15,45), E(-5,5), F(-10,20), G(-15,45)

[100] Answers may vary. Sample: Income is the money that a business or a company makes or receives. Expenses are any money that a business or a company spends.

[101] A

[102] A

[103] Answers will vary.

[104] B3: D3 – C3; C5: D5 – B5

[105] B7: B6/4; C7: C6/4

[106] A profit since the income exceeded the expenditures.

Chapter 10: Algebra: Integers and Graphing

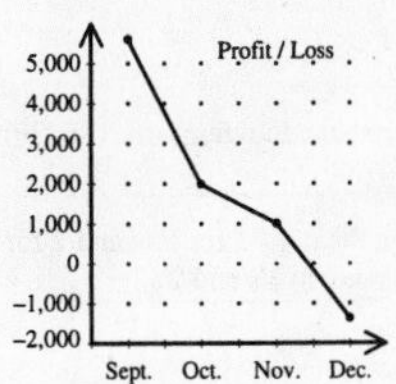

[107] Conclusions: Answers may vary. Sample: The company made a profit in all months except December. The profits have been steadily decreasing. If this trend continues, the company will eventually go bankrupt.

[108] Answers may vary. Sample: To find the profit or loss, find the sum of the monthly profits (positive numbers) and the monthly losses (negative numbers). If the sum is a positive number then the company has made a profit. If the sum is a negative number then the company has a loss.

[109] June

[110] Sample: Consider what the R.A.F. Company produces. Is the product seasonal? Were there layoffs during a particular month? Consider vacation time.
Stories should reflect some of the reasons for fluctuating profits and losses.

[111] $5,412

ANSWERS

Chapter 11: Exploring Probability

[1] C

[2] 0.5

[3] Yes, here is an example of a fair game using this spinner. Spin the spinner. If a player spins a 1, player A wins. If a player spins a 2, player B wins.

[4] A

[5] No. You can tell what object you are picking by its shape.

[6] By using logical reasoning students should agree with Danny. Since the number 7 does not appear on a die, it has zero chances of occurring. Therefore, Probability(7) = $\frac{0}{6} = 0$.

[7] Unfair. The Probability(5) = $\frac{1}{6}$ and the Probability(heads) = $\frac{1}{2}$. The outcomes are not equally likely.

[8] D

[9] vanilla, caramel
vanilla, strawberries
vanilla, pecans
peppermint, caramel
peppermint, strawberries
peppermint, pecans

[10] The game is unfair. Each player does not have an equal chance to win. Marcus has a better chance of winning since there are more even products than odd products.

[11] A game is fair if the outcomes are equally likely to occur and unfair if the outcomes are unequally likely to occur. Fair game example: Toss a coin; if a head appears player A wins and if a tail appears, player B wins. Unfair game example: Toss two number cubes; if the sum is less than seven, player A wins. If the sum is an even number, player B wins.

[12] Answers may vary. You may use a spinner with six numbers and a die.

[13] C

[14] Answers may vary. Sample: The number of points received for each number, odd or even, should be the same. Add another index card with the number 10 so that the number of odd and even numbers is equal.

Chapter 11: Exploring Probability

[15] red, red; red, green; red, blue; green, green; green blue; blue,blue

[16] C

[17] D

[18] Tom

[19] 20; 80

[20] 132, 123, 213, 231, 321, 331; 132 and 312

[21] 15

[22] 20

[23] 258, 285, 528, 582, 825, 852; 6 possible numbers

[24] 21

[25] 2

[26] D

[27] $\frac{1}{10}$

[28] $\frac{1}{8}$; Simulations may vary.

[29] Answers may vary. Sample: You can write a computer program to simulate a problem. Computers can generate random digits very quickly.

[30] Answers may vary, but should include some choice of 3 options in sets of 10.

[31] Answers may vary. Check students' work.

[32] 100,000

[33] Answers may vary. Sample: Have the computer generate random numbers from 1-4 in sets of 10.

[34] Answers may vary. Sample: Have computer generate random numbers 1-3 in sets of 30.

[35] Both numbers have an equal chance of being listed.

Chapter 11: Exploring Probability

[36] Tables may vary. $P(\text{odd sum}) = \frac{1}{2}$.

[37] Answers may vary. Sample: Generate random numbers 1–6. Find the probability that a number repeats.

[38] Answers may vary. Sample: Assign the digit 1 for true and 2 for false. Have a computer program generate random 1's and 2's.

[39] B

[40] $\frac{7}{18}$

[41] Express the number of favorable outcomes as a fraction of the total number of outcomes. You can express the probability as a fraction, decimal, or percent.

[42] The total number of possible outcomes and whether each outcome is equally likely or not.

[43] Answers may vary. Sample: 2, 4; 4, 8; 6, 12, etc.

[44] C

[45] D

[46] 2

[47] $\frac{1}{3}$

[48] $\frac{11}{25}$

[49] $\frac{43}{69}$

[50] $\frac{21}{50}$

[51] $\frac{29}{50}$

[52] a. 1; b. $\frac{5}{7}$; c. Sample: $\frac{1}{1{,}000{,}000}$; d. $\frac{1}{36}$; e. 0

Chapter 11: Exploring Probability

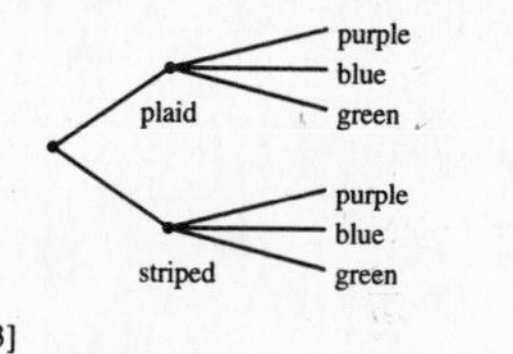

[53]

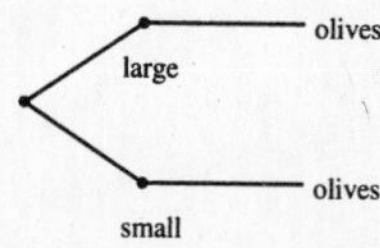

[54]

[55] Answers may vary. Sample: A tree diagram is a visual method of displaying all possible choices in a particular situation. A tree diagram can be used when all outcomes are equally likely to occur and when an event has two or more stages. A tree diagram can be used to find the probability of an event by using it to find the number of possible outcomes and the number of favorable outcomes. Dividing the number of favorable outcomes by the number of possible outcomes gives the probability of the favorable outcome occurring.

[56] Answers will vary. A sample answer could be a problem involving sports lessons, such as tennis or golf, and sessions throughout the day.

[57] B

[58] C

[59] A

[60] 40

ANSWERS

[61] Answers will vary. Sample: You can find the number of outcomes for an event with more than one stage by multiplying the number of outcomes at each stage.

[62] 12. The first stage has four choices. The second stage has three choices.

[63] 9 combinations: beef/spinach; beef/broccoli; beef/carrots; chicken/spinach; chicken/broccoli; chicken/carrots; fish/spinach; fish/broccoli; fish/carrots.

[64] There are 24 combinations. Lists will vary.

[65] The probability of choosing floral wallpaper is $\frac{1}{2}$. The probability of choosing purple paint and floral wallpaper is $\frac{1}{12}$.

[66] There are 24 total possible ways to choose a scarf, gloves, and a hat $(4\times3\times2)$. Of these 24 combinations, only 12 of them have a red hat. And of these 12, only 4 have black gloves. Therefore there is a 4 in 24 chance of selecting a red hat and black gloves. Therefore the probability of Tamara choosing a red hat and black gloves is $\frac{1}{6}$.

[67] 96 possibilities. Answers may vary. Richelle may find it easier to use the counting principle because there are 96 possibilities. It would be tedious and inefficient to draw a tree diagram to find out the same information.

[68] $\frac{1}{60}$

[69] B

[70] no

[71] Two events are independent if the outcome of one event does not depend on the outcome of the other.

[72] Explanations may vary. a and b describe dependent events. In each case, after the first event, there are fewer possibilities remaining for the second event. c describes independent events. d may result in different answers. Most will say that the events are not independent, but some may suggest that Jordan's doing poorly was unrelated to his staying up late. e describes independent events.

[73] C

Chapter 11: Exploring Probability

[74] A

[75] The probability is $\frac{1}{36}$. The answer can be found by using a factor tree or by finding the probability for getting a 5 on each roll and multiplying the two probabilities together. Multiplying the probabilities of two independent events is the same as dividing favorable outcomes by possible outcomes.

[76] A

[77] A

[78] $\frac{1}{4}$

[79] $\frac{1}{27}$. The probability of choosing an orange is $\frac{3}{9}$ and the probability of choosing cranberry juice is $\frac{1}{9}$. The answer is the product of the two possibilities.

[80] a. $\frac{3}{50}$; b. $\frac{3}{20}$; c. $\frac{1}{25}$

[81] $\frac{1}{8}$

[82] $\frac{4}{25}$

[83] $\frac{1}{50}$

[84] $\frac{7}{54}$

[85] Answers will vary. Samples: Drawing a tree diagram, making an organized list, or using the counting principle to determine all the possible arrangements. There are six possible arrangements.

[86] Answers will vary. Accept all logical responses. A sample would be that a student has three chores or responsibilities each evening. What are the possible orders in which he/she can do them? Students should use the counting principle to verify the answer of six possible orders. They should show $3\times2\times1=6$.

Chapter 11: Exploring Probability

[87] Answers may vary. Because 15 is a high number, drawing a tree diagram or making an organized list are both tedious and slow processes. The counting principle is the most efficient way of calculating that there are a huge number (15!) of possible orders in which the guests might arrive.

[88] There are 6 arrangements. They are 345, 354, 435, 453, 534, 543

[89] D

[90] 120

[91] B

[92] B

[93] 120

[94] 40,320

[95] 24

[96] 720

[97] 40,319. There are 40,320 possible arrangements minus the one listed in the question.

[98] 23 incorrect guesses. There are 24 possible arrangements.

[99] Answers will vary. Students should explain that a population is a group about which you seek information. Because it is inefficient, if not impossible, to get information about every member of the population, you must select a portion of the population to study. This portion is called a sample. If the sample is chosen well, it will represent the whole population.

[100] Answers may vary. a. random and most likely representative. b. may be random within Tennessee, but not random throughout the population; not representative. c. not random because counting is done on the same day of the week at the same time of the day for only two counts; not representative.

[101] 46. The size of the sample is 100 molecules.

[102] D

[103] 380

[104] B

Chapter 11: Exploring Probability

[105] D

[106] $\frac{1}{4}$

[107] 1,200

[108] 60. The sample size is 10.

[109] 70 would say yes and 130 would say no. No, the prediction will not always hold true because of variations in samples. However, as samples get larger, the results should get closer and closer to the survey results.

[110] Answers will vary. Check student answers for logic and accuracy. Students should compile a chart showing that 75% said yes, 15% said no, and 10% were unsure. Summaries will vary but should explain that a random sample of 1,000 people was studied to make predictions about the total number of visitors who went to the park during the given week. Students should then explain that by multiplying the percentage of the sample that said yes by the total number of visitors during the week, they are able to determine the total number of those visitors that will return. They should find that 337,500 visitors plan to return.

[111] 40

[112] a. The sample size is 4,000. b. According to the information, 7,350 households would watch America's Funniest Home Videos. Students must calculate 21% of 35,000.

Standardized Test Practice Exercises on the Software

Your *Prentice Hall Computer Item Generator with Standardized Test Practice* software includes a special feature—practice exercises that have been correlated to the mathematics objectives of the standardized tests below.

	Level of Prentice Hall *Middle Grades Math*		
	Course 1	**Course 2**	**Course 3**
California Achievement Tests, 5th Ed. (CAT5)	Level 16	Level 17	Level 18
Comprehensive Tests of Basic Skills (CTBS), Terra Nova	Level 16	Level 17	Level 18
Iowa Tests of Basic Skills (ITBS), Form M	Level 12	Level 13	Level 14
Metropolitan Achievement Tests, 7th Ed. (MAT7)	Intermediate 1	Intermediate 2	Intermediate 3
Stanford Achievement Test, 9th Ed. (SAT9)	Intermediate 2	Intermediate 3	Advanced 1
TAAS	Grade 6	Grade 7	Grade 8
NC End-of-Grade	Grade 6	Grade 7	Grade 8

The pages that follow show the objectives for the various standardized tests and the numbers of the items in the software that address each objective. You can use this information as an aid in creating worksheets and practice tests. You can also use the numbers to order worksheets or tests via Prentice Hall's exclusive Dial-A-Test® service. (See page vii for details.)

TEST 1

CAT5 Level 16

Test Objective	Standardized Test Practice Item Numbers
Computation	
Add whole numbers	**1.1, 1.2**
Subtract whole numbers, no regrouping	**1.3, 1.4**
Subtract whole numbers, regrouping	**1.5, 1.6**
Multiply whole numbers, no regrouping	**1.7, 1.8**
Multiply whole numbers, regrouping	**1.9, 1.10**
Divide whole numbers, no remainder	**1.11, 1.12**
Divide whole numbers, remainder	**1.13, 1.14**
Add, subtract, multiply, and divide decimals	**1.15, 1.16, 1.17, 1.18, 1.19, 1.20, 1.21, 1.22, 1.23, 1.24**
Add, subtract, and multiply fractions	**1.25, 1.26, 1.27, 1.28, 1.29, 1.30, 1.31, 1.32, 1.33, 1.34**
Order of operations	**1.35, 1.36, 1.37, 1.38**
Concepts and Applications: Numeration	
Order numbers	**1.39, 1.40, 1.41, 1.42**
Fractional part	**1.43**
Recognize numbers	**1.44, 1.45**
Place value	**1.46, 1.47**
Estimate, round	**1.48, 1.49, 1.50, 1.51, 1.52, 1.53, 1.54, 1.55, 1.56**
Concepts and Applications: Number Theory	
Number properties	**1.57, 1.58**
Divisibility	**1.59, 1.60, 1.61**
Equivalent forms	**1.62, 1.63, 1.64, 1.65, 1.66, 1.67**
Factors	**1.68, 1.69, 1.70**
Multiples	**1.71, 1.72, 1.73**
Odd, even numbers	**1.74**
Number sequence	**1.75, 1.76**
Concepts and Applications: Data Interpretation	
Graphs	**1.77, 1.78, 1.79, 1.80, 1.81, 1.82, 1.83**
Probability, statistics	**1.84, 1.85, 1.86, 1.87, 1.88, 1.89, 1.90**
Table, chart, diagram	**1.91, 1.92, 1.93, 1.94, 1.95**

CAT5 Level 16 (Continued)

Test Objective	Standardized Test Practice Item Numbers
Concepts and Applications: Pre-Algebra	
Find the missing element in an equation	**1.96, 1.97, 1.98, 1.99, 1.100, 1.101**
Write a number sentence to solve a problem	**1.102**
Use ratio, proportion to solve problems	**1.103, 1.104, 1.105, 1.106, 1.107, 1.108**
Function, pattern	**1.109, 1.110, 1.111**
Apply problem-solving strategies	**1.112, 1.113, 1.114, 1.115, 1.116, 1.117**
Concepts and Applications: Measurement	
Time	**1.118, 1.119, 1.120, 1.121, 1.122, 1.123**
Temperature	**1.124**
Length	**1.125, 1.126, 1.127, 1.128, 1.129, 1.130, 1.131**
Mass, weight	**1.132, 1.133, 1.134**
Perimeter	**1.135, 1.136**
Area	**1.137, 1.138, 1.139, 1.140, 1.141, 1.142, 1.143**
Volume, capacity	**1.144, 1.145, 1.146, 1.147**
Concepts and Applications: Geometry	
Recognize geometric elements	**1.148, 1.149, 1.150, 1.151, 1.152, 1.153**
Angles	**1.154, 1.155, 1.156, 1.157, 1.158**
Congruence	**1.159, 1.160**
Properties of plane figures	**1.161, 1.162, 1.163, 1.164, 1.165, 1.166**
Coordinate geometry	**1.167, 1.168**
Transformation	**1.169, 1.170**
Logical reasoning	**1.171, 1.172, 1.173**

TEST 2

CTBS Terra Nova Level 16

Test Objective	Standardized Test Practice Item Numbers
Number and Number Relations	
Demonstrate an understanding of number, number sense, and number theory by ordering numbers, representing numbers in equivalent forms, identifying relationships, interpreting numbers in real-world situations, and applying number concepts in real-world situations.	**2.1, 2.2, 2.3, 2.4, 2.5, 2.6, 2.7, 2.8, 2.9, 2.10, 2.11, 2.12, 2.13, 2.14, 2.15, 2.16, 2.17, 2.18, 2.19, 2.20, 2.21, 2.22, 2.23, 2.24, 2.25, 2.26, 2.27, 2.28, 2.29, 2.30, 2.31, 2.32, 2.33, 2.34, 2.35**
Computation and Numerical Estimation	
Demonstrate proficiency in computation procedures, solve real-world computation problems, apply estimation strategies, and determine reasonableness of results.	**2.36, 2.37, 2.38, 2.39, 2.40, 2.41, 2.42, 2.43**
Measurement	
Demonstrate an understanding of measurement systems, units, and tools by describing, calculating, or estimating size, location, and time; by using the concepts of perimeter, area, volume, capacity, weight, and mass; and by identifying appropriate degrees of accuracy. Solve problems involving principles of measurement, rate, and scale.	**2.44, 2.45, 2.46, 2.47, 2.48, 2.49, 2.50, 2.51, 2.52, 2.53, 2.54, 2.55, 2.56, 2.57, 2.58, 2.59, 2.60, 2.61, 2.62, 2.63, 2.64, 2.65, 2.66, 2.67, 2.68**
Geometry and Spatial Sense	
Demonstrate spatial sense and an understanding of geometry by visualizing and identifying two- and three- dimensional objects, classifying shapes, recognizing symmetry, using transformations, applying geometric formulas, and evaluating properties of geometric figures.	**2.69, 2.70, 2.71, 2.72, 2.73, 2.74, 2.75, 2.76, 2.77, 2.78, 2.79, 2.80, 2.81, 2.82, 2.83, 2.84, 2.85, 2.86, 2.87, 2.88, 2.89, 2.90, 2.91, 2.92**
Data Analysis, Statistics, and Probability	
Analyze, interpret, and evaluate data in various forms; and apply the concepts and processes of data analysis, statistics, and probability to real-world situations.	**2.93, 2.94, 2.95, 2.96, 2.97, 2.98, 2.99, 2.100, 2.101, 2.102, 2.103, 2.104, 2.105, 2.106, 2.107, 2.108, 2.109, 2.110, 2.111, 2.112, 2.113, 2.114, 2.115, 2.116, 2.117, 2.118**
Patterns, Functions, Algebra	
Recognize and extend patterns.	**2.119, 2.120, 2.121, 2.122**

CTBS Terra Nova Level 16 (Continued)

Test Objective	Standardized Test Practice Item Numbers
Demonstrate an understanding of functional relationships, algebraic processes, variables, and inequality.	**2.123, 2.124, 2.125, 2.126, 2.127, 2.128**
Recognize algebraic representations of problem situations and apply algebraic methods to solve real-world problems.	**2.129, 2.130, 2.131, 2.132, 2.133, 2.134, 2.135**
Problem Solving and Reasoning	
Select and apply problem-solving strategies, identify necessary information, use patterns and relationships to evaluate situations, apply inductive and deductive reasoning and spatial and proportional reasoning, and solve a variety of non-routine, real-world problems.	**2.136, 2.137, 2.138, 2.139, 2.140, 2.141, 2.142, 2.143, 2.144**
Communication	
Relate daily vocabulary to mathematical terminology; and relate models, diagrams, and pictures to mathematical ideas.	**2.145, 2.146, 2.147, 2.148, 2.149, 2.150, 2.151, 2.152**
Multiply Whole Numbers	
Multiply whole numbers.	**2.153, 2.154**
Divide Whole Numbers	
Divide whole numbers.	**2.155, 2.156**
Decimals	
Add, subtract, multiply, and divide decimals.	**2.157, 2.158, 2.159, 2.160, 2.161, 2.162, 2.163, 2.164, 2.165**
Fractions	
Add, subtract, multiply, and divide fractions.	**2.166, 2.167, 2.168, 2.169, 2.170, 2.171, 2.172, 2.173, 2.174, 2.175, 2.176, 2.177, 2.178, 2.179, 2.180, 2.181, 2.182, 2.183, 2.184, 2.185**
Percents	
Solve computational problems involving percents.	**2.186, 2.187, 2.188, 2.189**
Order of Operations	
Solve computational problems involving the standard order of operations.	**2.190, 2.191, 2.192, 2.193, 2.194, 2.195, 2.196, 2.197**

TEST 3

ITBS Form M Level 12

Test Objective	Standardized Test Practice Item Numbers
Concepts: Numeration and Operations	
Compare and order	**3.1, 3.2, 3.3, 3.4**
Properties of number systems	**3.5, 3.6, 3.7**
Classify numbers: divisibility	**3.8, 3.9, 3.10, 3.11, 3.12, 3.13, 3.14, 3.15, 3.16, 3.17, 3.18**
Place value	**3.19, 3.20, 3.21**
Standard form	**3.22, 3.23**
Use negative numbers	**3.24, 3.25, 3.26, 3.27, 3.28, 3.29**
Numerical patterns	**3.30, 3.31, 3.32, 3.33, 3.34, 3.35, 3.36**
Perform fundamental operations	**3.37, 3.38, 3.39, 3.40, 3.41**
Concepts: Geometry	
Identify figures	**3.42, 3.43, 3.44, 3.45, 3.46, 3.47, 3.48, 3.49**
Classify figures	**3.50, 3.51, 3.52, 3.53, 3.54, 3.55, 3.56**
Patterns	**3.57, 3.58**
Volume	**3.59, 3.60, 3.61, 3.62**
Concepts: Measurement	
Estimate measurements	**3.63, 3.64, 3.65, 3.66**
Identify appropriate units	**3.67, 3.68, 3.69, 3.70**
Time	**3.71, 3.72, 3.73, 3.74, 3.75**
Concepts: Fractions/Decimals/Percents	
Interpret representations	**3.76, 3.77, 3.78, 3.79, 3.80, 3.81, 3.82, 3.83, 3.84, 3.85, 3.86, 3.87, 3.88, 3.89, 3.90, 3.91, 3.92, 3.93, 3.94, 3.95, 3.96, 3.97, 3.98**
Compare and order	**3.99, 3.100, 3.101, 3.102**
Perform fundamental operations	**3.103, 3.104, 3.105, 3.106, 3.107, 3.108, 3.109, 3.110, 3.111, 3.112, 3.113, 3.114, 3.115, 3.116, 3.117, 3.118, 3.119, 3.120, 3.121, 3.122**

ITBS Form M Level 12 (Continued)

Test Objective	Standardized Test Practice Item Numbers
Ratio	3.123, 3.124, 3.125, 3.126, 3.127, 3.128, 3.129, 3.130, 3.131, 3.132, 3.133, 3.134, 3.135, 3.136
Concepts: Probability and Statistics	
Apply probability concepts	3.137, 3.138, 3.139, 3.140
Central tendency	3.141, 3.142, 3.143, 3.144, 3.145, 3.146
Concepts: Equations and Inequalities	
Relational symbols	3.147, 3.148
Evaluate algebraic expressions	3.149, 3.150, 3.151, 3.152
Solve equations	3.153, 3.154, 3.155, 3.156
Estimation	
Standard rounding	3.157, 3.158, 3.159, 3.160, 3.161
Order of magnitude	3.162, 3.163, 3.164
Compensation	3.165, 3.166, 3.167, 3.168, 3.169
Problem-Solving	
One-step problems: addition or subtraction	3.170, 3.171
One-step problems: multiplication or division	3.172, 3.173
Multiple step problems	3.174, 3.175, 3.176, 3.177, 3.178, 3.179, 3.180, 3.181, 3.182
Problem-solving strategies	3.183, 3.184, 3.185, 3.186, 3.187, 3.188, 3.189, 3.190
Data Interpretation	
Read amounts	3.191, 3.192, 3.193, 3.194, 3.195
Compare quantities	3.196, 3.197, 3.198, 3.199
Interpret relationships	3.200, 3.201, 3.202, 3.203, 3.204, 3.205, 3.206, 3.207
Math Computation	
Whole numbers	3.208, 3.209, 3.210, 3.211, 3.212, 3.213, 3.214
Fractions	3.215, 3.216, 3.217, 3.218, 3.219, 3.220, 3.221
Decimals	3.222, 3.223, 3.224, 3.225

TEST 4
MAT7 Intermediate 1

Test Objective	Standardized Test Practice Item Numbers
Concepts	
Numeration	**4.1, 4.2, 4.3, 4.4, 4.5, 4.6, 4.7, 4.8, 4.9, 4.10, 4.11, 4.12, 4.13, 4.14, 4.15, 4.16, 4.17, 4.18, 4.19, 4.20, 4.21, 4.22, 4.23, 4.24, 4.25, 4.26**
Number theory	**4.27, 4.28, 4.29, 4.30, 4.31, 4.32, 4.33, 4.34, 4.35**
Patterns and relationships	**4.36, 4.37, 4.38, 4.39, 4.40, 4.41, 4.42, 4.43, 4.44, 4.45, 4.46, 4.47, 4.48, 4.49, 4.50, 4.51, 4.52, 4.53, 4.54**
Measurement	**4.55, 4.56, 4.57, 4.58, 4.59, 4.60, 4.61, 4.62, 4.63, 4.64, 4.65**
Geometry	**4.66, 4.67, 4.68, 4.69, 4.70, 4.71, 4.72, 4.73, 4.74, 4.75, 4.76, 4.77, 4.78, 4.79, 4.80, 4.81, 4.82, 4.83, 4.84, 4.85, 4.86, 4.87, 4.88, 4.89, 4.90, 4.91, 4.92, 4.93, 4.94**
Algebra	**4.95, 4.96, 4.97, 4.98, 4.99**
Problem Solving	
Solution sentences	**4.100, 4.101, 4.102, 4.103, 4.104, 4.105**
Estimation	**4.106, 4.107, 4.108, 4.109, 4.110, 4.111**
Statistics and probability	**4.112, 4.113, 4.114, 4.115, 4.116, 4.117, 4.118, 4.119, 4.120, 4.121, 4.122, 4.123, 4.124, 4.125, 4.126, 4.127, 4.128, 4.129, 4.130, 4.131**
Strategies	**4.132, 4.133, 4.134, 4.135, 4.136, 4.137, 4.138, 4.139, 4.140, 4.141, 4.142, 4.143, 4.144, 4.145, 4.146, 4.147, 4.148, 4.149, 4.150, 4.151, 4.152, 4.153, 4.154, 4.155, 4.156, 4.157, 4.158, 4.159**

MAT7 Intermediate 1 (Continued)

Test Objective	Standardized Test Practice Item Numbers
Procedures	
Whole numbers	**4.160, 4.161, 4.162, 4.163**
Decimals	**4.164, 4.165, 4.166, 4.167, 4.168, 4.169, 4.170, 4.171, 4.172, 4.173, 4.174, 4.175, 4.176, 4.177, 4.178, 4.179, 4.180, 4.181, 4.182, 4.183**
Fractions	**4.184, 4.185, 4.186, 4.187, 4.188, 4.189, 4.190, 4.191, 4.192, 4.193, 4.194, 4.195, 4.196, 4.197, 4.198, 4.199, 4.200, 4.201, 4.202, 4.203, 4.204**

STANDARDIZED TEST PRACTICE

TEST 5

SAT9 Intermediate 2

Test Objective	Standardized Test Practice Item Numbers
Measurement	
Determine measurements indirectly from scale drawings.	**5.1, 5.2, 5.3, 5.4, 5.5**
Identify elapsed time.	**5.6, 5.7, 5.8, 5.9, 5.10**
Compare areas.	**5.11, 5.12**
Convert between units within the same system.	**5.13, 5.14, 5.15, 5.16, 5.17, 5.18**
Measure length.	**5.19, 5.20**
Select appropriate customary and metric units.	**5.21, 5.22, 5.23, 5.24**
Estimation	
Identify reasonableness.	**5.25, 5.26, 5.27**
Use estimation in operations with decimals and money.	**5.28, 5.29, 5.30, 5.31, 5.32, 5.33**
Use estimations in operations with whole numbers.	**5.34**
Problem Solving Strategies	
Identify missing information.	**5.35**
Solve problems using non-routine strategies.	**5.36, 5.37, 5.38, 5.39, 5.40, 5.41, 5.42**
Number and Number Relationships	
Compare and order decimals.	**5.43, 5.44, 5.45**
Compare and order fractions.	**5.46, 5.47**
Identify alternative representations of a fraction or mixed number.	**5.48, 5.49, 5.50, 5.51**
Identify equivalent fractions, including lowest terms fractions and improper fractions.	**5.52, 5.53, 5.54, 5.55**
Identify the name for a 7-digit whole number.	**5.56**
Identify alternative representations of a decimal.	**5.57, 5.58, 5.59, 5.60, 5.61, 5.62**
Number Systems and Number Theory	
Identify the least common multiple or greatest common factor of two numbers.	**5.63, 5.64, 5.65, 5.66, 5.67**
Identify a number that is 100 more or 100 less than a given number.	**5.68**

SAT9 Intermediate 2 (Continued)

Test Objective	Standardized Test Practice Item Numbers
Identify the place value of a digit in a decimal.	**5.69, 5.70**
Identify the place value of a digit in a whole number.	**5.71**
Identify whole numbers expressed in expanded notation.	**5.72**
Patterns and Functions	
Identify missing elements in number patterns.	**5.73, 5.74, 5.75, 5.76**
Identify missing elements in geometric patterns.	**5.77, 5.78**
Identify the output of functions (number machines).	**5.79**
Algebra	
Identify a solution sentence equivalent to a problem expressed in words.	**5.80, 5.81, 5.82, 5.83, 5.84**
Identify number sentences that represent the inverse operation of a give number sentence.	**5.85**
Identify equivalent expressions representing the commutative property of multiplication.	**5.86**
Statistics	
Determine measures of central tendency and dispersion.	**5.87, 5.88, 5.89, 5.90, 5.91, 5.92**
Extrapolate from bar graphs.	**5.93, 5.94, 5.95**
Extrapolate from line graphs.	**5.96, 5.97, 5.98**
Extrapolate from tables.	**5.99, 5.100, 5.101, 5.102**
Read and interpret line graphs.	**5.103, 5.104**
Read and interpret tally charts.	**5.105, 5.106**
Probability	
Determine combinations and permutations.	**5.107, 5.108, 5.109, 5.110**
Identify probabilities.	**5.111, 5.112, 5.113, 5.114**
Predict outcomes.	**5.115, 5.116, 5.117, 5.118, 5.119**
Geometry	
Classify angles.	**5.120, 5.121, 5.122, 5.123**
Classify polygons.	**5.124, 5.125, 5.126, 5.127, 5.128, 5.129**

SAT9 Intermediate 2 (Continued)

Test Objective	Standardized Test Practice Item Numbers
Identify lines of symmetry.	**5.130, 5.131, 5.132, 5.133**
Identify transformations: translations, rotations, reflections.	**5.134, 5.135**
Calculate area of plane figures.	**5.136, 5.137, 5.138, 5.139, 5.140, 5.141, 5.142, 5.143**
Calculate perimeter.	**5.144, 5.145, 5.146**
Identify coordinates.	**5.147, 5.148, 5.149, 5.150**
Computation, Using Symbolic Logic	
Multiplication and division of whole numbers	**5.151, 5.152, 5.153**
Operations with rational numbers	**5.154, 5.155, 5.156, 5.157, 5.158, 5.159, 5.160, 5.161, 5.162, 5.163, 5.164, 5.165, 5.166, 5.167**
Computation in Context	
Operations with whole numbers in context	**5.168, 5.169, 5.170**
Multiple operations in context	**5.171, 5.172, 5.173**
Operations with decimals, money, percents in context	**5.174, 5.175, 5.176, 5.177, 5.178, 5.179**
Operations with fractions and mixed numbers in context	**5.180, 5.181, 5.182, 5.183**
Rounding	
Round to estimate and solve problems.	**5.184, 5.185, 5.186**

TEST 6
TAAS Grade 6

Test Objective	Standardized Test Practice Item Numbers
Concepts: The student will demonstrate an understanding of number concepts.	
Compare and order nonnegative rational numbers, excluding whole numbers.	**6.1, 6.2, 6.3, 6.4, 6.5, 6.6, 6.7, 6.8, 6.9, 6.10, 6.11, 6.12**
Round whole numbers and decimals (to nearest tenth, one, ten, or hundred).	**6.13, 6.14**
Determine relationships between and among fractions (denominators of 2, 3, 4, 5, 6, 8, 10), decimals and percents.	**6.15, 6.16, 6.17, 6.18, 6.19, 6.20, 6.21, 6.22, 6.23, 6.24**
Use exponential notation to represent whole number expressions.	**6.25, 6.26**
Factor whole numbers.	**6.27, 6.28, 6.29, 6.30, 6.31**
Find the least common multiple and greatest common factor.	**6.32, 6.33, 6.34, 6.35, 6.36, 6.37, 6.38, 6.39, 6.40**
Concepts: The student will demonstrate an understanding of mathematical relations, functions, and other algebraic concepts.	
Use nonnegative rational number properties and inverse operations.	**6.41, 6.42, 6.43, 6.44, 6.45**
Determine missing elements in patterns.	**6.46, 6.47, 6.48, 6.49, 6.50**
Find relationships between ratios.	**6.51, 6.52, 6.53, 6.54, 6.55, 6.56, 6.57, 6.58, 6.59, 6.60, 6.61**
Solve simpler linear equations.	**6.62, 6.63, 6.64**
Identify ordered pairs on the coordinate plane.	**6.65, 6.66, 6.67**
Use number line representations of fractions and decimals.	**6.68, 6.69**
Concepts: The student will demonstrate an understanding of geometric properties and relationships.	
Recognize properties of 2- and 3-dimensional figures.	**6.70, 6.71, 6.72, 6.73, 6.74, 6.75, 6.76, 6.77, 6.78, 6.79, 6.80, 6.81, 6.82, 6.83, 6.84, 6.85, 6.86**
Identify translations, reflections, rotations, and their applications.	**6.87, 6.88**
Recognize similarity, congruence, and symmetry.	**6.89, 6.90, 6.91, 6.92, 6.93, 6.94, 6.95, 6.96**

TAAS Grade 6 (Continued)

Test Objective	Standardized Test Practice Item Numbers
Concepts: The student will demonstrate an understanding of measurement concepts using metric and customary units.	
Use metric and customary units.	**6.97, 6.98, 6.99, 6.100, 6.101, 6.102, 6.103, 6.104, 6.105**
Convert within the metric system.	**6.106, 6.107, 6.108, 6.109**
Convert within the customary system.	**6.110, 6.111, 6.112**
Find perimeter and circumference.	**6.113, 6.114, 6.115, 6.116**
Determine area (with and without grids) and volume.	**6.117, 6.118, 6.119, 6.120, 6.121, 6.122, 6.123, 6.124, 6.125, 6.126, 6.127, 6.128, 6.129, 6.130, 6.131, 6.132**
Concepts: The student will demonstrate an understanding of probability and statistics.	
Use counting arrangements.	**6.133, 6.134, 6.135, 6.136, 6.137, 6.138, 6.139**
Use sample spaces to find fractional probability.	**6.140, 6.141, 6.142, 6.143, 6.144, 6.145**
Predict possible outcomes from a sample.	**6.146, 6.147**
Analyze data and interpret graphs.	**6.148, 6.149, 6.150, 6.151, 6.152, 6.153, 6.154, 6.155, 6.156**
Find means (averages).	**6.157, 6.158**
Operations: The student will use addition to solve problems.	
Add whole numbers, fractions, and decimals.	**6.159, 6.160**
Operations: The student will use subtraction to solve problems.	
Subtract whole numbers, fractions and decimals.	**6.161, 6.162**
Operations: The student will use multiplication to solve problems.	
Multiply whole numbers and decimals.	**6.163, 6.164**
Operations: The student will use division to solve problems.	
Divide whole numbers and decimals.	**6.165, 6.166, 6.167, 6.168**
Problem Solving: The student will estimate solutions to a problem.	
Estimate with whole numbers and decimals.	**6.169, 6.170, 6.171**

TAAS Grade 6 (Continued)

Test Objective	Standardized Test Practice Item Numbers
Problem Solving: The student will determine solution strategies and will analyze or solve problems.	
Formulate strategies or solve problems using basic operations with whole numbers, fractions, and decimals.	**6.172, 6.173, 6.174, 6.175, 6.176, 6.177, 6.178, 6.179, 6.180, 6.181, 6.182, 6.183, 6.184, 6.185**
Analyze or solve problems through the use of similarity, congruence, and symmetry.	**6.186, 6.187, 6.188, 6.189, 6.190**
Analyze or solve problems using probability and statistics concepts.	**6.191, 6.192**
Problem Solving: The student will express or solve problems using mathematical representation.	
Formulate solution sentences.	**6.193, 6.194, 6.195, 6.196**
Analyze or interpret graphs and charts and use the information derived to solve problems.	**6.197, 6.198, 6.199, 6.200, 6.201, 6.202**
Problem Solving: The student will evaluate the reasonableness of a solution to a problem situation.	
Evaluate reasonableness.	**6.203, 6.204, 6.205**

TEST 7

NC End-of-Grade 6

Test Objective	Standardized Test Practice Item Numbers
The learner will demonstrate an understanding and use of rational numbers.	
Use models to relate percent to fractions and decimals; record, read, and explain.	**7.1, 7.2, 7.3, 7.4, 7.5**
Use models and pictures to demonstrate ratios, proportions and percents; explain relationships.	**7.6, 7.7, 7.8**
Read, write, and use numbers in various forms, including fractions, decimals, percents, and exponential notations, choosing the appropriate form for a given task.	**7.9, 7.10, 7.11, 7.12, 7.13, 7.14, 7.15, 7.16, 7.17, 7.18**
Find the prime factorization of a number less than 100.	**7.19, 7.20, 7.21**
Use prime factorization to investigate common factors and common multiples using a calculator when appropriate.	**7.22, 7.23, 7.24, 7.25**
Explore relationships among whole numbers, fractions, decimals, and percents using money, concrete models, or a calculator.	**7.26, 7.27, 7.28, 7.29**
The learner will demonstrate an understanding and use of geometry.	
Build models of 3-dimensional figures (prisms, pyramids, cones, and other solids); describe and record their properties.	**7.30, 7.31, 7.32**
Classify and use angles (interior, exterior, complementary, supplementary) and pairs of lines including skew lines.	**7.33, 7.34, 7.35, 7.36**
Construct congruent segments and congruent angles. Construct bisectors of line segments; using a straightedge and compass.	**7.37**
Identify and distinguish among similar, congruent, and symmetric figures, name corresponding parts.	**7.38, 7.39, 7.40, 7.41**
Recognize the results of translations, reflections, and rotations using technology when appropriate.	**7.42, 7.43**

NC End-of-Grade 6 (Continued)

Test Objective	Standardized Test Practice Item Numbers
The learner will demonstrate an understanding and use of patterns, relationships, and pre-algebra.	
Represent number patterns in a variety of ways including the use of calculators and computers.	**7.44, 7.45, 7.46**
Use patterns to explore the rules for divisibility.	**7.47, 7.48**
Use graphs and tables to represent relations of ordered pairs, using a calculator or computer where appropriate; describe these relationships.	**7.49, 7.50**
Identify and use patterning as a strategy to solve problems.	**7.51, 7.52**
Use realistic models to represent concepts and properties of variables, expressions, and equations. (Identity property of zero, property of one.)	**7.53, 7.54, 7.55, 7.56**
Use the order of operations to simplify numerical expressions, verifying the results with calculator or computer.	**7.57, 7.58**
The learner will demonstrate an understanding and use of measurement.	
Convert measures of length, area, volume, capacity, and weight in a given unit to other units in the same measurement system.	**7.59, 7.60, 7.61, 7.62**
Determine whether a given measurement is precise enough for the specific situation; determine when estimates are sufficient for the measurement situation.	**7.63, 7.64**
Explore the relationship of areas of triangles and rectangles with the same base and height. Demonstrate formulas for finding areas of triangles, parallelograms, and circles.	**7.65, 7.66, 7.67, 7.68, 7.69, 7.70**
Explore the effect on area and perimeter when changing one or two of the dimensions of a rectangle.	**7.71, 7.72**
Develop the concept of volume for rectangular solids as the product of area of base and height using models.	**7.73**
Estimate solutions and solve problems related to volumes of rectangular solids.	**7.74, 7.75, 7.76, 7.77**

NC End-of-Grade 6 (Continued)

Test Objective	Standardized Test Practice Item Numbers
The learner will solve problems and reason mathematically.	
Use an organized approach to solve non-routine and increasingly complex problems involving numeration, geometry, pre-algebra, measurement, graphing, computation, probability and statistics.	**7.78, 7.79, 7.80, 7.81, 7.82**
Analyze problem situations and apply appropriate strategies for solving them.	**7.83, 7.84, 7.85, 7.86, 7.87, 7.88**
Use inductive and deductive reasoning to solve problems.	**7.89, 7.90, 7.91**
Select an appropriate method for solving problems including estimation, observation, formulas, mental math, paper and pencil calculation, calculator and computers.	**7.92, 7.93, 7.94, 7.95**
The learner will demonstrate an understanding and use of graphing, probability, and statistics.	
Create and evaluate graphic representations of data, including circle graphs.	**7.96, 7.97, 7.98, 7.99, 7.100, 7.101**
Use measures of central tendency (mean, median, and mode) and range to describe meaningful data; compare two sets of unequal data.	**7.102, 7.103, 7.104, 7.105, 7.106**
Display data using computer software and explore the use of spreadsheets.	**7.107, 7.108**
Locate ordered pairs in meaningful situations using whole numbers, fractions, and decimals in the coordinate plane.	**7.109, 7.110**
Estimate the likelihood of certain events from experiments or graphical data.	**7.111, 7.112**
Interpret a statistical statement and discuss the extent to which the results of a sample can be generalized.	**7.113, 7.114, 7.115**
Find probabilities of simple events and discuss the implications.	**7.116, 7.117, 7.118, 7.119**
The learner will compute with rational numbers.	
Use whole number operations to solve real world applications, demonstrating competence with and without calculators (multiplication and division up to 3 digits by 2 digits).	**7.120, 7.121**

NC End-of-Grade 6 (Continued)

Test Objective	Standardized Test Practice Item Numbers
Select appropriate strategies, solve a variety of application problems and justify the selection.	**7.122, 7.123, 7.124, 7.125, 7.126, 7.127**
Divide decimal numbers, record results and explain procedure (1- and 2-digit divisors).	**7.128, 7.129, 7.130**
Within a context, estimate results and apply appropriate operations with decimals.	**7.131, 7.132, 7.133, 7.134, 7.135, 7.136, 7.137, 7.138**
Use models and pictures to demonstrate multiplication and division of fractions and mixed numbers, recording and explaining results.	**7.139, 7.140, 7.141**
Within a meaningful context, use estimation and operations with fractions less than one.	**7.142, 7.143, 7.144, 7.145**
In problem situations, use estimation and operations with fractions and mixed numbers.	**7.146, 7.147, 7.148, 7.149, 7.150**
In meaningful contexts develop the concept of adding and subtracting integers; record results.	**7.151, 7.152, 7.153, 7.154, 7.155, 7.156**
Translate word sentences that use integers.	**7.157, 7.158**
Estimate percents in real world situations and justify the estimate.	**7.159, 7.160**
Use mental math to solve problems involving simple fractions, decimals, and percents.	**7.161, 7.162**
Relate common fractions to frequently used percents; estimate and calculate using these percents.	**7.163, 7.164, 7.165**
Use ratios and proportions to explore probability and other interesting problems, discussing reasonableness of results.	**7.166, 7.167, 7.168, 7.169**

Prentice Hall *Computer Item Generator with Standardized Test Practice*
SYSTEM REQUIREMENTS AND INSTALLATION

Macintosh

System Requirements

PH Computer Item Generator will run on any Mac with a 68030 or better processor, at least 8MB of RAM, System 7.0 or later, at least 5MB of hard drive space available, and a printer.

Installation

- Insert the Prentice Hall *Computer Item Generator with Standardized Test Practice* CD into your CD-ROM drive.
- Open the PHCIG CD icon.
- Double-click **Install PHCIG**.
- Follow the instructions on screen.

You can choose either "Standard" or "Custom" installation. Choose "Custom" only if you are re-installing a portion of the PH Computer Item Generator software.

The installation program will prompt you to choose a location for the folder containing the PH Computer Item Generator software.

After installation is complete, your computer will re-start. You can now use Prentice Hall *Computer Item Generator with Standardized Test Practice*. For detailed instructions, consult the User's Guide by opening the CIG User's Guide icon.

Windows

System Requirements

PH Computer Item Generator will run on a PC with a 66 MHz 486DX or better processor, at least 8MB of RAM, VGA color graphics display, at least 5MB of hard drive space available, and a Windows-compatible printer. **NOTE**: PH Computer Item Generator requires a math coprocessor; it will not run with a 486SX processor.

Installation with Windows 95

- Insert the Prentice Hall *Computer Item Generator with Standardized Test Practice* CD into your CD-ROM drive.
- Click the **Start** button.
- Choose **Run...** from the **Start** menu.
- Type **X:\SETUP** (where X is the letter of your CD-ROM drive).
- Click the **OK** button.
- Follow the instructions on screen.

Installation with Windows 3.1

- Insert the Prentice Hall *Computer Item Generator with Standardized Test Practice* CD into your CD-ROM drive.
- Choose **Run...** from the **File** menu.
- Type **X:\SETUP** (where X is the letter of your CD-ROM drive).
- Click the **OK** button.
- Follow the instructions on screen.

You can choose a "Complete" or "Custom" installation. Choose "Custom" only if you are re-installing a portion of the PH Computer Item Generator software.

The setup program will prompt you for the directory and program folder names for PH Computer Item Generator. We suggest you accept the defaults provided.

After installation is complete, your computer will re-start. You can now use Prentice Hall *Computer Item Generator with Standardized Test Practice*. For detailed instructions, open the PH CIG User's Guide in the PH Computer Item Generator program group.